V&Runipress

NATIONAL **T**AIWAN
UNIVERSITY **PRESS**

Reflections on (In)Humanity

Volume 5

Edited by
Sorin Antohi, Chun-Chieh Huang and Jörn Rüsen

Assistant Editors: Stefan Jordan (München), Marius Turda (Oxford),
Editorial Assistants: Stephen J. Byrne (Oxford), Angelika Wulff (Witten)
Editorial Board: Aziz Al-Azmeh (Budapest), Dipesh Chakrabarty (Chicago), Pumla Gobodo-Madizikela (Cape Town), Yehuda Elkana (Jerusalem / Berlin), Moshe Idel (Jerusalem), Oliver Kozlarek (Morelia), Grazia Marchianò (Montepulciano), Jutta Scherrer (Paris / Berlin), Hayden White (Santa Cruz), Zhang Longxi (Hong Kong)

Marius Turda (ed.)

Crafting Humans

From Genesis to Eugenics and Beyond

V&R unipress

National Taiwan University Press

This book series is sponsored by the Berendel Foundation.

Published in cooperation with the Institute for Advanced Studies in Humanities and Social Sciences, National Taiwan University.

Bibliographic information published by the Deutsche Nationalbibliothek

The Deutsche Nationalbibliothek lists this publication in the Deutsche Nationalbibliografie; detailed bibliographic data are available in the Internet at http://dnb.d-nb.de.

ISBN 978-3-8471-0059-1 [Print, without Asia Pacific]
ISBN 978-986-03-6159-9 [Print, Asia Pacific only]
ISBN 978-3-8470-0059-4 [E-Book]

© Copyright 2013 by V&R unipress GmbH, D-37079 Goettingen
© Copyright 2013 by National Taiwan University Press, Taipei, Taiwan
All rights reserved, including those of translation into foreign languages. No part of this work may be reproduced or utilized in any form or by any means, electronic or mechanical, including photocopying, microfilm and recording, or by any information storage and retrieval system, without permission in writing from the publisher.
Cover image: El hombre como palacio industrial. Man as palace of industry.
© Wellcome Library, London
Page 2: Engraving by Johann Heinrich Meyer for the title page of Johann Gottfried Herder, *Briefe zur Beförderung der Humanität*.

Contents

Preface and Acknowledgements 7

Frank Ankersmit
Aftermaths and "Foremaths": History and Humans 9

Moshe Idel
Crafting a Golem: the Creation of an Artificial Anthropoid 39

Antonis Liakos
The End of History as the Liminality of the Human Condition: From
Kojève to Agamben 63

Roger Griffin
Bio-nomic Man (and Woman): Fantasies of Anthropological Revolution
as a Reaction to Modernity's Nomic Crisis 71

Merryn Ekberg
Eugenics: Past, Present, and Future 89

Marius Turda
Crafting a Healthy Nation: European Eugenics in Historical Context . . . 109

Maria Sophia Quine
Making Italians: Aryanism and Anthropology in Italy during the
Risorgimento 127

Alison Bashford
Julian Huxley's Transhumanism 153

List of Contributors 169

Bibliography 173

Index of Names 195

Preface and Acknowledgements

This volume is based partly on papers presented at the Berendel Foundation's second annual conference held at Queen's College, Oxford between 8 and 10 September 2011. The conference benefitted from the generous financial support of the Berendel Foundation and the Wellcome Trust (Grant no. 096561). I am grateful to these two institutions and to the participants for making the conference the success that was.

'Crafting humans' – and its corollary human enhancement – is a contested topic, both in medical sciences and the humanities. With continuing advances in science and technology, scientists and the general public alike are aware that the basic foundations of the human condition are now at stake. This is amply evidenced in the 'Superhuman' exhibition (19 July – 16 October 2012) at the Wellcome Collection in London. One important message of this exhibition is that the human body could be changed and transformed through the enhancement of basic physical and mental capacities. Yet, the current discussion of human enhancement – as illustrated by the specialists invited to contribute and whose opinions have been recorded for the exhibition – has largely ignored the (pre-) history of theories of social and biological improvement. The biological malleability of the 'human' is something that is now taken for granted but this volume questions this aptitude to change and improve humans, highlighting three critical aspects: the role of religion; the importance of historical time and the corporeality of historical subjects, like races, nations and societies. Despite the rapid growth of interest in the interconnectedness of technological progress, biomedical sciences and ethics, alongside the health benefits of recent discoveries in genetics and genomics, discussing current theories of human enhancement within their historical, religious, philosophical, and cultural contexts, from Antiquity onwards, remains yet to be achieved. In the decisive debates over the excesses and disastrous effects of human dreams of perfectibility (particularly since the Holocaust), the problematic connotations of 'crafting humans' are ever present. And if this prompts us to be more careful when discussing the intellectual sources of contemporary technologies of human improvement, than it is crucial that we take such claims seriously. Understanding the human must, therefore, be as much a form of moral introspection and historical responsibility as a quest for scientific knowledge and adaptability to technological progress.

This volume is but a modest contribution to this growing body of work. To some extent, it complements the Wellcome exhibition on the 'Superhuman' by considering the historical, ethical, and philosophical questions raised by the project of crafting and enhancement. The chapters included here offer insights into some of the reflections and imaginaries that have inspired and legitimated both theoretical and practical programmes for 'crafting' humans, ranging from the religious/spiritualist and the philosophical/cultural, to the secular and the scientific/scientistic; from the mystical quest for human perfection, to the biopolitical eugenic state of the twentieth century, and current genetic theories of human enhancement. While vast bodies of scholarship have been devoted to each of these individual topics, this volume discusses them in a synchronized way, as interrelated variants of the most central story in history, that of human perfectibility.

*

Above and beyond these general comments, there are some specific aknowledgements that I would like to make. Firstly, for permission to reproduce the photo on the cover, I am grateful to the Wellcome Library, London. Secondly, due to unforeseen circumstances Sorin Antohi could not join me in editing this volume. However, my discussions with him about 'crafting humans' have been inspiring and he has left a last inprint upon this volume. As such, I am grateful for his unfailing support and encouragment. Thirdly, this volume would not exist without the editorial support and occasional stylistic veto of Stephen Byrne. This is certainly a better book as a result of our collaboration. Finally, the volume is dedicated to Yehuda Elkana, who unfortunately passed away as this volume was prepared for publication. His illness precluded him from submitting his contribution but his complicitous humor and critical acumen, displayed so vividly during the conference, are not forgotten. He was a great scholar and a true friend.

London, 10 October 2012   Marius Turda

Frank Ankersmit

Aftermaths and "Foremaths": History and Humans*

The struggle between Kant and Herder about the meaning of history, or, to be more precise, about the destination of humanity and its relationship to nature and culture, belongs to the most important intellectual events of the late 18th century.[1]

Introduction

George Steiner once characterized our own time as follows: 'We came after, and that is the nerve of our condition. After the unprecedented ruin of human values and hopes by the political bestiality of our age.' Needless to say, Steiner referred here to the unprecedented moral catastrophe of the Holocaust and he wanted to express with his words that the memory of this moral catastrophe will be with us for the foreseeable future, if not forever. The foreseeable future is here essentially an 'after': so, indeed, we are living 'beyond or in the aftermath of the Holocaust'.

But suppose now that a catastrophe like the Holocaust is *in wait* for us and that in some way or other we have a strong premonition of its advent – a premonition so strong that we have as little doubt about this future Holocaust as about the warming up of the climate next year, when spring will turn again into summer. And this is not just some weird *Gedankenspiel*, for our expectations about the course of next year's climate has its analogue on a far larger scale in the predictions by climate-scientists about the consequences of global warming and that may result, according to them, in an ecological catastrophe of unprecedented proportions. From the perspective of such predictions we do not live in the *aftermath* of a previous catastrophe, such as the Holocaust, but in the *foremath* of a coming one, if you allow me to introduce this neologism into the English language.

---

* All translations from German are mine unless otherwise indicated
1 See John Zammito, 'Herder, Kant, Spinoza und die Ursprünge des deutschen Idealismus', in *Herder und die Philosophie des deutschen Idealismus*, ed. by Marion Heinz (Amsterdam: Rodopi, 1997), pp. 107–144 (p. 111).

It is sometimes added that the imminent ecological crisis is even exemplary of what our future will be like. That is to say, in the future the nature of the present will be determined by *premonitions* of the future rather than by the *memory* of the past. The centre of gravity of the present, so to say, will then, shift from the past to the future; today will be the first day of the future rather than the last day of the past.² If so, and if, moreover, it is true that history is the story of catastrophes and misfortunes rather than of happiness, the (historical) present will not be the *aftermath* of the catastrophes of the past but rather the *foremath* of catastrophes to come. The question then arises of what will happen if terrible and potentially traumatic events are a thing of the future rather than of the past. We have endlessly discussed the issue of how societies or civilizations react to their terrible pasts, but how do they anticipate their terrible futures? That's a new question and the one I wish to address in this chapter.

World-history

The writing of history and historical awareness is the most sensitive and subtle seismograph for detecting the reverberations of the great earthquakes of human history. Think of how the cataclysm of the French Revolution reverberated all through nineteenth-century historical writing, and of how the Holocaust determined much of contemporary historical thought. But is the reverse conceivable as well? Could some future catastrophe cast its shadow on the present; could we have a premonition or presentiment of some future French Revolution or Holocaust, whose ominous threat colours the experience of the present already? In much the same way that the traumatic experience of the past may make the past more powerful than the present?

At first, it may seem that this would be at odds with the arrow of time: how could traumatic experience possibly precede what it is a traumatic experience of? But, if Nietzsche is right, the idea of such sudden reversals of the arrow of time is less preposterous than might seem at first sight. In his *Will to Power* Nietzsche discussed the notion of causality. He denied to causality its scientific aspirations by emphasizing its anthropomorphism. Causality is an anthro-

---

2 Thus, according to Domanska: '(…) historians, too, should, begin to approach the past from the vantage point of the future rather than the present. Our choice of research problems and research methods, our way of constructing knowledge about the traces of the past should be guided by this future-oriented perspective and ought to address the question: What kind of knowledge of the past will humans need in a transnational, diasporic, or posthuman world?'. See Ewa Domanska, *Biohistory and the Contemporary Human and Social Sciences,* Paper for the VIII International Conversation on History: History and Globalization. Pamplona, University of Navarra, October 6–9, 2010, p. 4.

pomorphist notion since it results from a projection of our own "will to power" onto the world. Our own will to power inspires us with certain desires or intentions and these function as causes for how we shall subsequently act. This is the anthropomorphist model we project on nature. The example offered by Nietzsche is the flash of lightning. In actual physical reality this is just one phenomenon. But the anthropomorphism of causality then invites us to pull it apart in a cause and an effect and to say that a cause – lightning – has caused a certain effect – the flash. As if the lightning had had the intention to produce the flash.[3] However, as Nietzsche goes on to argue, if anthropomorphism structures our conception of causality then we may just as well reverse the order of cause and effect. For suppose our will to power requires us to find out what is the case of a certain effect that we have established. In that case the effect precedes the cause – for without the effect we had not asked for its cause.

And, indeed, one can think of an example illustrating Nietzsche's claim. I have in mind here the interesting fact of the combination of, on the one hand, impending ecological crisis predicted by so many and, on the other, a recent variant of historical writing, namely so-called world-history. World-history was put on the historian's agenda in the 1960s – William McNeill being one of its most influential advocates – so at a time when the idea of the ecological crisis was still a thing of the future. Nevertheless, much of world-history operates within the same matrix as present scientists when discussing the ecological crisis. World-history singled out for attention exactly the same variables that are considered crucial in the emergence of the ecological crisis that has so much been on our minds in the last ten to twenty years. So it might seem that the practitioners of world history had had a *premonition* of that crisis.

To be sure, world-history focuses not on ecological issues only. To begin with, world-historians will argue that history has now brought us to a stage where all that used to isolate one nation, culture, or civilization from others has been overcome. So the history of what had always *united* us – without our taking notice of it – must now rank highest on the historian's agenda. The historian should now reveal to us the history we have always unwittingly shared and that traditional historiography had therefore always remained blind to. Not only will this be a wholly new variant of historical writing, not only will it tell us a story that we have never heard before but, above all, this is the kind of history we desperately need now that we are all united within one all-encompassing global system. We must read backwards, so to say, our united globalist present into the past and do so right back to the dawn of mankind.[4] Doing so will *unite* us, by

---

3 Friedrich Nietzsche, 'Wille zur Macht', in *Friedrich Nietzsche. Werke*, vol. 3, ed. by Karl Schlechta (Munich: Carl Hanser Verlag, 1969), p. 502.
4 Self-evidently, the idea loses much, if not all of its plausibility if one agrees with authors such

revealing our shared past, instead of *dividing* us, as political and cultural history always tended to do. And is this not what we are in need of in our shared global future?⁵

Secondly, there is a close affinity between cultural anthropology, on the one hand, and the world-historian's musings about the earliest origins of mankind. Both have their roots in what is called 'conjectural history' and its speculations about the earliest stages of mankind focusing on how human society is formed by the most universal and elementary material conditions of all human life. 'Conjectural history' has its venerable *apriorist* roots in natural law philosophy, and its *aposteriorist* ancestor in nineteenth-century cultural anthropology, finding its empirical data primarily in still existing primitive societies, from the Sioux to the Azandes.⁶ World-history can be said to continue and develop *aposteriorist* conjectural history insofar as it attempts to account for how the factors that determined the origins of human society and civilization went on to decide humanity's fate down to the present day. And, indeed, to the extent that world-history is successful in demonstrating the lasting causal significance of these factors, it gives us the story of all of humanity. This would certainly help to justify its claim to be the variant of historical writing we need most in a globalizing world. For these universal factors have in our present universalist global reality a counterpart that is congenial to them; it may seem that these factors can only now exert their causal power, unhindered and untrammelled by the local peculiarities that had always interfered with them until quite recently. Human history has, finally and after the most uncertain and erratic vagaries, been reset on the path of its most powerful causal determinants and is now ready follow their guide. Just like an orchestra suddenly producing a majestic Beethoven

---

as Jacques Sapir arguing that globalization is a neo-liberal illusion. See Jacques Sapir, *La Démondialisation* (Paris: Seuil, 2011).

5 World-history must be distinguished from global history. For global history does not have such pretensions: it is content to observe that an all-encompassing global system emerged in the last half century and is content to investigate its present functioning. Global history merely is a new and ambitious variant of contemporary history: of what, in Germany, is called 'Zeitgeschichte'.

6 One may think here of Friedrich Creuzer, *Symbolik und Mythologie der alten Völker, besonders der Griechen* (Leipzig und Darmstadt: Bei Heyer Und Lesk, 1819); Johann Jakob Bachofen, *Das Mutterrecht* (Stuttgart: Krais & Hoffman 1861); Lewis Morgan, *Ancient Society* (Cambridge, Ma: Belknap Press of Harvard University, 1964 [1877]; Edward Burnett Tylor, *Primitive Culture: Researches into the Development of Mythology, Philosophy, Religion, Art and Custom* (London: J. Murray, 1871); J.G. Frazer, *The Golden Bough: A Study in Magic and Religion* (New York: Macmillan, 1890). For a synopsis of the development of of anthropology since the 19th century, see Annemarie de Waal Malefijt, *Images of Man: A History of Anthropological Thought* (New York: Knopf, 1974) and the fascinating Uwe Wesel, *Der Mythos vom Matriarchat* (Frankfurt am Main: Suhrkamp, 1980). Freud's *Totem und Tabu, Moses und Monotheismus* and his *Das Unbehagen an der Kultur* are also worth mentioning in this context.

symphony after a chaotic and cacophonous opening, and in which each member of the orchestra still played a score different from that of all the others. History has, finally, come to itself.

Thirdly, world-history can be said to carry on the venerable tradition of so-called speculative philosophies of history (think of St. Augustine, Bossuet, Hegel, Comte, Marx, Spengler, Toynbee etc.) trying to discover in history some hidden pattern and a type of historical agent whose appearance determined the nature of this pattern. Contemporary practitioners of world-history are, however, quite well aware of the criticism traditionally levelled at speculative philosophies of history by authors such as Popper, Hayek, Mandelbaum, Danto, and others, from which it never recovered. Indeed, speculative philosophy of history is dead, and contemporary practitioners of world-history will be amongst the first to sign its death-warrant. In fact, world-history was born from the rejection of speculative philosophy of history. For when William McNeill introduced world-history, Arnold Toynbee's *Study of History* served as his *repoussoir*.[7] As a result, contemporary world-history succeeds in combining the scope of speculative philosophy of history with the empirical solidity of "ordinary" historical writing.

Finally, the achievements of world-history can be summed up in the following four claims:

In the first place, we encounter here this reversal of causality that Nietzsche had in mind. For world-history projects the realities of actual, global history on all of our past. We now analyze all of our past in terms of the kind of causalities at stake in global history and in this sense the effect of the historical process – contemporary global society – is the cause of the discovery of world-history. With the result that the causal mechanisms discovered in the past by world-history are, in fact, the effects of the emergence of a global society in the last few

---

7 Arnold Toynbee, *A Study of History* (Oxford: Oxford University Press, 1935–1954); William McNeill, *The Rise of the West: A History of the Human Community* (Chicago: Chicago University Press, 1963). Speculative philosophies were criticized for two reasons: it was said that their holism was a source of the totalitarian temptation and, next, that each speculative system was based on at least one empirically unverifiable and, hence, metaphysical assumption. Such as the metaphysical belief that all history is the history of God's actions with humankind, of the march of Reason through history, or of the class-struggle. Now, for Toynbee all history was the history of civilizations; and he tailored the historical facts accordingly. Hence, he tended to downplay the interaction between civilizations and even argued, for example, that the Spaniards had had little to do with the death of the Aztec civilization. For the life-cycle of this civilization had come to an end already. In order to avoid such patent absurdities McNeill defended so-called 'diffusionism' and focused precisely on the *interaction* between cultures. He claimed that cultures originated from the interaction between people who are strangers to each other – while even emphasizing diffusionism to such a degree that it threatened to become an alternative historical metaphysics – as McNeill was willing to recognize later on. See William McNeill, *Keeping Together in Time: Dance and Drill in Human History* (Cambridge, Ma: Harvard University Press, 1995).

decades. This is, needless to say, a radicalization of the old claim that we often, if not always read history backwards, that is, as seen from the perspective of the present.[8]

In the second place, world-history always aimed to correct the Euro-centrism of most of Western historical writing. And it has undoubtedly been marvellously successful in this. In world-history one will rarely come across the traditional high-points in the history of the West, such as the Fall of the Roman Empire, the Wars of Religion, the French Revolution and its aftermath, or the two world wars of the previous century: the expansion of the West being the only exception to this. World-historians offer an account of human history with which each inhabitant of this globe, wherever he or she happened to be born, can identify him or herself.

Thirdly, there is a dramatic change in what are seen to be the principal agents in human history. Most of historical writing dealt with the *faits et gestes* of human beings for the last one to three thousand years. In traditional history, Western or non-Western, human beings make history, even if we leave ample room for Adam Ferguson's most perceptive observation that 'nations stumble upon establishments, which are the result of human action, but not the execution of any human design',[9] so for the unintended consequences of intentional human action. But now books like Jared Diamond's immensely successful *Guns, Germs and Steel* present human history as a mere response to accidental facts about man's climatological and biological environment.[10] Or think of Cavalli-Sforza's work on how mankind spread over the globe in the period from 700,000 to 150,000 years ago.[11] And then one does not know what impresses us more: the fact that such a history can be written at all, or the complete irrelevance here of all that "ordinary" historians had always considered to be of importance in their approach to the past. No less amazing are books on the history of the human genome or books like Richard Dawkins's bestseller *The Selfish Gene* with the profoundly unsettling message that not *we*, but our *genes*, are the real agents in the history of mankind. We are merely the material they need for securing their own perfectibility. Or, to take one more striking example, think of love, of that

---

8 The theme is brilliantly discussed in Peter Novick, *That Noble Dream: The 'Objectivity Question' and the American Historical Profession* (Cambridge: Cambridge University Press, 1988).

9 Adam Ferguson, *An Essay on the History of Civil Society* (Cambridge: Cambridge University Press, 1995 [1767]), p. 119.

10 Jared Diamond, *Guns, Germs and Steel: A Short History of Everybody for the last 13,000 years* (London: Jonathan Cape, 1997). Diamond argued here that civilization might just as well have come into being in New Guinea, if the Papuans had been so lucky as to have the same mix of cattle, pets, and corn that happened to be available in Mesopotamia.

11 Luigi Luca Cavalli-Sforza, *Genes, Peoples, and Languages* (New York: North Point Press, 2000).

most sublime and most poetic of all human feelings and that was sung by Homer, Shakespeare, Goethe, and innumerable others; and observe, then, how Günther Dux explained the origins of that feeling in terms of a number of simple and trivial physical differences between men and women.[12] So what have traditional historians always been talking about, in the end? We are reminded of Braudel's accusation that they did little more than study 'the foam of history'.[13] In sum, world-history is a radically de-humanized history, an account of the past without human agency.[14]

Fourthly, world-history tells us a story about the past in which human history is merely an epiphenomenon of natural history, or rather of life in general. We're merely the last stage in the evolution of life that started and that will continue after man has disappeared from the scene; unless mankind is so successful in destroying the conditions for the possibility of life on this planet that life will disappear together with us. We are just one stage that life passes through on its long way from the first organisms of two billion years ago to some wholly unimaginable future. And then the historian, or rather the world-historian, will have little use for the kind of skills that historians are traditionally taught. In 2001 at the occasion of the 115th annual meeting of the American Historical Association Edmund Wilson, founder of socio-biology claimed that future historians wishing to understand the driving forces of humanity would need to know the principles of ecology, population genetics and even molecular biology.[15] Nine years later Ewa Domanska was even more explicit:

> Indeed, just as the humanities of the 1980s could not exist without semiotics and such key concepts such as text, narrative, discourse, or sign, today's humanities cannot exist without its deepening relationship with science or concepts that begin with the prefix "bio" such as biopower, biohistory, biosocial, bioheritage, biocitizenship, biocolonization, biofact, biovalue[16].

In sum, history is bio-history; mankind is, basically, a biological phenomenon and its history should be written accordingly.

---

12 Günter Dux, *Geschlecht und Gesellschaft: Warum wir lieben* (Frankfurt am Main: Suhrkamp, 1994).
13 Less subversive is, perhaps, Ernst Gellner, *Plough, Sword and Book: The Structure of Human History* (London: Collins Harvill, 1988), in which he described these three things as history's main agents.
14 Folz even goes further than that: 'world history, if done properly – that is expanding the theme of interactions to include all actors, not just human ones – is not only good scholarship, it may be vital to saving the planet'. Quoted in Domanska, *Biohistory*, p. 4. One may agree with all of Folz's statement; but not with his anthropomorphist proposal to see nature as an agent: nature is not an agent. Unless, of course, Folz would have a convincing argument for such a vitalist or animist conception of nature.
15 Quoted in Domanska, *Biohistory*, p. 6.
16 Domanska, *Biohistory*, p. 1.

Man and nature

I have presented world-history here as expressing a premonition of the contemporary conflict between man and nature and of how nature might avenge on mankind its irresponsible behaviour. So it may then come as a bit of surprise that the issue of the relationship between man and nature was already on the agenda in the eighteenth century. Since the more philosophical implications of world-history have up till now rarely been discussed, the eighteenth century debate on history and nature acquires a sudden relevance. So retracing the main pattern in these discussions on man and nature of two and half centuries ago may be of help for a better understanding of world-history and of how it relates to the problem of the ecology.

Two positions can be discerned in the eighteenth century debate. In the first place there is the Neapolitan polymath Giambattista Vico (1668–1744). In his *La Scienza Nuova* he argued that there is a strict divide between the object of research of the sciences and that of the humanities. He expressed his claim in his famous claim of *verum et factum convertuntur* (roughly: '*truth* is to be found in what has been *made*'). It was his big idea that we can understand *history* better and deeper than *nature* because we have made it ourselves whereas nature was made by God. Of course, one cannot doubt that this "better and deeper" widely overstated the matter because of the immense successes of the sciences, and that was evident already in Vico's own time. So historicist and hermeneuticist theorists of either German or Anglo-Saxon pedigree watered down Vico's bold assertion to the more modest claim that both the sciences and history have their own object and research-methods. Self-evidently, this agrees with how we always used to think about history: history studies what has been said by human beings, either individually or collectively. Nature has no role to play here and is a reality of a completely different order.

But half a century after Vico had separated the domains of nature and history Johann Gottfried Herder (1743–1804) united them again in his major work *Ideen zur Philosophie der Geschichte der Menschheit* (1784–1791), which is one of the most important books in both historical writing itself and in the history of historical thought.[17] In fact, the book could well be described as the first book on world-history. For just like the practitioners of world-history Herder emphasizes our dependence on our environment and of how detrimental our intervention with the environment may be for ourselves.[18] He is aware of the necessity of

---

17 For some remarks on later discussions of the relationship between man and history on the one hand and nature on the other, see Dipesh Chakrabarty, 'The Climate of History: Four Theses', *Critical Inquiry*, 35 (2009), 197–222.
18 See Johann Gottfried von Herder, *Ideen zur Geschichte der Philosophie der Menschheit. Band 1* (Riga und Leipzig: Hartknoch, 1785), p. 89.

photo-synthesis by plants for the production of oxygen and for the right balance in the air we breathe.[19] *Klima* is his favourite term and designates the balance in environmental factors decisive for life in general and for ourselves in particular: we are *Zöglinge der Luft*.[20] And life varies with the natural conditions under which it has developed and sustains itself. Climate even is the condition for the emergence of life in general. In agreement with all this Herder's *Ideen* courageously removes humanity from the centre of things; human agency is no less absent in his work as it is in world-history. Not only is the history of the West a mere epiphenomenon in his account,[21] not only are the names of emperors, Popes, kings and so on – even of Christ – wholly absent from his tale, even more so, humanity as a whole is brutally removed from the prestigious place it always occupied in human reflection on the past.

Above all, in his effort to upset all traditional categories for understanding the past, Herder situates his argument in the widest possible context; namely, the context of the cosmical variables from which life in general and human history could arise. His book opens with explaining – with Kant and Laplace – how our stellar system came into being, from an original nebula of dust finally crystallizing out in the sun and its planets by the forces of gravitation: which, more or less, still is the accepted theory. He then tells how life began with unicellulars and mosses, gradually developed plants and animals and, finally, man. And he insists that precisely this genealogy should inspire humanity with the greatest modesty with regard to itself. As he insists, we must have the courage to recognize animals as 'our elder brothers'.[22] What we share with them, namely having a food canal,[23] is absolutely basic in all of animal life and should prevent us from ever seeing ourselves as belonging to a wholly different order than other animals. Since Darwin one and a half centuries have passed to accustom us to this most sobering insight. Seeing animals such as apes (described most respectfully by Herder[24]) as our 'elder brothers' is of course a mere platitude nowadays; but saying things like that in the 1780s was no less revolutionary than the great revolution beginning at the end of that same decade.

So how could Herder at the end of the eighteenth century write a book with a message putting him at the vanguard of historical writing at the beginning of the

---

19 Addressing himself to plants Herder exclaims: 'wholesome childern of the earth what we breathe out pestiferously, what destroys us, is what you set to work on'. Herder, *Ideen. Band 1*, p. 87.
20 Herder, *Ideen. Band 1*, p. 37.
21 See Johann Gottfried von Herder, *Ideen zur Geschichte der Philosophie der Menschheit. Band 4* (Riga und Leipzig: Hartknoch, 1792). The history of the West is presented here as a mere 'afterthought' and as being of no particular relevance for an understanding of history.
22 Herder, *Ideen. Band 1*, p. 90.
23 Herder, *Ideen. Band 1*, p. 112.
24 Herder, *Ideen. Band 1*, p. 191

twenty-first century? What made him present human history as little more than an *entr'acte* in natural history – as also is the case in contemporary world history? The answer lies in Herder's Spinozism: Spinoza's doctrine of the single substance, of which all the objects in this world are mere modifications, made him annul all categorical differentiations between man and nature, or between human history and natural history. Everything is included in the all-encompassing order of the single substance, and should be perceived as such. So we should not even think of granting to man some special place as was done by Vico – and in the practice of the writing of history down to the present.²⁵

Mentioning Herder's Spinozism brings us to the so-called *Pantheismusstreit* in the Germany of the late 1780s, which has been one of the greatest intellectual debates in all of history, in which practically all German philosophers, theorists, and men of letters participated, from minor figures now wholly forgotten to Herder himself, Kant, Fichte, Schelling, Hegel, Goethe, Schiller, Schlegel, Novalis, Hölderlin and so on. The debate most importantly contributed to the formation of what one might call 'the German mind', as it would crystallize out in the nineteenth century. Since the *Pantheismusstreit* has been decisive for the matrix defining the relationship between history and nature down to the present day, it will be necessary to say a few things about it here.

The debate began when Friedrich Heinrich Jacobi's revealed that Lessing – at that time the unchallenged leader of the German Enlightenment – had confessed to him shortly before his death that he had always been a Spinozist and a believer in Spinoza's 'εν και παν',²⁶ hence, in the idea that all things in this world, natural and human, are modifications of the One Substance, which is God or Nature (*Deus sive Natura*). Since Spinoza was still considered a *nomen nefandum,* and since the accusation of Spinozism could effectively wreck anybody's intellectual

---

25 At the same time Herder is generally regarded as one of the most important precursors of later German historicism and for which the opposition of history and nature was no less self-evident than it had been for Vico. Perhaps the paradox can be solved by distinguishing between two conceptions of 'nature'. For 'Herder 'nature' was what we now commonly understand by that word, though it had for him, as for most of his contemporaries, still the typically Aristotelian ring of 'φυσις' (derived from the verb 'φυειν' meaning 'to grow'). So nature was for him, above all, organic nature. Later historicists would primarily associate 'nature' with the workings of political power (above all as described by Machiavelli and by *raison d'état* theorists) and with what can be said about history from the perspective of the social sciences. If understood in this way Spinozism would, indeed, remain very much alive in all of the historicist tradition, though rather as a moral aporia to be wrestled with than as the indisputable philosophical truth that it had been for Herder.
26 In this expression is concentrated the whole magic of Spinozism: it stands for synthesis, totality, holism, for what both reason and feeling aspire to; it is the bridge between subject and object, between the sign and what the sign stands for, between is and ought, between desire and its fulfillment, between man and nature'. See Zammito, 'Herder, Kant, Spinoza', p. 114.

career at that time, the term "confession" is quite appropriate here. Though Jacobi had probably intended little more than to attract the attention to himself, his indiscretion calked all existing disputes in the German intellectual world of that time, especially those occasioned by Kant's revolutionary critical philosophy.[27]

The main effect of Kant's first *Critique* had been to radically break with rationalist *logos*-philosophy in which the order of Thought or Knowledge and that of Being were still reassuringly held together by Reason or *logos*.[28] Kant's transcendental philosophy placed the order of thinking within the purely epistemological and cognitive sphere of the transcendental self and by doing so cut through all its ties with the order of Being. So from the perspective of Kant's critical philosophy no philosophical system could be more erroneous than that of Spinoza, uniting both the (knowing) subject and the (known) object within the domain of the one Substance, of which both were to be seen as mere modifications. So where Spinoza is, there is no room for Kant, and *vice versa*. Though Kant never seems to have bothered to study Spinoza, he was well aware of the irreconcilable enmity between his own philosophical system and that of Spinoza.

All the more was he worried by the popularity gained by Spinozism in the *Pantheismusstreit*, and even more so by the fact that his own philosophy paradoxically further contributed to its popularity. For his own radical separation of Knowledge and Being, of what we can say about the world, on the on hand, and *noumenal* reality, on the other, could not fail to make his own followers desperate for more clarity about the ontological anchors of knowledge. All the more so since Kant, with his radical pulling apart of the *noumenon* and the *phenomenon*, could never answer that question adequately himself. In this way Kant was driving his own followers – much to his disgust and distress – right into the arms of Spinoza. Spinoza's thought was generally regarded as the only reliable remedy for the inherent "nihilism" and "fatalism" of the Kantian system and was, therefore, appealed to in order to 'protest against all forms of dualism, whether Kantian, Fichtean or Cartesian. Schelling and Hegel greatly admired Spinoza for his monism, for showing how to overcome dualism when Kant, Fichte and Jacobi had only reinstated it'.[29]

---

27 Friedrich Heinrich Jacobi, *Briefe über die Lehre Spinozas* (Leipzig: Bey Georg Joachim Goeschen, 1786).
28 This is where one might disagree with Gadamer. Gadamer relates the end of logos philosophy to the death of the Hegelian system in the 1830s and 1840s. He is certainly right when characterizing Hegel as the last great representative of logos philosophy. But that should not make us forget that Kant had already dealt the death-blow to logos–philosophy with his first *Critique*. All the more so since the unexpected revival of Spinozist logos philosophy can well be seen as a reaction to Kant. See Hans-Georg Gadamer, *Wahrheit und Methode* (Tübingen: Mohr, 1972), p. 207.
29 Frederick Beiser, *Hegel* (New York and London: Routledge, 2005), p. 64.

It might be argued that the *Pantheismusstreit* was the constellation under which modern historical writing was born. On the one hand, there is the legacy of both Vico and Kant separating history and nature in the name of knowledge; on the other hand, there is the legacy of Herder advocating Spinozism with all of his redoubtable rhetorical powers and insisting on their ontological commonground. The former option manifested itself in the historicist's reflection on the nature of historical knowledge and which made historicists confident to postulate a firm and insurmountable ontological divide between the object of investigation of the physicist and that of the historian. On the other hand, they had inherited enough from Herder to make them prepared to discern a quasi-natural dimension in the historical order. This dimension they attributed to political power in its Machiavellian or *raison d'état* manifestation (as in the case of Meinecke),[30] or in a higher naturalism that we may get access to when the historian has fulfilled his tasks and that will bring us to the level of the highest knowledge, superseding the opposition between history and nature (as in the case of Burckhardt).[31] In the case of Meinecke the problem of the (re-)unification of history and nature itself was still stated in Kantian terms (i.e. in terms of the opposition between the natural, and the moral order), while he tried to overcome the problem with an appeal to a Spinozist pan(en)theismus.[32] Whereas Burckhardt appealed to Schopenhauer's short-cut of an identification of the transcendental self with the ontological category of the Will. However different Meinecke's and Burckhardt's solutions may have been, both wrestled with the legacy of modern historical thought in the *Pantheismusstreit*, and with the insoluble conflict between Spinoza and Kant.[33]

One last comment on the *Pantheismusstreit* and its two main protagonists, Kant and Herder, is due here. Undoubtedly Kant's philosophical genius outshone by far Herder's often so regrettably chaotic intellectual efforts. Herder was no match for Kant – arguably the greatest philosopher of all times, after all – and Herder was painfully aware of this, no less than his contemporaries such as Goethe and Schiller. For Herder the conflict with Kant, formerly his adored master at Königsberg University, was the most bitter experience of his life and it cast a dark shadow over his last years. All the more so since he probably had been

---

30 Friedrich Meinecke, *Die Idee der Staatsräson in der neueren Geschichte* (Munich: Oldenbourg, 1976).
31 Burckhardt was fascinated by how the Age of Constantine the Great presents itself to the historian as 'metamorphosis' ('Verpuppung') of Greek and Roman antiquity into the Christian world of the Middle Ages – juts as a caterpillar may change into a butterfly.
32 The term 'Panentheismus' was used for the first time by Karl Christian Krause (1781 – 1832). See, Zammito, 'Herder, Kant, Spinoza', pp. 113, 131. See also, Reinbert A. Krol, 'Friedrich Meinecke: Pantheism and the Crisis of Historicism', *Journal of the Philosophy of History*, 4:2 (2010), 195 – 209.
33 See also note 25.

insufficiently aware himself of how his *Ideen* ran up against the very essence of Kant's first *Critique*. He even believed to have written in Kant's spirit when so courageously presenting the coming into being of the solar system as the beginning of human history.

At the same time, Kant was also unbalanced himself by his encounter with Herder. Zammito even goes as far as to claim that the *Critique of Judgment* – especially the analysis of teleology of presented there – was a response to the challenges presented to him by Herder's *Ideen*.[34] Whatever may be the truth about that, it cannot be denied that Kant's own effort to outline a philosophy of history – his *Idee zu einer allgemeinen Geschichte in weltbürgerlichen Absicht* – has some striking similarities with Herder's *Ideen*. Think of the following passage:

> nature does not do anything superfluous and is never wasteful in the means it uses for achieving its aims. So when it granted to man reason and, hence, freedom of the will, that was already a clear indication of what it must have had in mind when fixing human nature in this way.[35]

So nature has a certain purpose with us and gave us the means – reason and freedom – in order to achieve that purpose dictated by nature. A Spinozist would find nothing to quarrel with in this, for obviously this is *logos* philosophy in *optima forma*.[36] Kant's brief essay dates from 1784, so two years before the outbreak of the *Pantheismusstreit,* and from the same year in which the first volume of Herder's *Ideen* came out. So perhaps Kant detested the *Ideen* so much because it made him painfully aware of his own unreflected Spinozism.[37]

With the wisdom of hindsight one might say that the disagreement between Kant and Herder boiled down, in the end, to the question how far one could or should go with the demand to historicize. Kant agreed to recognize Reason,

---

34 Zammito, 'Herder, Kant, Spinoza', p. 110. See also John Zammito, *The Genesis of Kant's Critique of Judgment* (Chicago: Chicago University Press, 1992).
35 See, Immanuel Kant, 'Idee zu einer allgemeinen Geschichte in Weltbürgerlichen Absicht', in Immanuel Kant, *Ausgewälte Kleine Schriften* (Hamburg: Felix Meiner, 1965), p. 30.
36 And in many ways an anticipation of Hegel's philosophy of history.
37 Zammito added a new dimension to the old discussion of the causes of the conflict between Herder and Kant. Zammito periodizes the German Enlightenment into periods of 'Popularphilosophie' and of 'Schulphilosophie'. He then goes on to say that both Kant and Herder were protagonists of 'Popularphilosophie' until Kant broke away from that tradition and began a new period of 'Schulphilopsophie' with his Copernican revolution in the 1770s. So not Herder (as is commonly assumed) but Kant was the one who broke up their cooperation. See John Zammito, *Kant, Herder, and the Birth of Anthropology* (Chicago and London: Chicago University Press, 2002). It must strike the reader of Zammito's erudite book that Spinoza is virtually absent from his discussion of Herder. The explanation probably is that Zammito aims at a rehabilitation of Herder; and then Herder's well-attested Spinozism may well be a hindrance rather than a help.

human Reason, as a gift of Nature; but he opposed, or would have opposed Herder's proposal to infer from this that we ought therefore include nature in (human) history as well. For him the emergence of human Reason out of the cosmic processes resulting in the solar system belonged to the history of Nature, and not to that of (human) History. And the former stopped where the latter began. Herder, however, was ready to consider human history as being part of natural history and unwilling to see any unbridgeable gaps between the two of them.

And, indeed, because of his Spinozism Herder could consistently argue this way, whereas the Kant of the first *Critique* could not possibly do so. For Kantian epistemology, as a theory of human knowledge, must *sui generis* remain indifferent to the trajectory of how it came into being from a *historical* point of view. For example, if you wish to know why the eye enables you to perceive visible reality, theories about the *history* of the eye will at most be of occasional interest, but cannot be of any real relevance to your inquiry. Optics and not history are then what you should rely upon. On the other hand, Herder could argue that Kant's decision to separate natural and human history is wholly arbitrary. For why should we restrict History, even human history, only to that of the species of the *Homo sapiens*? Does *homo sapiens* not have a history anterior to its emergence? All the more so, is human history not embedded in a natural history in which human history is a mere accidental detail?

Or, as the practitioners of world-history might urge, is the impending ecological crisis not impressive proof of the revenge that natural history may well have on human history – with the implication that human history has become part of natural history? Have we not exceeded the limits within which nature had enclosed us and our history, so that we are now in a state of war with that all-encompassing natural context? Is this then not the story we will have to tell in order to inform humanity about where it presently is in its history? Klaus Meyer-Abich would agree: 'the conflict with nature caused by industrialization must remind us of the fact that we do not intervene in the world from the outside, theistically, so to say, but are part of that world ourselves'.[38] We are not the Gods of the natural order, but merely one of its more modest modifications, to use Spinozist language. And if we had paid more attention to Herder's philosophy of history, we would have known this all along. We would then have had a historical writing continuously warning us about the dangers of our interactions with nature.

But as this imaginary discussion between Kant and Herder suggests, we have

---

38 See Klaus M. Meyer-Abich, 'Herders Naturphilosophie in der Naturkrise der Industriegesellschaft', in *Herder und die Philosophie des Deutschen Idealismus*, ed. by Marion Heinz (Amsterdam: Rodopi, 1997), p. 328.

reached an impasse here. How far we should go with the demand to historicize is, in the end, an arbitrary decision. We may opt here for either Kant or Herder, but we will then necessarily do so on the basis of choices unrelated to the issue itself that is *sub judice* here – for example, on the basis of why we like Spinozism (Herder) or epistemology (Kant). The concept of history *itself* can offer no help here, for we would make ourselves guilty of the sin of circular argument when trying to derive the concept of history from itself.

Hegel

In an erudite essay on the origins of German idealism, Jack Zammito made abundantly clear what is wrong with the traditional picture that Herder's influence on the emergence of idealism was zero. Indeed, he was Kant's antipode. But precisely of this his Spinozism could not fail to attract the attention of all those wrestling with the problems occasioned by the Kantian system. I already mentioned the fascination that Spinozism had on Kant's own disciples.[39] Think furthermore of Hölderlin,[40] or of Schelling who wrote to Hegel in a letter in 1795 'ich bin indessen ein Spinozist geworden'. Indeed, much of Idealism and Romanticism evolved in the polarity between Spinozism and Kantianism. This is why Herder's thought became the model for many German thinkers at the turn of the century.

There is no more impressive proof of this claim than Hegel. In the first place, both were Spinozists. Consider Hegel's statement on Spinoza in his *History of Philosophy*: 'when one begins to philosophize one must be first a Spinozist. The soul must bathe itself in the aether of the single substance, in which everything one has held dear is submerged'.[41] And no less than Herder was Hegel attracted to Spinoza since the latter's notion of the single substance promised a way-out of the dualisms of the Kantian system.[42] Above all that of subject and object, since both should be seen as mere modes of that single substance.[43] A substance,

---

39 See Zammito, 'Herder, Kant, Spinoza', p. 123.
40 Margarethe Wegenast, *Hölderlins Spinoza-rezeption und ihre Bedeutung für die Konzeption des "Hyperion"* (Tübingen: Niemeyer, 1990).
41 Quoted in Beiser, *Hegel*, pp. 46–47.
42 Though is must be added that where Kant had for Herder been the main challenge in his intellectual life, Hegel seems to have been much more indifferent to Kant. In fact, an adequate description of the Hegelian system is possible without any reference to Kant. Surely, this is completely different for Fichte and Schelling.
43 A claim that was radicalized by Schelling's identity philosophy and which went as far as to postulate the actual *identity* of subject and object, of mind and nature. See Heinrich Schipperges, 'Natur,' in *Geschichtliche Grundbegriffe. Historisches Lexikon zur politisch-*

moreover that both Herder and Hegel were happy to characterize as 'nature'. However, both Herder and Hegel unambiguously rejected Spinoza's requirement to proceed *more geometrico*, and his mechanistic and deterministic conception of nature.[44] In opposition to Spinoza both warmly embraced an *organicist* conception of nature,[45] and that was accepted by most of their contemporaries:

> the organic worldview seemed enormously appealing to a whole generation of thinkers at the close of the eighteenth century. The great attraction of the organic paradigm is that it seemed to uphold the unity and continuity of nature by explaining both the mental and the physical according to a single paradigm. It seemed to realize that long-sought ideal of all science since the seventeenth century: a non-reductive yet naturalistic explanation of life and the mind. The organic paradigm is non-reductivist since it explains everything holistically, by showing how they play a necessary role in a whole. The organic paradigm is also naturalistic, (…) because it understands all events according to laws, where these laws are holistic rather than mechanistic (…).[46]

So, in agreement with intellectual climate of the time both Herder and Hegel 'vitalized' Spinoza. Moreover, both welcomed the introduction of Aristotelian formal and final causes when describing this vitalized nature; both discerned in nature entelechical principles, called 'ideas' by Hegel,[47] striving for their real-

---

sozialen Sprache in Deutschland, vol. 4, ed. by Otto Brunner, Werner Conze, Reinhart Koselleck (Stuttgart: Ernst Klett, 1978), p. 237.

44 Here Kant might have expressed his qualified agreement; think of his observation in the third *Critique* that there could never be a Newton for the growth of a blade of grass. And Kant adds here that we can only fully comprehend what we have made ourselves, thus introducing unwittingly Vico's famous historicist thesis of the 'verum et factum convertuntur' in his otherwise so very anti-historicist thought.

45 'Herder, pointing beyond his age as part of the rising organistic trend and opposing the mechanistic and rationalistic schemes of his times, was firmly rooted in his own time and naturally reflects some of its character'. See Edgar Schick, *Metaphorical Organicism in Herder's Early Works: A Study of the Relation of Herder's Literary Idiom to his World-view* (The Hague; Paris: Mouton, 1971), p. 121.

46 Beiser, *Hegel*, pp. 85–86. Beiser agrees here with Zammito's general characteristic of the German idealists: 'they did not want to deny to the Absolute life and existence, but understood life itself as εν και παν. Since the young idealists conceived of primeval Being as being essentially fused with Being, they united a far from lifeless Absolute with animated nature. Nature was for them more than mere matter, nature was a life force'. See Zammito, 'Herder, Kant, Spinoza', p. 128.

47 It is here that Hegel argument shows a striking resemblance to the so-called 'doctrine of the historical ideas' advocated by early historicists such as Leopold von Ranke and Humboldt. Discussing Hegel's Aristotelianism Beiser comments: 'following Aristotle's critique of Plato, Hegel thinks that universals do not exist as such but only *in re*, in particular things. As forms inherent in things, as concrete universals, universals are, in Aristotle's language, the *formal-final* causes of things. The formal cause consists in the essence or nature of a thing, what makes it the thing it is, and the final cause is the purpose the object attempts to realize, the goal of its development' (see Beiser, *op. cit.*; 67). This completely captures the historicist notion of the 'historical idea'. See Frank Ankersmit, 'The Necessity of Historicism', *Journal of the Philosophy of History*, 4:2 (2010), 226–240.

ization and both considered these principles to be the *trait d'union* between the domains of nature and those of life and of human history.

But the differences between Herder and Hegel are no less striking. Herder never associates entelechy and its purposes with Reason. He would never have seen Reason as History's final cause.[48] This is different with Hegel; Hegel not only naturalizes history with Herder, he also "rationalized" it. Reason is for him immanent in nature; as Zammito succinctly puts it: 'Nature as a living force is both in the world and its higher principle. It is *immanent Reason*'.[49] We encounter here Hegel's return to *logos* philosophy, and where he refers, with one majestic gesture, the whole effort of Kantian critical philosophy to the dustbin.[50]

Let me offer a clarification here. In both Stoicism and natural law philosophy of the seventeenth and eighteenth centuries Reason had *two* habitats, instead of just *one* (i. e. in the human mind). Reason was believed to be present in the world itself in the sense that the Stoic's 'λογοί σπερματικοι' – i. e. 'logical seeds' – guaranteed the rational and predictable behaviour of the things of the world. Objects do not suddenly fall to the ceiling, if we drop them from our fingers but they will consistently fall to the ground. So it as if there is some hidden 'principle' in them "forcing" them to this most "rational" behaviour. This is what Hegel calls 'objective Reason or Mind' ('objektiver Geist'), but the very same Reason is also present in our mind, enabling us to fathom the secrets of nature, and this is 'subjective Reason or Mind' ('subjektiver Geist'). Within this picture it is Reason's world-historical task to *recognize*, on the level of the subjective Reason, objective Reason as its own *alter ego*. But this is a most complicated and laborious process that, in fact, will only be achieved at the end of history. The process requires such a tremendous effort since it is a kind of fusion of the domains of knowledge and that of being, of the universal and the particular. The universal and knowledge are first in the order of explanation since explanation requires an

---

48 'In contrast to Vico, accordingly, Herder postulates no ultimate explanations in term of an allegedly recognizable coincidence between divine purposes *of* history and actual human purposes *in* history'. See Frederick Barnard, *Herder on Nationality, Humanity and History* (Montreal and London: McGill-Queen's University Press, 2003), p. 110. Much the same picture arises when one contrasts Herder not with Vico but with Hegel. Herder reserved his teleological argument for the components of (both natural) and human history, but excluded the whole of the historical process from it.
49 See, Zammito, 'Herder, Kant, Spinoza', p. 128; see also pp. 130, 131. Or think of how Hegel put it himself when writing about philosophy of history: 'the only thought it brings along with itself is, however, the simple thought of Reason, hence, that Reason governs the world and that therefore world history is a rational process'. See Georg Wilhelm Friedrich Hegel, *Vorlesungen über die Philosophie der Weltgeschichte. Band 1. Die Vernunft in der Geschichte* (Hamburg: Meiner, 1970), p. 28.
50 Thus, Beiser writes: 'it is indeed striking that Hegel commended the old rationalism precisely because it assumed that thinking could grasp reality in itself, and in this respect he even held that it stood on a higher level than Kant's critical philosophy'. See Beiser, *Hegel*, p. 55.

appeal to universals; the particular is first in the order of existence, since whatever exists is given us as particulars. Hence, if subjective Reason is to recognize itself in its *alter ego*, objective Reason, it has to cross – and also *close* – the gap between the order of knowledge and that of being.

Dialectics is given the task of closing that gap; and dialectics needs nothing less than all of history to achieve this tremendous feat of the reconciliation of knowledge and being, finally resulting in the 'absolute Mind'. It also follows, as I should emphasize, that dialectics is a kind of go-between between knowledge and being; it therefore inhabits both domains. Consequently, the distinction between knowledge or language, on the one hand, and the world or being, on the other – a distinction that is conditional for all contemporary philosophy of language – does not apply to the Hegelian system. All that is of importance and interest in Hegel's philosophy cuts right across that to us so familiar language versus world opposition.

Vanamonde

Self-evidently, this raises the question of how to give some actual concrete content to Hegel's bold assertions about the fusion of the order of being and of knowledge, of the universal and the singular, and of the dialectics of language and the world – all of them finally resulting in the 'absolute mind'. Hegel himself never bothered to answer that question, nor any of his many disciples, as far as I know.[51] But we can be sure that it must be a figure of the future – of 'the end of history' on Hegelian assumptions. This, then, is where the imagination of the writers of science-fiction literature could be of assistance.[52] For does SF not give us a premonition of the future, and of the ultimate goals of mankind? There can be no doubt about that the unsurpassed genius of SF-literature – a genre more or less dead by now – has been Sir Arthur Clarke (1917 – 2008). And, indeed, in four of his novels – *Against the Fall of Night, The City and the Stars, Childhood's End*, and *2001: A Space Odyssey* – a theme occurs that seems to fit the Hegelian model of the end of history, one that may give some concrete and imaginable substance

---

51 Hegel's praise of liberal constitutional monarchy should not be read as implying that history had come to an end in his own time, but only as indication what should be seen, according to him, as most progressive at the time he was writing. Hegel was no conservative, let alone a reactionary: he admired Napoleon and right to the end of his life he always toasted on the French Revolution on 14 July.
52 That Fukuyama's *End of History* comes not even remotely close to what we should associate with Hegel's conception of it, will be too obvious to be stated. And the same is true of any other attempts to locate Hegel's end of history in the foreseeable future, or, even worse, in the present.

to Hegel's visions of the end of history. I shall be the first to admit that Clarke's image of the future are very weird; but after the discussion in recent Anglo-Saxon philosophy on "brains in a vat", on people exchanging hemispheres of their brains, on what it is like to be a bat and so on, we have little reason to complain that Clarke's speculations should be too bizarre to be taken seriously. Or think of Leibniz's monadology: that system even is immeasurably weirder than anything Clarke has to tell us

2001: A Space Odyssey gives the basic pattern. The idea here is that as we now already have prostheses for amputated limbs, science will enable us replace all parts of the human body with more reliable substitutes. In the end our brains will also be replaced by some more perfect and enduring substitute.[53] At that stage, the opposition of mind and matter, of knowledge and being would have been overcome.[54] This certainly seems to go a long way to realize Hegel's predictions about the end of history.

But one might object that we are not yet where we would have to be according to Hegel. For exchanging all our present bodily parts for technologically more reliable alternatives still leaves us much the same human beings whom we have been all of the time. At least, if all our prostheses are functioning as they should. We would then still remain individual human beings, and be no less dependent on our more advanced physical machinery than we presently are on our so much more imperfect biological make-up. More particularly, there would still be no fusion of the Hegelian particular – i.e. individual human beings – with the Hegelian universal – i.e. the technological knowledge required for turning us into such machine-like images of our former selves.

But in the other three novels Clarke presents us with even more ambitious premonitions of the future. Whereas in *2001. A Space Odyssey* the issue is addressed from the perspective of matter, he there attacks it from that of mind. As Clarke most powerfully puts it:

> imagine that every man's mind is an island, surrounded by the ocean. Each seems isolated, yet in reality are linked by the bedrock from which they spring. If the ocean were to vanish, that would be the end of the islands. They would all be part of one continent, but their individuality would have gone.[55]

---

53 The speculation is of special interest from the perspective of Vico's claim that history offers us a knowledge superior to that of science, since we have made history ourselves, whereas nature is the product of God's hands. We might now accuse Vico of having forgotten that we, as human beings, do also belong to nature and, hence, to the domain created by God. So how could we understand history? Only if we assume that who we are should be of no relevance to history. But that assumption is most implausible: surely our natural desires, our passions, and even our biological constitution are most prominently present in human history.
54 Arthur C. Clarke, *2001: Een ruimte-odyssee* (Utrecht: A. W. Bruna, 1969), p. 146.
55 Arthur C. Clarke, *Childhood's End* (New York: Ballantine Books, 1964), p. 146.

Surely this gives us a fusion of the universal and the particular, as Hegel demanded. But not in the way such fusion was achieved in the writings of the mass-psychologists of the early 1900s, such as Gustave Le Bon or Gabriel Tarde. For there such fusion is a loss in our awareness of the world; Le Bon's and Tarde's masses are blind forces waiting to be guided into any direction that their leader takes them. However, here this awareness is increased immensely; for it results in a pure mind in which the awareness of the world, of matter or being, is complete.[56] This does certainly sound very Hegelian, especially if we recall that *awareness*, the recognition by the subject (subjective reason) of itself in the object (objective reason) is absolutely basic to the Hegelian system. In this quasi-Hegelian absolute mind the universe comes to a complete awareness of itself. And the speculation is no less Spinozist, for that matter, since in Clarke's construction mind and matter could well be seen as emanations, or modifications of the Spinozist single substance. But even this is not yet the end of the story.

For in both *Childhood's End* and *The City and the Stars* Clarke goes on to say a few more things about this model of the absolute mind. As Clarke insists strange things may happen when and where it manifests itself. When in *Childhood's End* humanity metamorphoses itself into the "absolute mind" the last man who still is like you and me witnesses its exploits:

> just a minute: I've noticed something else. *My weight is decreasing.* What does that mean? I've dropped a pencil – it's falling slowly. Something's happened to gravity. (…) The buildings round me, the ground, the mountains – everything's like glass – *I can see through it.* Earth is dissolving. My weight has almost gone. (…) There goes the river. No change in the sky, though. I can hardly breath. Strange to see the Moon still shining up there. I'm glad they left it, but it will be lonely now. The light! From *beneath* me – inside the Earth – shining upward, through the rocks, the ground, everything – growing brighter, brighter, blinding.[57]

Here the report breaks off – and the last man is also dissolved into nothingness, with everything else. As will be clear from this quote, the "absolute mind" may indulge in playing with the laws of nature and change them in agreement with its wishes. And this also is as it should be. A mind that is pure awareness, and awareness only, still upholds the distinction between awareness and what it is awareness *of*. The truly absolute mind must overcome this distinction and does so by being master of the laws of nature. And there is, again, a deep message in this. Dissolving the Earth and its last human inhabitant as described by Clarke presupposes a *will* to do so. In this way Clarke's variant of Hegel's absolute mind

---

56 At the admittedly enigmatic end of *2001. A Space Odyssey* Clarke even has the courage to describe how the 'mutation' of a mind like our own, into such a quasi-Hegelian absolute mind, might take place.
57 Clarke, *Childhoods' End*, pp. 216–17.

comes close to Schopenhauer's will – the *noumenal* ground of all of *phenomenal* reality.[58] And where there is a will, there must be an entity doing the willing. This entity is thus a reconciliation of the concrete entity it is and the laws of nature willed by it, thus perfectly satisfying Hegel's notion of the "concrete universal". But as such it still retains something – as it must do – of the particular and can, hence be assigned a proper name. Clarke gives it the name 'Vanamonde',[59] which certainly is a much more poetic and fascinating name than that of God.[60]

Premonitions

One last aspect of Clarke's vision of the future of mankind is of interest in the present context. *Childhood's End* begins with the invasion of the so-called Overlords, to whom the task was given of supervising humanity in the process ending with its transformation into the 'absolute mind', as described in the previous section. At the end of the book one of these Overlords refers to that invasion in a discussion with the last human inhabitant of the Earth:

> when our ships entered your skies (…) you feared and recognized us, as we knew that you would. It was not precisely a memory. You have already had proof that time is more complex than your science ever imagined. For that memory was not of the past, but of the *future* – of those closing years when your race knew that everything was finished. (…) It was as if a distorted echo had reverberated round the closed circle of time, from the future to the past. Call it not a memory, but a premonition.[61]

In sum, the invaders were feared so much since mankind had a vague but no less compelling premonition of what would happen to it. Not an "aftermath", but a "foremath", so to say. When pondering this, once again so thought-provoking conjecture, the first thing to come to mind is Samuel Johnson's initially counter-intuitive statement that 'nothing settles a man's mind so much as the knowledge that he will be hanged tomorrow'. Of course this is not a matter permitting of easy generalizations – and many examples seem to contradict Johnson's observation. Nevertheless, in his last book Douwe Draaisma discusses the letters written by the victims of Robespierre's Regime of Terror on the eve of their

---

58 Schopenhauer himself would not have agreed with having his own system grafted upon that of Hegel, for whom he felt only hatred and contempt.
59 Arthur C. Clarke, *The City and the Stars* (New York: Harcourt, Brace and Company, 1956), p. 164.
60 In fact, whereas wisdom is ordinarily considered to be one of God's most prominent attributes, Clarke associates his variant of the absolute mind with the playfulness of children. The 'absolute mind' still has to grow up, as it seems. And then the intriguing question is what meaning could be given to this though-provoking conjecture.
61 Clarke, *Childhood's End*, p. 207.

execution, which have been preserved for posterity since Fouquier-Tinville's subordinates never bothered to pass them on to their addressees. Most striking in these letters is the tone of resignation and apparently their writers worried more about how they would live on in the memory of their wives, husbands and children than about their encounter of the next day with the guillotine.[62] Even more so, in the last chapter of his best known book Draaisma discusses 'near death experiences' (NDE's); hence, what went on in the mind of persons being certain that they would die in the next few seconds. So mountaineers in an apparently fatal fall, swimmers about to drown or people involved in a dramatic car-accident. Again, there is neither panic nor despair here. Rather, an impulse of dissociation and of quiet objectification, often going together with what is called "panoramic memory", that is, the tendency to survey all of one's life within one comprehensive whole. If these stories are true, dying must be less of an ordeal than we ordinarily believe (so much the worse, one might add, for Heidegger's 'Sein zum Tode').[63] Strangely enough, the prospect of *imminent death* seems to be less traumatic than the *survival of death*. Whereas we would expect death to be such a terrible event that its *foremath* must be far worse than its *aftermath*, for whatever may happen in the aftermath, one apparently had had the good luck to avoid the worst by having survived the potentially fatal event itself.

But suppose now that the newspapers were to announce tomorrow that scientists have ascertained that sooner or later we shall all die. The message would universally be recognized as idiotic; not only because this is no news to us, but also since few people really worry about the inevitability of their own death.[64] But if the newspapers were to tell us that because of some inescapable cosmic catastrophe the end of humanity is to be expected in some two hundred years – thus after all those people living now will have died – this news would come to us as a tremendous shock. Apparently, there is an asymmetry in how we react to our own death, on the one hand, and that of humanity as a whole, on the other. Arguably, this could be seen as one of the more redeeming features of the human individual; apparently the capacity to transcend our own narrow perspective on the world is somehow innate in human nature. Supposing, then, that human beings may strangely be more sensitive to the end of humanity than to their own death – perhaps because of some gene that evolution has written into our DNA – Clarke's idea that we may have a premonition of some future catastrophe affecting all of humanity can be considered intellectually less irresponsible than it might initially seem to be. And that would get us back to our conjecture at the

---

62 Douwe Draaisma, *Vergeetboek* (Groningen: Historiche Uitgeverij, 2010), pp. 229–249.
63 Douwe Draaisma, *Why Life Speeds up as you Get Older: How Memory Shapes our Past*, trans. by Arnold and Erica Pomerans (Cambridge: Cambridge University Press 2004), esp. ch. 17.
64 Or – as Spinoza argues – by blinding ourselves to that fact by experiencing our lives as eternal.

beginning of this essay that world-history is, perhaps, the *foremath* of the ecological catastrophe predicted by climate-scientists.

For a *juste milieu* between Spinoza and Kant

I expect that most of us will be impressed by Hegel's apocalyptic vision of mankind's future and probably even more by Clarke's so singularly powerful and convincing poeticization of the Hegelian vision. These kinds of stories, about the last things, are always fascinating however sceptical we may be with regard to their plausibility. Who does not read St. John's *Apocalypse* without being deeply impressed by its language and the scenes depicted in it? There is a cosmic poetry in all such texts that must remind us of Burke and Kant's notion of the sublime, which we may find (with E.T.A. Hoffmann) in Beethoven's great symphonies or in the work of painters such as Francisco Goya, David Kaspar Friedrich or, John Martin.[65] These works of art give us an intimation of eternity, of the vastness of the universe, of the powers of nature and, in opposition to all that, of our own littleness and utter insignificance. And yet we have ourselves a role to play as well in these sublime visions; if only to accentuate our own insignificance. The creators of these sublime works of art therefore never omit a hint of the human.[66] They need the futility of mankind in order to exalt a sublime nature, or reversely, a sublime nature in order to suggest our own futility. Nevertheless, the two of them, nature and mankind, remain tied to each other; and in this way sublime art seems to honour Spinozist speculations about the one single substance and to which we belong along with huge mountain-peaks, raging seas, or the cold and inhospitable infinity of the universe. Or rather, as argued by theorists of the sublime, we are nauseatingly caught up in the paradox of being forced to such a sense of belonging, whereas, at the same time, we are sure that we will never actually *succeed* in extending the sense of belonging to those mountain-peaks, raging seas and so on.

Indeed, in all these intimations of sublimity nothing is left of the human being and of humanity; he is completely swallowed up by the immense forces of nature whose powers far beyond his own fragile powers. So it is, too, in world-history – perhaps one more variation on the theme of the sublime – and where genes, germs, epidemics, the rhythm of the glacial periods, the accidents of the dis-

---

65 See, for the sublime in music, the dissertation by Kiene Brillenburg Wurth, *The Musically Sublime: Indeterminacy, Infinity, Irresolvability* (New York: Fordham University Press, 2009).
66 A striking illustration of this claim is John Martins's (1789–1854) impressive 'Sadak in search of the waters of oblivion' of 1812 (now in the Saint Louis Art Museum). Think away the tiny human figure on the foreground – and the painting becomes meaningless.

tribution of corns, grasses and livestock, and so on determine humanity's fate. The human species is presented here as well, but as in the sublime work of art as merely the helpless and passive plaything of quasi-divine powers infinitely larger than itself.

No doubt this is an important message, especially now. We had forgotten about nature and about the undeniable fact that human history is, in the end, part of natural history. There was natural history before human history and there will, again, be aeons of natural history after the end of human history – 'man came and went', to quote the title of one more deeply moving story by Arthur Clarke. Hence, Hegel is right when insisting that 'an awareness of the objective' or nature is a condition of our own perfection. And now that an ecological catastrophe is imminent if the scientists are right, this is truer than ever. Without such awareness, without the awareness of nature's reaction to our most irresponsible behaviour towards her, not even a beginning can be made with resetting the balance between nature and man. So let nature cloth itself in its most sublime garb, so that we cannot fail to become aware of it powers again. And then we cannot read enough of Hegel and Clarke.

But Hegelian awareness is not enough. We also need the notion of human agency; and it would be the stupidest of mistakes to eliminate human agency since it performed so poorly and counter-productively in the past one and a half centuries. To paralyze human agency is the danger of sublimity and of the effect that the work by authors such as Hegel and Clarke writing in the style of the sublime may have on us. It needs human agency to redress the errors of previous human agency – and without it all will be lost. But Hegel's vision of the "absolute mind" leaves no room for agency. For him the end of history is the end of action. What could one?, us?, God? still meaningfully do after having reached that ultimate stage? What prospect of real action is left to the Hegelian "absolute mind"? It can do little else than sit down and ponder the road whence it came. All is then history, and the future has been wiped away. So it is in Clarke's operationalization of Hegel: Clarke's absolute minds are either outright destructive (the mad mind), childishly playful by making, for example, rivers run uphill instead of the reverse, or most often simply unsure about what they could meaningfully do. Thus Clarke lets the Hegelian 'absolute mind', as presented in *2001: A Space Odyssey*, somewhat despondently declare at the end the novel: 'for though he was now master of the world, he did not yet know exactly what he should do. But he will think of something'.[67] But, again, what could it/he still meaningfully do at all?

It is much the same in world history, as written by McNeill and his many

---

67 Introduce some cosmic variant of the master/slave relationship would probably be Hegel's own suggestion.

followers. History as presented here nowhere shows a juncture for meaningful actions simply because all human action, either individual or collective would be wholly irrelevant from the perspective they ordinarily adopt. World-history is the history of the irreversible *faits accomplis*, of the facts that we could neither prevent nor change. It is history that rages over us like a thunderstorm. Traditional historical writing was too humanist; it saw in our collective past only the hands and mind of man – the Spinozism of Herder, Hegel and of contemporary world-history adopted the other extreme and saw human history as a mere extension of natural history. So where to find the *juste milieu* between these two extremes, between the Menippean satire of the traditional Vichian, humanist picture of the world,[68] on the one hand,[69] and the cosmic sublimity of Spinoza, Hegel and Clarke, on the other? Where to find the right balance between the human species and it always liked to tell its history, on the one hand, and nature, on the other?

At this stage two options suggest themselves as the *juste milieu* between these two extremes. The first would be to return to a metaphysically defined division between the domains of man and nature, as was typically provided by Vico and that presented us with the so very reassuring clear cut demarcation between the domain of the sciences and that of the humanities, hence between nature and man. But such a solution would fail to do justice to our present predicament which, if anything, throws into our faces a dramatic rearrangement of the domains of nature and man, a rearrangement that we could not even hope to discuss meaningfully on the assumption that both nature and man have their preordained role to play on the scene of history.

At this stage we would do well to recall the discussion about the relationship between man and nature was occasioned by the *Spinozismusstreit*, with Kant and Herder as their main protagonists. And that discussion was, essentially, not a discussion about how to carve up the world in a domain proper to nature and one that is proper to mankind. This discussion was rather a debate epistemology versus metaphysics. Kant asked himself the question of the conditions of the possibility of human knowledge of the world both natural and human. And this epistemological approach enabled him too to propose a division reminiscent of that of that of Vico. On the basis of his epistemology there is, on the one hand, the domain of the transcendental self and, on the other, that of the phenomenal

---

68 For a clarification of the Menippian satire, see Hans Kellner, *Language and Historical Representation: Getting the Story Crooked* (Madison, Wis.: University of Wisconsin Press, 1989), p. 172. Kellner brilliantly argues here that Braudel's *La Méditerranée et le monde Méditerranéen à l'époque de Philippe II* was written in this style.
69 With regard to the humanist picture of the world one might well risk the paradox that we should begin with becoming less humanist than we have been, if the human species is to be saved from the dangers presently threatening its survival.

world as the object of the transcendentalist self's knowledge of that world. Vico's metaphysical division was now transformed into an epistemological division. This was, in fact, the great revolution effected by Kant: all (formerly) ontological disputes were now discussed from the perspective of the Kantian transcendental self. Which, by the way, did not in the least prevent that on the new Kantian vocabulary would produce results closely resembling those that had been fashionable during the pre-Kantian regime of ontology or metaphysics. For example, the older, Vichian division between the domains of nature and man would be reformulated by the neo-Kantians at the end of the nineteenth century in terms of the transcendental self and the objects of its knowledge.

However, of specific importance in the present context is Kantian ethics. As we all know, Kant applied the transcendental approach to ethics as well by asking himself the transcendental question of how ethics is possible. That is to say, ethics should not be founded, as used to be the case, on merely empirical or rational principles. Such principles will have to be summoned for the tribunal of transcendental reason questioning their very possibility. As Kant puts it:

> we will therefore have to investigate the possibility of a categorical imperative wholly aprioristically, since we sadly miss here the advantage that its reality should be given to us in experience so that this possibility would not be necessary for the fixation of the categorical imperative, but only for explaining it.[70]

And, again, as we all know this made Kant ask himself the somewhat surprising question whether the mere form of the, or a categorical imperative did not yet contain already itself the clue to its formulation. This was actually the case, as Kant insisted, with the result that the categorical imperative runs as follows: 'always act in agreement with a principle of action that you could be will to become a general law'.[71] Later on Kant comes up with different variants of the categorical imperative and I now quote one such reformulation that is of specific interest in our present discussion:

> since the universality of laws determining effects is which is called Nature in the most general sense of the word (in agreement with its form) and since therefore the being of things is determined by universal laws – the universal, categorical imperative could be formulated as follows: always act in such a way that the maxim of your action could, by virtue of your own will, become a UNIVERSAL LAW OF NATURE.[72]

---

70 See Immanuel Kant, *Grundlegung zur Metaphysik der Sitten* (Stuttgart: Philipp Reclam, 1970), p. 66.
71 Unfortunately, Kant never tells us what criteria we have for deciding whether we can, or ought to will some maxim of action to become a general law, or not. But perhaps the notion of contradiction could help him out here: for example, it could be argued that making the maxime of theft into a general law would be in contradiction with the notion of property.
72 See Kant, *Grundlegung zur Metaphysik der Sitten*, p. 68

Hence, Kant presents our ethical obligations here as a supplement to the laws of nature: there are the already existing general laws of nature, but we ought to add to them – as additional laws of nature – the also general moral laws that are dictated by transcendental practical reason.

This, then, is where Kant can be said to strike the right balance between the order of nature and that of man, between the Spinozist tradition of Herder, Hegel and Clarke on the one hand, and that Vichian humanism, on the other. Spinozist ethics is little more than a (Stoic) subjection to the laws of nature; but Kant adds to these laws the morals laws originating in transcendental *human* reason. Observe, finally, that this synthesis is achieved on the level of a *moral* obligation. So this prescribes to us the duties that we have towards 'nature', and that we forgot with Vichian humanism.

Conclusion

If the climate-scientists are right – and it would be most unwise to ignore their warnings – we are presently living in what one might call the *foremath* of a most serious catastrophe involving the future of mankind. No one can deny any longer that nature will have a terrible revenge on us if we fail to drastically reduce carbon-dioxide emissions, the size of the world's population, our ecological foot-print and our most irresponsible exploitation of this world's natural resources. As authors such as Mark Lynas, Edmund Wilson and a host of others have made chillingly clear World War II and the Holocaust are idylls if compared to the catastrophe awaiting us stubbornly refuse to acknowledge this absolutely basic fact about the chances of humanity's persistence in the future.[73] It is true, these authors always hopefully add that we may still escape this catastrophe if we were to collectively agree upon some quite painful measures. But after Kyoto, Copenhagen, Cancùn and, more recently, Durban, it will be clear that we had better forget about this. With the credit and debt crises of 2008 and 2011 we have other, and more pressing things on our mind. So if there is an ecological catastrophe in wait for us, we can be sure to get all of it.

The imminent catastrophe is, basically, a conflict between man and nature. Self-evidently, phrases like 'a conflict between man and nature' are anthropomorphist metaphors and not to be taken literally. No law of nature will be

---

73 Mark Lynas, *Six Degrees: Our Future on a Hotter Planet* (Washington, D.C.: National Geographic, 2008) (a profoundly unsettling book), Edward O. Wilson, *The Future of Life* (New York: Knopf, 2002) (arguing that we are, what he calls, 'the bottleneck' generation: if we fail to take the right decisions right now, we will destroy the future of the next generations). For an enumeration of other works relevent in this context, see Dipesh Chakrabarty, 'The Climate of History: Four Theses', *Critical Inquiry* 35:2 (2009), 197–222, p. 200, n. 8.

sinned against in the case of such a catastrophe; and our defeat in that conflict with nature will be wholly in agreement with the laws of nature, down to the minutest detail. There will be no Vanamonde bending these laws in our favour; however much the inherent anthropomorphism of the humanist conception of history may invite us to believe otherwise. Nor should "nature" be literally seen as an opponent having come into conflict with humanity; "nature" has neither desires nor purposes and the fighting out of conflicts with humanity is not on its agenda. Nevertheless, the metaphor certainly makes sense: whereas "nature" remained outside human history until quite recently, apart then from accidental earth-quakes, volcanic eruption, or tsunamis, it has now become a factor in human history of considerable, and even decisive significance. And, reversely, whereas humanity had no perceivable impact on "nature" until the Industrial Revolution, humanity may now change the Earth into an arid and lifeless desert.

From that perspective we may say with Paul Crutzen that we presently live in the 'anthropocene', a geological age whose character is to a large extent determined by human agency.[74] This should urge us to reconsider the question of the relationship between human history and natural history and that was so much at stake in the *Pantheismusstreit* of the end of the eighteenth century. In that battle, with Herder and Kant as its main protagonists, discussion focused on two issues and that were not often clearly distinguished. In the first place, are man and nature both part of the one single substance, as Spinoza had argued? From the perspective of our present ecological conflict with nature one might feel inclined to sympathize with the Spinozist position. Is it not true that Vichian humanism made us forget about nature and believe that we are living in some separate ontological realm reassuringly inaccessible to nature? So should we not all become Spinozists again now that 'nature' has made it so abundantly clear that it will not allow itself to be declared irrelevant?

But this brings me to the second issue. Kant's main achievement has been to definitively discredit *logos* philosophy and of which Spinozism certainly was an exponent. Spinoza postulated a rationality in reality itself – the single substance – and required the knowing subject to recognize that rationality, even more so, to surrender completely to it. Hegel can be said to have effected a radical historicization of Spinozism – and no one can fail to be impressed by how he did so. But if all is said and done, his system was a rehabilitation of *logos* philosophy. And such rehabilitation was only possible on the condition of ignoring Kant's critical philosophy.

So that places us for the dilemma of abandoning Kant (or not) in favour of Spinozism, since the latter seems to be so much more in agreement with what we expect from philosophy in the *foremath* of an ecological catastrophe. All the

---

74 Chakrabarty, 'The Climate of History', 207–212.

more so since we are all well aware of Kant's scientistic inclinations: and was it not precisely science that got us in our present predicament?

Nevertheless, I would prefer the Kantian horn of the dilemma. To begin with, though Spinozist conceptions of history may present us with fascinating vistas of the human past and present by including human history in natural history, the price to be paid for this is the sacrifice of human agency. And this sacrifice is neither realistic nor opportune under the present circumstances. In the second place I would consider the return to *logos* philosophy a regrettable and reactionary philosophical strategy. We may go *beyond* Kant, but not go back to a phase *antedating* his critical philosophy. That does by no means imply that we should embrace Kantian epistemology lock, stock and barrel; there are other ways for overcoming *logos* philosophy.[75]

---

[75] As advocated, for example, in my book, *Meaning, Truth and Reference in Historical Representation* (Ithaca, N.Y.: Cornell University Press, 2012).

Moshe Idel

Crafting a Golem: the Creation of an Artificial Anthropoid

Introduction: Modernity and Premonitions

To create a full-fledged man artificially is tantamount to being perfect in oneself. This presupposes a competition with the first creator of a man, God, whose ultimate result was conceived of as not being completely perfect. The possibility of such a human creation was thus implausible in a culture that promoted a vision of a fallen man – whose original sin created an original guilt – as was the case in Christian Europe over the last two millennia. Within this theological framework, the attempt to generate a perfect being may be conceived of as in competition with the divine creative act, the pre-lapsian perfect Adam. Perfection, if such was attainable in the lapsian situation, was extra-mundane, to be achieved by detaching the soul from the body, by means of askesis, or mystical techniques. Assumptions as to the fallen nature of man, coupled with an idea of divine perfection, stymied the emergence of the possibility that man may create a perfect being, body and soul together, and it cast a long shadow of ambiguity over the possibility of human perfection, even after Christianity began to lose its grip on the mind of the Europeans.

There are, however, some texts, such as Mary Shelley's *Frankenstein*, that anticipated the ambivalent developments in modern Europe. The new sciences, and their radical potential, were conceived of as being fraught with somber, even deleterious results. Thus Shelley's artificial anthropoid turned out to be a monster. This dichotomous approach toward a new and more powerful man, who uses scientific tools for his own purpose, could in principle, be understood as a positive development, but it was imagined in the novel to be in fact a dangerous enterprise. A 'fallen' Victor successfully created a monster through science, and subsequently life became a nightmare. Accordingly, Victor's success can also be described as a disaster.

Although Shelley deals expressly with some of the ambivalence expressed toward early-nineteenth century science, she also drew some inspiration also from the atmosphere of Prague, which she became acquainted with while starting to write the novel in 1804. It was then that the city underwent a transformation, traces of which can still be seen: it became the scene for the development of a variety of traditions concerning the creation of an artificial anthropoid, the Golem, a problematic figure whose image haunts the city even nowadays.[1] It is part of an incredible example of a process of *Zauberung*, which started to grow slowly but steadily in opposition to the Enlightenment tendency towards *Entzauberung*.[2]

The problematic involved in the transition from the magically created man, found in many Jewish medieval texts, to a scientifically fabricated one, is not just the result of the intuition of a gifted novelist. Artificially created anthropoids started to populate the imagination of Central Europe in an accelerated manner during the nineteenth and early-twentieth centuries, each of them carrying a different message, rarely a message of hope, more often of strongly articulated menaces and fears.[3] This development can be summarized as the technology that turned against the scientist, or to use a Hebrew dictum: the Golem turned against its creator. And it took less than a century and a half until the new scientific developments that produced this unease were put to service of one of the most horrible events in history, the Holocaust, which took place primarily in Central and Eastern Europe. The power to act when dissociated from a structure of positive ideals and strong inhibitions was revealed to be a curse, though initially promising so many good things. Power and darkness were collaborating just when the light of reason was beginning to improve the plight of humankind.

Undoubtedly, it is the power of magic, and not science, which looms behind many of these premonitions. Yet, there are areas of magic that have inspired, if not the practice at least the reflections, of modern scientists. This is the case with

---

[1] Hillel Kieval, 'Pursuing the Golem of Prague: Jewish Culture and the Invention of a Tradition', *Modern Judaism*, 17 (1997), 1–20, reprinted in his *Languages of Community: The Jewish Experience in the Czech Lands* (Berkeley; London: University of California Press, 2000), pp. 95–113; John Neubauer, 'How Did the Golem Get to Prague?', in *History of the Literary Cultures of East Central Europe: Junctures and Disjunctures in the 19th and 20th centuries, vol. IV, Types and Stereotypes*, ed. by Marcel Cornis-Pope and John Neubauer (Amsterdam: John Benjamin, 2010), pp. 296–307. See also my forthcoming 'On Astral Golems, Dalai Lama and the Maharal', in *Essays for a Jewish Lifetime: The Burton D. Morris Jubilee Volume*, ed. by Menachem Butler and Marian E. Frankston (New York: Hakirah Press, 2012).

[2] Compare to the essay of Jeffrey H. Chajes, '*Entzauberung* and Jewish Modernity – on "Magic", Enlightenment and Faith', in *Simon-Dubnow-Institut Jahrbuch – Yearbook* VI (2007), pp. 191–200.

[3] For the theme of the *Golem* in modern cultures, see: Gad Yair and Michaela Soyer, *The Golem in German Social Theory* (Ladham, MD.: Lexington Books, 2007); Cathy S. Gelbin, *The Golem Returns: From German Romantic Literature to Global Jewish Culture, 1808–2008* (Ann Arbor: University of Michigan Press, 2011); Emily Bilsky (ed.), *Golem! Danger, Deliverance and Art* (New York: Jewish Museum, 1989); and the comprehensive survey in Byron L. Sherwin, *Golems Among Us: How a Jewish Legend Can Help Us Navigate the Biotech Century* (Chicago: Ivan R Dee, 2004).

one of the founders of Cybernetics, Norbert Wiener, and his 1966 book, *God and Golem, Inc.: A Comment on Certain Points where Cybernetics Impinges on Religion*. As the title of the book indicates, the relationship between the magically generated Golem, and the technologically generated machine that would emerge from the development of cybernetics, was one of inspiration rather than menace. Similarly, at the Weitzman Institute in Rehovot, one of the first computers has been named Golem.[4]

Let me now turn to a short history of one aspect of European magical culture, the Golem, and a more optimistic and active approach that developed in Europe, since the late Middle Ages: an approach in which Man was conceived as being capable of becoming divine, or obtaining divine knowledge, and thus also capable of creating a creature, which was not negative, at least not in principle.

Three Pillars of European Culture

There are three main pillars that have underpinned European culture as it has developed since the Middle Ages: the religious or sacramental one, the philosophical or critical one, and finally the magical or performative one. These three approaches to reality were only rarely separated from each other, but for heuristic aims I shall first discuss them separately and point out later the interactions.

The first of these pillars, the religious or sacramental, can be identified with the Judeo-Christian tradition, which puts the emphasis on sacred books, religious beliefs and rituals, and a confidence that these represent the highest way of life, leading to some form of redemption, individual or collective. It is an approach that stipulates the centrality of a supernal power that can be worshiped and which, in many cases, can respond to that worship. In most cases, this ideal was backed by powerful establishments, which were eager to impose the superiority of the religious approach and sacramental way of life, creating and policing the categories of the faithful and the heretic. This approach attempted to shape the personality – including one's belief and behaviour – rather than the intellect or the body: claiming that man is a combination of two elements, body and soul.

The second approach is the philosophical-critical one, basically the Platonic and the Aristotelian forms and their medieval elaborations. Led by those who attempted to articulate comprehensive visions of reality, more than of community or theology, this approach advanced the idea of free investigation as the

---

4 See Gershom Scholem, *The Messianic Idea in Judaism* (New York: Schocken, 1972), pp. 335–340.

highest form of human activity, in short it was a mentalist approach that placed emphasis upon intelligence as the most important human organon. Though controlled by the Church authorities for long periods of the Middle Ages, this more critical approach experienced a resurgence during the seventeenth century and produced some of the best of modern philosophies, with their critical acumen. Scientific investigation was an important part of this approach, and the affinity between philosophy and science had been advanced since the time of Pythagoras or Thales. In modern times this affinity returned with, for example, Giordano Bruno, Gottfried Wilhelm Leibniz, and Isaac Newton. This approach was less concerned with affecting the soul or the body (though it investigated them), rather it sought to influence the intellect, which was most conducive to a critical attitude and a commitment to discovering the abstract, often immutable structures of reality.

The third approach, which will concern us here much more, and which is less widely mentioned in the more general analyses of European culture, is the magical.[5] It differs from the first two approaches both by the immediacy of it aims and by the concreteness of its methods. It is concerned much less with knowing the structures of reality than with the power to change them. Although it assumed the reality of an invisible world, the concrete approach was less concerned with issues of belief and understanding, and more about the possibility of its easy manipulation by humans. This approach was mainly concerned with demons, and angels. However, from time to time it also addressed the divinity, understood as a source of power that could be used to the specific purposes of the magician or his client. As the widespread lore on popular magic and witchcraft shows, in many of its forms this was a less elitist approach. Nevertheless, there were also several forms of elitist magic, found, for example in some late forms of Neoplatonism, in Hermeticism and in their various echoes during the Middle Ages and the Renaissance. We shall return to this issue later on in this chapter.

There was a continuous tension between the magical approach and the religious one, since both competed on a common ground: guiding, to a certain extent, the behaviour of large masses of the population. The conflict between the long-term commitment of the religious approach and the short-term solution that magic and witchcraft promised created not only intellectual divergences between the two, but many well-known persecutions and exterminations – as in the case of the witch-hunts of the fifteenth to eighteenth centuries. Philosophers were, in broad terms, less antagonistic toward the magical than the religious

---

5 See the pioneering studies of Lynn Thorndike, especially the multi-volume *History of Magic and Experimental Science* (New York: McMillan, 1925–1928), and his *The Place of Magic in the Intellectual History of Europe* (New York: AMS Press, 1967).

authorities were, though some of them, like Maimonides, sharply criticized both magic and astrology.

The experimental nature of magic, together with the gradual weakening of religious authority from the sixteenth century, combined with more philosophical-critical approaches, shaped the more practical aspect of pre-modern science. A social vision of the impact of magic should, therefore, be envisioned within a framework which incorporates the contest with – and eventual cooperation of – the two other approaches. Its decline did not necessarily mean its disappearance but rather a restructuring, as chemistry emerged out of alchemy and astronomy emerged out of astrology.

The interplay between the three approaches, struggling with each other, but also coexisting and sometimes even cooperating, lasted throughout the Middle Ages until the pre-modern time, when the balance between them changed, allowing for critical and experimental attitudes to acquire a more predominant role than the religious approach. My concern below is with what a magical approach can contribute to the images of man within the broad confines of European culture.

Magical Literatures

Unlike the religious or the philosophical approaches, which produced vast, comprehensive, and systematic literatures, covering a broad variety of topics, that related to the magical approach is quite modest. It rarely consisted in voluminous writings, and even the longer treatises it produced – such as the Book of Picatrix, or the various versions of the Book of Raziel – though written by educated elites, cannot compete with the writings of either philosophers or theologians in terms of their number, comprehensiveness, or systematic basis. A perusal of part of the extant magical literature, especially the Hebrew one, shows that it consists in innumerable but much shorter pieces: recipes, exorcist formulas, or short prayers. Since the study of these smaller pieces is only at its inception, it is hard to estimate their number, distribution, or impact. However, what may be safely said is that they constitute a body of practices, which existed on a pan-European scale for an extensive period of time. Furthermore, we may assume that some of the once existing recipes perished as they were principally passed along through oral transmission.

One of the genres of recipes from the Hebrew literature consists of instructions on how to create an artificial human being, an enterprise attributed to third century legalistic figures, mentioned in the Talmud.[6] I collected their in-

---

6 Moshe Idel, *Golem: Jewish Magical and Mystical Traditions on the Artificial Anthropoid* (Albany: State University of New York Press, 1990), pp. 27–43.

structions and printed them, together with some analyses in my monograph on the Golem.⁷ These Hebrew texts, consisting of somewhere between a few lines and a page and a half of text, instruct the reader in a variety of techniques for creating an artificial anthropoid. The basic methodology involved the use of dust and water to shape a plastic form of a man, followed by the infusion of vitality into its limbs by means of the recitation of a variety of combinations of letters.

Almost all of the letter combinations advanced are related to permutation theories found in an authoritative text entitled the *Book of Formation, Sefer Yetzirah*, in Hebrew.⁸ This is a concise and rather enigmatic treatise, which advances an original cosmogony: the world is created out of all the combinations of the 22 Hebrew letters that God carved from primordial air, together with the ten divine numbers, *sefirot*, which stem from God and return to him. It also includes a strong emphasis on the microcosm-macrocosm theory and, according to some versions, with the patriarch Abraham's *imitatio Dei:* operating in the same manner God did when He created the world, by combining letters. The book was variously attributed to the patriarch Abraham or to the seminal rabbinic figure rabbi Akiva. Scholarly opinion is divided as to the time of its composition, between the first century CE to the eighth one, depending on accepting or not the Muslim influence.

Although the book is certainly not concerned with magic as its principal subject-manner, it ends with the description of the forefather Abraham imitating God by combining letters, an operation that is described as being successful. The precise meaning of this success is not clear from the book, however, I am strongly inclined to see in it a success in accomplishing that which was achieved by God, namely the creation of something.

---

7 Idel, Golem; *idem, Kabbalah in Italy, 1280–1510: A Survey* (New Haven: Yale University Press, 2011), pp. 236–267; and, *idem*, 'Golems and God: Mimesis and Confrontation', in *Mythen der Kreativitaet*, ed. by Oliver Krueger, Refika Sarioender, and Annette Deschner (Frankfurt am Main: Lembeck, 2003), pp. 224–268. On the Golem see also the groundbreaking study of Gershom Scholem, *On the Kabbalah and Its Symbolism*, trans. by Ralph Manheim (New York: Schocken, 1977), pp. 158–204, and Byron L. Sherwin, *The Golem Legend: Origins and Implications*, (Lanham, MD.: University Press of America, 1985).

8 The secondary literature on the book is vast. See for example, Yehuda Liebes, *Ars Poetica in Sefer Yetzirah* (Tel Aviv: Schocken, 2000) (in Hebrew); Paul Fenton, *Sefer Yesirah ou le Livre de la Création: Exposé de cosmogonie hébraïque ancienne* (Paris: Rivage, 2002); A. Peter Hayman, *Sefer Yesira, Edition, Translation and Text-Critical Commentary* (Tuebingen: Mohr Siebeck, 2004); Meir Bar-Ilan, *Astrology and other Sciences among the Jews of Israel, in the Roman-Hellenistic and Byzantine Periods* (Jerusalem: Mossad Bialik, 2001) (in Hebrew); Ithamar Gruenwald, 'A Preliminary Critical Edition of Sepher Yetzirah', *Israel Oriental Studies*, 1 (1971), 132–177; *idem*, 'Some Critical Notes on the First Part of *Sefer Yezira*', *Revue des études juives*, 132 (1973), 475–512; Nicholas Sed, 'Le *Sefer Yesira*, l'edition critique, le texte primitif, la grammaire et la metaphysique', *Revue des études juives*, 132 (1973), 513–528; and, more recently, Tzahi Weiss, 'Soft and Hard: More Comments on the Syrian Context of *Sefer Yesira*', *Kabbalah*, 26 (2012), 229–241 (in Hebrew).

> When Abraham our father came, and looked. And saw and investigated and understood and carved and combined and hewed and pondered and succeeded, the Lord of All was revealed to him. And he made him sit in his lap, and kissed him upon his head. He called him his friend and named him his son,[9] and made a covenant with him and his seed forever.[10]

Thus, in my opinion, a magical element maybe discerned in this book, and it is obviously the issue of imitating God. This practice is conceived as positive, provoking a sympathetic reaction from the divine, and many of the techniques for creating the Golem by means of letter-combinations are derived from this text. The book also had an immense impact on the development of medieval Jewish esoteric literatures, each putting in relief another dimension of its enigmatic content. Its impact in European culture can be discerned in the ars combinatoria of such authors as Raymond Lull, Giovanni Pico della Mirandola, Johannes Reuchlin, and William Postel, to mention only the most important figures in this topic.[11]

Despite the affinities between these recipes and the idea that God created the world by combining letters, the assumption that a perfect man can be created by such a recipe is not found. The vast majority of the golem recipes, mentioned above, assume that it is only possible to create a deficient anthropoid, namely one that cannot speak or, according to some descriptions, cannot procreate.[12] Indeed, in some Kabbalistic sources, even the attempt to create a Golem was conceived of as dangerous. The following formula, stemming from a Kabbalist who was either close to the Kabbalist Abraham Abulafia, or was Abulafia himself, highlights this:

> And [then] a likeness [*demut*][13] will emerge…and it is forbidden to do like the deed of the Creator, and you shall not study it in order to perform it, but you shall study it in order to understand and to teach, and to cleave to the great name of God, praised be He.[14]

---

9 On this issue, see Moshe Idel, *Ben: Sonship and Jewish Mysticism* (London; New York: Continuum, 2007), pp. 133–134.

10 VI:8, Hayman, *Sefer Yesira*, pp. 181–182; Idel, *Golem*, pp. 9–26; and, A. Peter Hayman, 'Was God A Magician? *Sefer Yesira* and Jewish Magic', *Journal of Jewish Studies*, 41 (1989), 225–237 (esp., p. 234).

11 Moshe Idel, 'Ramon Lull and Ecstatic Kabbalah', *Journal of the Warburg and Courtauld Institutes*, 51 (1988), 170–174; Umberto Eco, *The Search for the Perfect Language*, trans. by James Fentress (Oxford; Cambridge, MA.: Blackwell, USA, 1995), pp. 53–69; Andreas Kilcher, *Die Sprachtheorie der Kabbala als Aestetisches Paradigma* (Stuttgart; Weimar: J.M. Metzler, 1998), pp. 152–175; and, Harvey J. Haimes, *The Art of Conversion, Christianity & Kabbalah in the Thirteenth Century* (Leiden: Brill, 2000), pp. 217–222.

12 See Idel, *Golem*, pp. 237–238.

13 This means that this is a vision rather than a corporeal creature.

14 Idel, *Golem*, pp. 97–98.

Study and mystical union – cleaving – are conceived of as being higher than the imitation of God by performance, namely the creation of an anthropoid. This is quite a medieval type of approach, and we shall return to this issue below when discussing the views of Frances Amelia Yates. What transpires, even in this case, is the possibility of the application of such knowledge, through mental activity, is given priority in quite an accentuated manner.

Perfect Kabbalist, Perfect Creature: A Theory by R. Isaac of Acre

From the late-thirteenth century onwards, however, another approach may be discerned. This approach appears in a most important text written by R. Isaac ben Samuel of Acre, one of the most interesting Kabbalists active at the end of the thirteenth century and beginning of the fourteenth century.[15] According to the available sources, R. Isaac was an itinerant figure, who had visited three continents in search for Kabbalistic lore. He was, therefore, an accomplished Kabbalist, who was, reputedly, acquainted with more forms of Kabbalah than anyone else before him. Recent studies, which have analyzed his concerns with magical recipes, have shown that he also had a special interest in magic.[16] It is this curiosity, combined with an inclination toward a more experiential (and perhaps also more experimental) form of Kabbalah that may account for his special interest in traditions and theories about the creation of an artificial anthropoid, which are found to a much greater extent in his writings than in those of any of the earlier Kabbalists.[17]

The following passage of his consists in a discussion which took place during a seminary that reflects a Kabbalistic trend of which he was part, at least for a certain period: namely, a group related to ecstatic Kabbalah and influenced, in some part, by its views. This type of Kabbalah was strongly concerned with the *Book of Yetzirah* and its various commentaries,[18] and there we also find a vivid interest in the concept of the Golem, conceived mainly as an intellectual creature. I assume that one of the members of this group was a certain R. Nathan ben Sa'adyah Harar, himself a student of Abraham Abulafia, who was also one of the

---

15 On this Kabbalist, see Eitan P. Fishbane, *As Light Before Dawn, The Inner World of a Medieval Kabbalist* (Stanford: Stanford University Press, 2009); and, Sandra Valabregue-Perry, *Concealed and Revealed: Ein Sof and Theosophic Kabbalah* (Los Angeles: Cherub Press, 2010), where the previous bibliography is found.
16 See Amos Goldreich, *Automatic Writing in Zoharic Literature and Modernism* (Los Angeles: Cherub Press, 2010) (in Hebrew), *passim*.
17 See Idel, *Golem*, pp. 108–111.
18 See Moshe Idel, '*Sefer Yetzirah:* Twelve Commentaries on *Sefer Yetzirah* and the Extant Remnants of R. Isaac of Bedresh's Commentary', *Tarbitz*, 79 (2010), 471–556 (in Hebrew).

Kabbalistic masters of R. Isaac.[19] The school of ecstatic Kabbalah afforded real significance to the process of creating spiritual entities, namely souls and intellects, but not bodies.[20] Understood in such a manner, this process was a way of imitating God.[21] In his account of the discussion R. Isaac quotes R. Nathan, as follows:

> And if she [the soul] will merit to cleave to the Divine Intellect, happy is she, since she returned to her source and root, and she is called, literally, Divine Intellect. And that person is called the Man of God, that is to say, a Divine Man, creating worlds. Behold Rava created a man, but did not yet merit giving him a speaking soul. And you have to understand that since the soul of man has reached a degree of the supernal degrees, his soul governs everything below this degree, and there is no need to elaborate upon this issue which is an axiom for every learned person.[22]

It is reasonable to assume that the introduction of Rava's creation of man serves as an example of a degree that can be transcended by certain persons, the Divine Men, who are able to rule over everything inferior to this degree, by cleaving to the highest degree. They could attain that which Rava did not yet merit. This reading is corroborated by the word '*Adaiyn* ('yet') which implies the possibility to surpass the achievement of the Talmudic master. If so, the Divine Man could, at least implicitly, introduce a speaking soul into the Golem, provided he was in union with the Divine Intellect. A perfect Golem may, therefore, be created only by a perfect man who is in a state of perfect mystical union, namely in a state of union between his soul and the Divine Intellect.

It should be pointed out that R. Nathan himself was not interested in magical performance though he was well aware of this aspect of Kabbalah. The paramount importance of the contact between the mystic and the divine intellect is reminiscent of the views of Abraham Abulafia, that the process of creating a creature is preceded by the reception of an influx of wisdom.[23] In both cases intellectual perfection is considered as a prerequisite for the creative process.

In what seems to me to be one of the most interesting passages dealing with the creation of the Golem ever generated by a Kabbalist, the above-mentioned R. Isaac follows the affinity between human perfection, of an intellectual brand, and

---

19 See Moshe Idel (ed.), *Natan ben Sa'adyah Har'ar, Le Porte della Giustizia*, trans. by Maurizio Motolese (Milano: Adelphi, 2001), pp. 52–62.
20 See esp., Idel, *Golem*, pp. 102, 105–106.
21 Idel, *Golem*, p. 102. On the possibility that this passage, which has been copied in Yohanan Alemanno's *Collectanea*, influenced Lodovico Lazzarelli, see *ibid.*, pp. 175–177; and, Idel, *Kabbalah in Italy*, pp. 258–261.
22 Amos Goldreich (ed.), *Sefer Me'irat 'Einayyim* (Jerusalem: Hebrew University, 1984), p. 223; Idel, *Golem*, pp. 106–107; and, Moshe Idel, *Studies in Ecstatic Kabbalah* (Albany: State University of New York Press, 1988), pp. 116–117.
23 See Idel, *Golem*, pp. 96–100.

the creation of a perfect golem. Though I dealt with this extended passage a number of times in my studies, this is an occasion to present it both in a much more detailed manner on the one hand, and in a broader framework, on the other:

> Once…I, the young[24], was sitting in the company of advanced students, lovers of wisdom.[25] One of them opened his mouth and asked me as follows: 'What is the difference between Creation [*Beriy'ah*] and Formation [*Yetzirah*]?' I told him: 'Why don't you ask also why Abraham our ancestor, did call his book [by the title] *Yetzirah*, which consists of wondrous deeds, by means of whom Rava created a man, and to R. Hiyya[26] and R. Hosha'yiah a three-year old calf has been created each time before the entrance of the Sabbath, and they were eating it during the day of Sabbath[27], and Jeremiah and Ben Sira created from it a speaking, wise and intelligent man,[28] as I have explained above[29], and why did he [namely Abraham] not call it the *Book of Beriy'ah*?' And he [the student] was not able [to answer me] and none of them answered me, since they did not know what is it [the answer?]. But I, the young, while I was speaking it, I have seen the correct rationale for it, which is as follows: 'You already know the secret of the [letter] *Yod* of the *'ABYA'* and the secret of the [letter] *Bet*. Since the majority of sons of man have no power to endow a speaking soul, *a fortiori* an intellective soul, on the matter shaped either in the form of an animal or a beast or a bird or a fish or a reptile, even not in the form of man, [using the capacity of] the *Book of Yetzirah*, but only the animal and appetitive soul [alone], as our sages said Rava created a man and he sent it to R. Zeira etc,[30] the book was called *Sefer Yetzirah* but not the book of *Beriy'ah*. The reason is that the animal and appetitive soul, which perishes with the death of the body, when the combination of the four elements is undone, stems from the intermediary world, which is the *Yod* of *'ABYA'*. But the secret of the speaking [and] intellective soul is from the supernal world, which is the [letter] *Bet* of *'ABYA'*. By saying the majority [of men] and not all [men] I intended to exclude Jeremiah the prophet, the disciple of Moses our master, peace on him, and Ben Sira and all those similar to them, who are very few, who attained a divine perfection, [so as] to create an animal, speaking, [and] intellective [being].[31] And if you shall argue that all the prophets…were the disciples of

---

24 Here and below, R. Isaac refers to himself as a young even when he was old, and it intends to point to his modesty. See Idel, *Studies in Ecstatic Kabbalah*, pp. 87–88, n. 43.
25 For another instance of mentioning a group of study by R. Isaac, see Moshe Idel, *The Mystical Experience in Abraham Abulafia*, trans. by Jonathon Chipman (Albany: State University of New York Press, 1987), pp. 117–118. For the question of groups of Kabbalists in the context of R. Isaac see Idel, *Golem*, pp. 112–113.
26 This is a mistake for R. Hanina.
27 Sanhedrin, fol. 65b.
28 On this Kabbalistic tradition, which has some earlier sources, which includes a warning against the creation of the Golem, see Idel, 'Golems and God', pp. 248–252.
29 Unfortunately such a discussion did not each us.
30 Sanhedrin fol. 65b.
31 R. Isaac distinguishes between the speaking faculty or soul, and the intellectual one. This is not a common view in the Middle Ages, but it is found in ecstatic Kabbalah, probably from a Pythagorean source. See also below, our discussion of this distinction.

Moses, our master, peace on him, so why did you mention Jeremiah in particular as a disciple of Moses? The answer is that you must pursue the Kabbalists in order to explain you the secret of the verse[32] 'The Lord thy God will raise up to thee a prophet from the midst of thee, of thy brethren, like me, to him you shall hearken' and then you will understand, for sure, my intention. However, concerning Jeremiah and ben Sira alone, I have received [a tradition] that they have drawn downward[33] a speaking soul from the root of *Bet* of *'ABYA'*,[34] that is the *'Alef* of *'ABYA'*, by the dint of their great degree and the perfection of their soul, being able to [perform] this wondrous deed.[35]

R. Isaac of Acre presents the act of creating the perfect golem within the frame of his own peculiar Kabbalistic Weltanschauung. This consists in the view that there are four cosmic layers: the highest one, that of *'Atzilut*, namely the world of Emanation, is the world of the divine powers – referred to by R. Isaac by the first 'A of the 'ABYA' acronym, that stands for the names of the four worlds. The next is the world of *Beriy'ah*, namely Creation, which is the world of the divine chariot, hinted at by the letter *Bet*. The third one, the world of Yetzirah, meaning of Formation, is the world of the angels, and corresponds to the letter Yod in the acronym. Finally, there exists the world of 'Asiyah, the lower, material world, which is to be understood as the world of Making. When the companion asked as to the nature of the difference between *Beriy'ah* and *Yetzirah*, he intended to ask what is the distinction between the two cosmic worlds? This was a view that was apparently new then, as the whole story is told in the past.

R. Isaac answered the question as if dealing with the nature of *Sefer Yetzirah*, which is focused, according to his interpretation, upon the capability of some mystics to induce only the animal and appetitive soul from the world of *Yetzirah*, into matter. This low soul stems from the world of *Yetzirah*, this being the reason, according to R. Isaac, that Abraham designated his book by the name *Yetzirah*. This is a rather low regard of this book, though this Kabbalist wrote a commentary on it, in the vein of the theosophical-theurgical Kabbalists, who envisioned the content of the book as dealing basically with the realm of emanation.[36] This possibility is conceived as indisputable for a fair range of persons, including the Talmudic figures.

Yet, as we learn from the passage, a higher spiritual faculty can be induced, though by the very few, specifically Jeremiah the prophet and Ben Sira, and by

---

32 Deuteronomy 18:15.
33 *Himshikhu*. This verb is found in 13th century Kabbalah in a variety of contexts. Here, however, it is obvious that it stands for some form of operation that draws down a soul from the divine realm into a human form.
34 I assume that here some words are missing, as we shall see below.
35 Ms. Sassoon 919, p. 217; Ms. Cambridge, Genizah, TS. K 12,4 p. 22. See also Idel, *Golem*, pp. 108–109.
36 See Gershom Scholem, 'R. Isaac of Acre's Commentary on the First Chapter of *Sefer Yetzirah*', *Qiryat Sefer*, 31 (1956), 379–396 (in Hebrew).

'those similar to them'. They are described, in a manner reminiscent of the earlier quote of R. Isaac, as possessing a "divine perfection": *shelemut 'elohi.* Human perfection is, therefore, not only a matter of a purified spirit clinging to God, but also of being capable of imitating God, by creating a full-fledged human being, including the body, in an artificial manner. Consequently, some few elite are considered to have access to the higher world, that of *Beriy'ah* or Creation, being able to draw down the speaking, and then the rational soul. However, the Kabbalist assumes that those few may be able to reach even the world of *'Atzilut,* as the phrase *Bet* of *'ABYA'* which is the *'Aleph* of *'ABYA'* implies. I see this sentence as deficient, and should be understood as follows: *Bet* of *Beriy'ah* point to the speaking soul, while *'A* stands for *'Atzilut,* which is the source of the intellectual soul, a statement missing from the form in which the text reached us in two manuscripts. If so, R. Isaac asserts that it is possible to create a golem that includes elements from all the three higher cosmic worlds, and so it seems to be reasonable to assume, also from the lowest world, which, apparently, would supply the prime-matter for the golem.

The assumption that man can create using elements from all the four cosmic worlds is tantamount, as I shall try to show, to the divine act of the creation of Adam. In other words, the above passage is an interesting replica to the Genesis discussion of the creation of man, as R. Isaac understood it. So, for example, we read in his commentary on the Kabbalistic secrets included in the Pentateuch, *Mei'rat 'Einayyim:*

> The secret of creation of man [refers to] the speculative soul [*ha-neshamah ha-ha-khamah*], which stands for ever. And the secret of his formation [refers to] the animal soul, which does not stand for ever […] And emanation and creation are more spiritual than formation.[37]

This last quote comprises, in nuce, the doctrine of the above discussion of the creation of the Golem. The implications of the views of R. Isaac are, however, more radical than they appears at a prima facie reading. The assumption that the two ancient masters were able to induce the spiritual element from the world of emanation implies that the magically created man has the highest spiritual capacity: which is not to be found automatically in a normally created man since, according to some Kabbalists, the highest soul is an achievement to be obtained by a mystical regimen vitae. The conclusion that the created man by Jeremiah and Ben Sira was endowed with a spiritual soul that is characteristic only of a mystic, is a far-reaching one since the sublime status of their creation is then undeniable. This view can be contrasted with the views of other authors who rejected the possibility that a golem could even speak. What seems to be

---

37 Goldreich, *Me'irat 'Einayyim*, p. 20, and Idel, *Golem*, pp. 110–111.

implicit here is a historiosophy of the creation of the anthropoid: the earlier masters, the prophet Jeremiah and his alleged son Ben Sira created a perfect man, speaking and intelligent, while the Talmudic masters flowering later on, created entities which were closer to animals. This generational decline is part of a wider historiosophy of this Kabbalist, who envisioned the period between late-antiquity and the late-twelfth century as one during which the Jews did not possess knowledge of the true God, before the Kabbalistic tradition restored the authentic theology.

The situation with R. Isaac of Acre is, in my opinion, not different. He inherited a theosophical theory about the four cosmic worlds discussed above. I assume that this theory has been adopted by him, and perhaps also adapted, from sources with which R. Nathan ben Sa'adyah Harar was acquainted. It is in the collection of Kabbalistic traditions that R. Isaac prepared, that the term 'ABYA' occurs for the first time.[38] Since R. Isaac states quite clearly in the lengthy quote adduced above that he received a tradition related to causing the descent of the sublime soul, one can assume that he conceived of his discussion as retrieving the understanding of the creation of the Golem as found in the works of the most accomplished Kabbalists: the ancient Ben Sira and Jeremiah.[39] Thus we may describe R. Isaac of Acre's approach as combining the views of R. Nathan ben Sa'adyah, who emphasizes the importance of the intellectual transformation of the operator as a requirement for magical activity, with the Jeremiah-Ben Sira tradition.

As part of this adoption and adaptation the possibility of reaching the highest realm in the divine sphere allows new possibilities insofar as both the mystical and the magical attainments of the Jewish masters are concerned: they are capable not only of cleaving to the *'Ein Sof,* a view characteristic of this Kabbalist,[40] but also of operating on the intra-divine structure by drawing down power from the world of Emanation to the lower worlds, and R. Isaac mentions in many cases his moments of contemplation, and deals with theurgical operations that a Kabbalist can accomplished within the world of emanation.[41] His in-

---

38 See Gershom Scholem, 'Hitpatehut Torat ha-'Olamot be-Qabbalat ha-Rishonim', *Tarbiz,* 2 (1931), 415–442; Gershom Scholem, 'Hitpatehut Torat ha-'Olamot be-Qabbalat ha-Rishonim', *Tarbiz,* 3 (1932), 33–66 (in Hebrew), and, Idel, *Studies in Ecstatic Kabbalah,* p. 88 n. 49.
39 It should be mentioned that in one of his writings, R. Isaac claims that Jeremiah did not die, but it is still alive nowadays, and that he is capable, at least in principle, to draw down the prophetic spirit. See *'Otzar Hayyim,* Ms. Moscow-Guensburg 775, fol. 163ab. It is hard to overlook the possible implication of such a view, which is probably related to a theory of metempsychosis, for the assumption of the creation of the anthropoid in the present.
40 See Moshe Idel, *R. Menahem Recanati, the Kabbalist,* (Tel Aviv: Schocken, 1998) (in Hebrew), p. 195; and, Valabregue-Perry, *Concealed and Revealed,* pp. 171–72.
41 See Fishbane, *As Light Before Dawn,* pp. 125–177; and, Valabregue-Perry, *Concealed and Revealed,* pp. 166–176.

structions for intentions in prayer assume that it is possible to contemplate the Infinite, a rather rare assumption in thirteenth century Kabbalah.[42] This intimacy with the divine is accompanied by a rather developed theosophy. Thus, though R. Isaac does not confess to the creation of a golem, perfect or not, he assumed the possibility of doing so in a manner that was unparalleled, and consonant with types of Kabbalistic activities, like combinations of letters, he believed that should be practiced in any case, including the drawing down of supernal influx.[43]

Interestingly enough, the same Kabbalist compares elsewhere the manner in which the anthropoid has been created: Rava created it without any utterance, while according to the mid-thirteenth anonymous Kabbalist, Jeremiah and Ben Sira did so by resorting to an utterance, *Ma'amar*.[44] There is no doubt that the impact of the anonymous theory found in mid-thirteenth century Kabbalah is conspicuous here but, again, the interdiction to create a golem, found in several earlier discussions he was acquainted with, has been obliterated in R. Isaac's passage. My assumption is that the *Ma'amar*, is related to the fact that those figures were capable to create a speaking anthropoid, unlike the mute figure created by Rava, according to the Talmudic legend.

In other words: the anonymous discussions about the creation of the golem, which served as a source of inspiration for R. Isaac, dealt with the creation of an artificial man by Jeremiah and Ben Sira, and the interdiction upon doing so has been changed by R. Isaac in an unambiguously positive manner. The very assumption that a perfect anthropoid can be created implicitly produces the assumption that it is licit to do so. This change is quite dramatic and, later on, we shall see a similar phenomenon in the eighteenth century discussions of R. Jacob Emden.

Conspicuously absent from these traditions, is the question of the creation of the anthropoid as a possible substitution from procreation, or the multiplication of the divine image in the world. In a religious culture where procreation was a major imperative, such an absence shows that the two acts were conceived of as unrelated.

---

42 Fishbane, *As Light Before Dawn*, pp. 178–247; and Valabregue-Perry, *Concealed and Revealed*, pp. 171–172.
43 Idel, *Studies in Ecstatic Kabbalah*, pp. 115, 118–119.
44 See Idel, 'Golems and God', pp. 25–252. In the versions discussed there, the Golem is depicted as speaking to its two creators.

Golem: From Magic Practice to Theology

Let me now turn to the affinities between the magic of the Golem, and the two other approaches mentioned above: religion and science. The golem recipes are based on the imitation of divine creation, either that of Genesis or that according to Sefer Yetzirah.[45] In the case of the latter an important development took place in the sixteenth century Kabbalah: the creative practice of God was portrayed in a manner that imitates the details of the creation of the Golem. This case of inversion certainly added a positive note to the entire question of whether or not one should create a golem.

The artificially created anthropoid, described in R. Isaac of Acre's quote, comprises in himself the whole range of creation, and therefore parallels the divine creation of the world. This understanding is consonant with a view, already seen in the traditions of R. Nathan, that the *macroanthropos*, identical with the intellectual man, comprises the whole cosmos, including its spiritual facets, whereby the material man is the *microanthropos*.[46] Moreover, this view also corresponds with a tradition found in an early-medieval exegetic treatise *Midrash 'Avkkir*, dealing with Adam: whose creation began before the creation of the world, and ended after the accomplishment of the creation of the world, and the whole universe was included in him.[47]

The assumption that the artificial man includes in itself the whole universe, including the four cosmic worlds of the Kabbalists, is reminiscent of the theory of Lurianic Kabbalah, where *'Adam Qadmon*, the Primeval Man, includes in itself the whole range of worlds. As I attempted to show elsewhere, it is reasonable to see that, in some of its elements, the Lurianic theory of *'Adam Qadmon* was indebted to late-thirteenth or early-fourteenth century Kabbalistic material, belonging to a school with which R. Isaac of Acre was acquainted: that of the late thirteenth-century Spanish Kabbalist R. David ben Yehudah he-Hasid.[48] Thus, far from envisioning the creation of the Golem as a dangerous or unlawful form of activity, it became for some important Kabbalists a paradigm for the process of theogony: God, assumed those Kabbalists, created *'Adam Qadmon* just as the Jewish magician created the Golem. God was first imitated, but with the emergence of Kabbalah it is God who is understood to act in a Kabbalistic manner, namely to imitate the Kabbalists. Following the attitude found at the first discussions of the Golem during the Middle Ages, which are based upon the

---

45 See Idel, 'Golems and God', pp. 225–228.
46 See Idel, *Studies in Ecstatic Kabbalah*, pp. 79–80.
47 See Moshe Idel, *Kabbalah: New Perspectives* (New Haven: Yale University Press, 1988), pp. 117–118.
48 Moshe Idel, 'The Image of Man above the Sefirot: R. David ben Yehuda he-Hasid's Theosophy of Ten Supernal *Sahsahot* and its Reverberations', *Kabbalah,* 20 (2009), 181–212.

principle of *imitatio Dei* – as for example in the late-fourteenth century *Sefer ha-Peliy'ah* – it is God in his theogonic emanation that is imitating the creation of the golem.[49]

Moreover, this creation of the *'Adam Qadmon,* in terms related to the creation of the Golem, is accompanied in many Lurianic texts since the second part of the 16th century by the assumption that this cosmic structure breaks as part of the theogonic process, the so-called *shevirat ha-kelim* – the breaking of the vessels – and it is the religious duty of the Kabbalist to help the reconstruction through the performance of ritual, so as to facilitate the return of the divine sparks to their primordial place. I see this development as part of a more positive attitude toward the creation of the Golem, which was accompanied by a proliferation of more speculative and legendary treatments dealing with the *Golem-imaginaire*.

The Golem: From Magic to Modern Science

Let me attempt to describe the above development that conceived the creation of a corporeal entity and its animation in a perfect manner as a positive activity – unlike the earlier medieval views, which regarded it as negative and dangerous. This development is reminiscent of an interesting remark by the famous scholar of the Renaissance, Dame Frances Amelia Yates, to the effect that:

> Fundamentally, the Greeks did not want to operate. They regarded operations as base and mechanical, a degeneration from the only occupations worthy of the dignity of man, pure rational and philosophical speculation. In the Middle Ages this attitude was perpetuated in the notion that theology is the crown of philosophy and the true end of man is contemplation.[50]

According to Yates, the change toward a much greater human activism is to be understood as related to:

> the religious excitement caused by the rediscovery of the *hermetica*, and their attendant *Magia*; in the overwhelming emotions, aroused by cabala and its magico-religious techniques. It is magic as an aid to gnosis which begins to turn the will in the new direction… Thus "Hermes Trismegistus" and the Neoplatonism and Cabalism associated with him, may have played during his[51] period of glorious ascendance over the mind of the western man a strangely important role in the shaping of human destiny.[52]

---

49 See Idel, *Golem*, pp. 144–145.
50 Frances A. Yates, *Giordano Bruno and the Hermetic Tradition* (Chicago: University of Chicago Press, 1979), pp. 155–156. On the centrality of contemplation in Greek culture see: A. J. Festugière, *Contemplation et vie contemplative selon Platon* (Paris: Vrin, 1950); and, Alberto Grilli, *Il problema della vita contemplativa nel modo Greco-romano* (Milano: Fratelli Bocca, 1953).
51 Namely Bruno's.

Yates situated the beginning of this development at the end of the fifteenth century in Florence, with the arrival of both the Platonic corpora (especially the various Hellenistic ones) and the Kabbalistic corpora to the city. For her, this confluence of a more experimental approach, critical toward the medieval intellectualistic heritage, was a crucial process in the crystallization of a new attitude that shaped pre-modern science, part of her famous thesis, explaining how the new scientific-technological attitude emerged.[53] Aware as I am of the critiques that have been addressed to her claims in this case, I nevertheless want to use her concepts and the idea of the concatenations between the various literatures she proposed, understood as triggering the development of the new sciences.[54]

It is possible to discern a similar synthesis of magic, Kabbalah, and Hermeticism in the passage of R. Isaac, quoted above, which took place no later than the beginning of the fourteenth century, apparently in Spain, or perhaps in Northern Africa, where the Kabbalist probably died. While the first two attitudes are obvious, the third one is less so. If we understand by Hermeticism a certain type of magical activity, namely astro-magic, which culminates in the attraction of supernal entities or powers within lower ones, prepared especially for capturing them,[55] then such a view may be discerned in the above passage: particularly

---

52 Yates, *Giordano Bruno*, p. 156. For an important thesis emphasizing the contribution of Kabbalah to a new, more optimistic idea of man in Christian circles starting with late 17th century thinkers, see the innovative studies of Allison P. Coudert, most recently her study where earlier references can be found: 'The Kabbalah, Science, and the Enlightenment: the Doctrines of Gilgul and Tikkun as Factors in the Anthropological Revolution of the Eighteenth Century', in *Aufklärung und Esoterik: Rezeption – Integration – Konfrontation*, ed. by Monika Neugebauer-Wölk (Tübingen: Max Niemeyer, 2008), pp. 299–316.

53 For a reassessment of the role of Hermetica in Renaissance magic see, for example, Brian Copenhaver, 'Hermes Trismegistus, Proclus, and the Question of a Philosophy of Magic in the Renaissance', in *Hermeticism and the Renaissance*, ed. by Ingrid Merkel and Allen G. Debus (Washington: Folger Books, 1988), pp. 79–110.
    For the contribution of the Hermetic magic of the Renaissance to later magical practices in various parts of Europe see, Keith Thomas, *Religion and the Decline of Magic* (New York: Scribner, 1971), pp. 222–231.

54 On the vast synthesis between magic and Kabbalah in the voluminous corpus of Kabbalistic writings produced in Spain in the last decades of the 15th century, contemporary to Marsilio Ficino, see, Moshe Idel, 'Magic and Kabbalah in the *Book of the Responding Entity*', in *The Solomon Goldman Lectures*, ed. by Mayer I. Gruber (Chicago: The Spertus College of Judaica Press, 1993), pp. 125–138. On this corpus and its protagonists, see Gershom Scholem, 'On the Story of R. Joseph della Reina', in *Hokhma Bina veDaat, Studies in Jewish History and Thought Presented to A. Altmann*, ed. by S. Stein and R. Loewe (Alabama: Alabama University Press, 1979), pp. 100–108 (in Hebrew); *idem*, 'The Maggid of Rabbi Joseph Taitatchek and the Revelations attributed to Him', *Sefunot*, 11 (1971–1978), 69–112 (in Hebrew); and, Moshe Idel, 'Inquiries in the Doctrine of *Sefer Ha-Meshiv*', *Sefunot*, 17 (1983), 185–266 (in Hebrew).

55 For Hermeticism in Judaism and especially in Kabbalah, see Shlomo Pines, 'Le *Sefer ha-*

when the Kabbalist speaks of the possibility to draw down a speaking soul, and later an intellective one, as the highest form of attainment, conducive to the creation of the perfect artificial man. Unlike the earlier approaches to the Golem, which were suspicious as to the nature of this enterprise, thereby restricting the realm of possible achievements of the magicians/Kabbalists, R. Isaac allows of the potential for the highest possible achievement, rare as it may be.

R. Isaac of Acre's vision for the possibility of creating a perfect anthropoid, accomplished by means of the Hermetic technique of drawing down the supernal soul within a anthropoid figure (that can be described also as a statue – *golem* is quite reminiscent of the Greek *agalma*, which means statue)[56] is quite novel in the Kabbalistic and other literatures of the thirteenth century. It combines the more linguistically oriented magic, found in many of the recipes of the Golem, with a more technical, astro-magic approach, and certainly with Kabbalistic theosophy and theurgy.

The Hermetic or astro-magical vision of this creature is also represented elsewhere in Kabbalah, it reappeared during the Renaissance, especially in the writings of R. Yohanan Alemanno, [c. 1430 – c. 1522] one of the Jewish teachers of Giovanni Pico della Mirandola.[57] Although Alemanno was certainly acquainted with R. Isaac of Acre's *Me'irat 'Einayyim*[58] it is difficult to ascertain whether he also knew of the other writings of the earlier Kabbalist. The manuscript, from which we quoted R. Isaac's lengthy passage, was quite a rare one. However, what cannot be denied is that in the voluminous writings of the Florentine Kabbalist, most of them still in manuscript form, he reflects the same synthesis between magic, Hermetic and other, Hermeticism, Neoplatonism, and Kabbalah, as does R. Isaac, and the synthesis that was described by Yates in the passage quoted above.

Like the medieval R. Isaac, Alemanno's sources for understanding the creation of the golem also include Hermetic ones. Not those stemming from Marsilio Ficino's translations from Greek, but from views found in Hebrew treatises, in

---

Tamar et les *Maggidim* des Kabbalists', in *Hommage à Georges Vajda*, ed. by Gerard Nahon and Charles Touati (Louvain: Peeters, 1980), pp. 333–363; *idem*, 'On the Term *Ruhaniyyut* and its Sources and On Judah Halevi's Doctrine', *Tarbiz*, 57 (1988), 511–540 (in Hebrew); Dov Schwartz, *Studies on Astral Magic in Medieval Jewish Thought*, trans. by David Louvish and Batya Stein (Leiden: Brill, 2005); Moshe Idel, 'Hermeticism and Judaism', in *Hermeticism and the Renaissance*, ed. by Ingrid Merkel and Allen Debus (Washington: Folger Books, 1988), pp. 59–76; and, *idem*, 'Hermeticism and Kabbalah', in *Hermeticism from Late Antiquity to Humanism*, ed. by Paolo Lucentini, Ilaria Parri, Vittoria Perrone Compagni (Turnhout, Belgium: Brespols, 2004), pp. 389–408.

56 See Idel, *Golem*, p. 299.
57 On his substantive treatments of the creation of the anthropoid see, Idel, *Golem*, pp. 167–175.
58 See for example, his untitled treatise extant in Ms. Paris, Biblioteque Nationale 849, fols. 96b, 121b.

extant books written in Spain or translated there since the early-fourteenth century.[59] To a great extent Alemanno's writings represent a development that was nourished by a plethora of texts by Jewish-Spanish authors, which he had at his disposal, at least for a while, and copied from, as excerpts in his *Collectanea*. Some of these excerpts served his as important building-blocks for his own writings. Thus, if we adopt Yates' thesis, in respect of the development of science out of magic, we may assume that a synthesis, like the one she described, may also be found independently in different contexts in the work of two Jewish writers, even before such a synthesis is known in the Christian sources.

Original as Yates' thesis is, it seems that it was not totally novel. The comparison between magic and science, or perhaps better, the vision of Jewish magic of the Golem as the real, secret science, was adumbrated by a famous, prolific, and influential figure in Central Europe during the second half of the eighteenth century, R. Jacob Emden (1697 – 1776).[60] In his book *Birat Migdal 'Oz*, there is a passage that deserves special attention in our context, where he wrote:

> ...as to the topic of *Ma'aseh Bereshit*[61], when the issue of creation will be comprehended in its essence and its causes, so that man will reach to its ultimate aim, he will be capable to innovate also a totally new creature, as in the case of R. H[anina] and R. '[Oshaya] who were preoccupied with *Sefer Yetzirah* and a three year calf emerged[62], in order to show the power and the wisdom of the supernal innovator, to distribute from His wisdom to those who fear Him and 'He revealed His secret to them'[63], the power of His holy names has been revealed, and to announce that He distributes to those who love Him, His glory, to make a [magical] use of His scepter, in order that they will imitate the Creator, to draw out new beings and He gave power in their hand to create worlds by the dint of the combination of names, as explained in *Sefer Yetzirah*.[64]

This is an ingenuous combination of two early Rabbinic statements, both dealing with prohibitions concerning the use of divine attributions: one prohibiting the use of the divine names, the other the prohibition on resorting to what was called the divine scepter.[65] In both cases, there is an attempt in the

---

59 See Moshe Idel, 'The Magical and Neoplatonic Interpretations of Kabbalah in the Renaissance', in *Jewish Thought in the Sixteenth Century*, ed. by Bernard Dov Cooperman (Cambridge, Ma.: Harvard University Press, 1983), pp. 186 – 242.
60 On his and his father's views on the Golem, see Idel, *Golem*, pp. 217 – 219. On him see more recently Yehuda Liebes, 'The Messianism of R. Jacob Emden and His attitude toward Sabbataianism', *Tarbiz*, 49 (1980), 122 – 65 (in Hebrew).
61 Namely the account of creation, an important topic in Jewish esotericism, sometimes related to the physical world.
62 Sanhedrin, fol. 65b.
63 Cf. the end of *Sefer Yetzirah*, where the revelation of a secret by God to Abraham is mentioned, and was quoted above.
64 R. Jacob Emden, *Sefer Birat Migdal 'Oz* (Jhitomir, 1884), fol. 25a.
65 See Mishnah, Sanhedrin II:5, and Mishnah, Avot I:13, respectively.

Rabbinic thought to keep the divine realm separated from the human one. However, here Emden inverts the Rabbinic approach, and emphasizes the possibility of imitating God, provided there was a divine intention to impart knowledge to some humans, those who are described as capable now to imitate God. This is quite a positive description of the possibility to create new beings, as a form of imitation Dei.

Unlike the prohibitions on the creation of an anthropoid, found in the recipes and legends mentioned above, or the assumption of its lower nature, Emden stipulates the importance of such a practice as an aim of knowledge. In Emden's case, however, this is not simply evidence for a shift in the attitude to this form of magic. There is also a quest for a form of retrospective validation for the creation of a golem by his great, great, grandfather, R. Elijah of Helm, an issue that had haunted his descendants.[66] The inversion of the Rabbinic interdictions shows a very significant shift here in comparison to earlier discussions. Nevertheless, the source of knowledge and power is conspicuously God's and it is His decision to impart the special knowledge to people. Therefore, in a way, the magician who creates a golem (including, implicitly, Emden's sixteenth-century ancestor) fulfills the divine will rather than rebelling against it. Beyond this family dimension, there is also another one, more comprehensive. In another book of his, Emden wrote:

> The natural science of the gentiles ['anshei ha-'olam] is a coarse and thick garment to the account of the creation [Ma'aseh Bereshit], that is the hidden fruit and the very essence of its issue. The natural science of the philosophers deals with the external shells that are thrown away, [because] they are not pleasant to be eaten by the intelligent [persons]. Since they [the philosophers] do perceive only the accidents... But God posited the true divine wisdom, which deals only with the inner part and the essence[67], and this is the reason why it is called the practical [wisdom],[68] because in its power is [the power] to innovate new creatures *in actu*...like Rava, who created a man, and R. H[anina'] and R. 'O[shayah], who created for themselves a three-year old calf and ate it, and the least of them is able to resurrect the dead, in addition to all the other miracles they performed.[69]

The shift here is to a positive description of the power of Jewish magicians, who are nourished by secret knowledge of divine extraction, in comparison with the

---

66 See Idel, *Golem*, pp. 207–12.
67 Of *Ma'aseh Bereshit*.
68 *Ma'asit*, an elyptic form for the phrase *Qabbalah ma'asit*.
69 R. Jacob Emden, *Sefer Mitpahat Sefarim* (Lemberg, 1871), p. 69, translated and discussed in Idel, *Golem*, p. 194 n. 94. In more general terms, see my thesis as to the ascent of discussions of the *golem* as a reaction to the emergence of alien sciences, as formulated in *ibid.*, pp. 165–195. See, also, Elhanan Reiner, 'The Attitude of Ashkenazi Society to the New Sciences in the Sixteenth Century', *Science in Context*, 10 (1997), 589–603.

lower order of knowledge of gentile scientists or philosophers. Emden refers to the so-called practical Kabbalah, namely the magical branch of Kabbalah, as superior to alien science. Thus, the magical aspect of Kabbalah is conceived as the inner lore, as the fruit in comparison to the shells. In a way this is an apotheosis of magic by a Central European Jew, who, orthodox as he was, had nevertheless been in good relations with the founder of the Jewish Enlightenment, Moses Mendelssohn, who regarded himself as his disciple. Thus, although not a philosopher or even one who was sympathetic with philosophy – Emden denied Maimonides' authorship of the Guide of the Perplexed, conceived by him as a forgery – he was in possession of a critical mind, capable not only of detecting Sabbatean allusions in abstruse Kabbalistic texts, but also ingenuous enough to discern traces of medieval terms in the canonical book of the Zohar, and pronounce the view that some parts of it were of later composition. In other words, he was one of the first important critical philologist in Jewish culture.

An Eighteenth-Century Apotheosis of Magic in European Jewry

Two different moments should be discerned as important in the transition between the traditional pictures of reality in the Middle Ages and those characteristic of modern science: the first one is the sharp process of secularization, a process that is entirely absent from the Hebrew passages discussed below. However, the other process, which I tried to emphasize above, that of putting a new accent on the positive aspects of human activity – seen in the context of crafting an anthropoid –and which endowed this form of magic with much more licit valences, is quite evident. In a way, this new, and more positive approach to golem-magic (as a form of machine, to use Norbert Wiener's terminology) is consonant with other developments in the eighteenth century. The ascent of the legend about the golem, the holy person with extraordinary powers, East European Hasidism, and especially the resurgence in the importance of the wonder-making holy man, the Tzaddiq,[70] from the second half of the eighteenth century onwards, can be described as a re-enchantment of some parts of European Judaism.

A seminal figure, who contributed much to Jewish culture, especially to the flowering of Kabbalah in the first half of the eighteenth century, R. Moshe Hayyim Luzzatto, was accused of practicing magic in order to obtain revelations,

---

70 See for example, Arthur Green, 'The Zaddiq as Axis Mundi in Later Judaism', *Journal of the American Academy of Religion*, 45 (1977), 327–347; Ada Rapoport-Albert, 'God and the Zaddik as the Two Focal Points of Hasidic Worship', *History of Religions*,18 (1979), 296–325; and, Moshe Idel, *Hasidism: Between Ecstasy and Magic* (Albany: State University of New York Press, 1995), pp. 149–70.

an accusation that I see as well founded.⁷¹ His much more influential contemporary, R. Israel Ba'al Shem Tov – the *Besht* – the founder of East European Hasidism, was known as a magician and healer.⁷² Their controversial contemporary, R. Yonathan Eibeschuetz – a major Halakhic expert and the favorite target of Emden's fiery and prolonged critique – wrote and distributed amulets, which included some Sabbatean overtones.⁷³ And, R. Elijah of Vilnius, was attributed the possibility to create a golem but he desisted from doing so.⁷⁴ Therefore, at least four of the central figures in Jewish life in eighteenth-century Europe, conceived of magic as licit, and sometimes even envisioned it as capable of solving practical problems in the present. This is a rather wide consensus in a culture where the leading figures in a given period rarely based themselves around shared positions. Let me also point out that the *Sefer Raziel ha-Malakh*, the most widespread book of Jewish magic, was printed for the first time in Amsterdam in 1701 and became a best-seller in Jewish Europe, second only to the Hebrew Bible. Some years ago I perused a compendium of two voluminous manuscripts of magical recipes and treatises. It is, perhaps, the largest collection of Jewish magic I am acquainted with, and is now held in a private collection in New York. The manuscripts were once in the possession of R. Isaac of Radvil, a late eighteenth century Hasidic figure. Thus, the surge of the interest in the golem is better seen as part of a broader phenomenon of interest and practice of magic.

The polemic nature of Emden's second passage, which rails against alien sciences, is quite obvious and it does not require the imposition of a scholar's efforts to understand it. It reflects a more practical interest in magic that is characteristic of the emergence of technology. An interest in the Golem is obvious at the beginning of the nineteenth century, for example in Franz Klut-

---

71 See Isaiah Tishby, *Netivei Emunah u-Minut* (Ramat Gan: Massada, 1964), pp. 184–85; and, Meir Benayahu, *Kitvei RaMHa"L be-Kabbalah* (Jerusalem, 1979), pp. 142–43, n. 13. I hope to dedicate to this topic a separate study.
72 See these important studies: Immanuel Etkes, 'The Place of Magic and the Masters of the Name in the Ashkenazi Society at the end of the 17th and 18th Century', *Zion*, 60 (1995), 69–104 (in Hebrew); *idem, The Besht: Magician, Mystic, and Leader,* trans. by Saadya Sternberg (Waltham, MA; Hanover, MA: Brandeis University Press; University Press of New England, 2004), pp. 7–45, 259–271; and, Yohanan Petrovsky-Shtern, 'The Master of An Evil Name: R. Hillel Ba'al Shem and His *Sefer Ha-Heshek*', *AJS Review*, 28 (2004), 217–248. See also: Zeev Gries, *Conduct Literature (Regimen Vitae), Its History and Place in the Life of the Beshtian Hasidism* (Jerusalem: Mossad Bialik, 1989) (in Hebrew), pp. 93–99; Zvi Mark, '*Dybbuk* and *Devekut* in the *Shivhe ha-Besht:* Toward a Phenomenology of Madness in Early Hasidism', in *Spirit and Spirit Possession in Judaism,* ed. by Matt Goldish (Detroit: Wayne State University Press, 2003), pp. 257–301; Gedalyah Nigal, *Magic, Mysticism, and Hasidism* (Tel Aviv: Yaron Golan, 1992) (in Hebrew); and, Idel, *Hasidism*, pp. 290, 315, 326, 334–335.
73 Gershom Scholem, *Researches in Sabbateanism*, ed. Yehuda Liebes (Tel Aviv: Am Oved, 1991), (in Hebrew), pp. 707–33.
74 See Idel, *Golem*, pp. 244–46.

schak's journal, *Panorama*,[75] which was printed in Prague in the 1840s. It is also apparent in the unparalleled anthropological interests in earlier forms of Judaism. This was expressed in the gloss that the mysterious figure who hides behind the name Ma'aravi added to the anonymous pseudo-historical novel *Me'ora'ot Tzevi*, which was printed in Lemberg in 1815, and dealt with the golem, Dalai Lama and Sabbatai Tzevi,[76] in a religiously comparative manner. Similarly, this interest is abundant in the various conceptual sources that nourished the late eighteenth-century influential Polish figure R. Pinehas Horowitz's rich and voluminous *Sefer ha-Berit*, which also deals with the Golem. Together, these elements point to a common geographical and intellectual background that id different from the concerns expressed in traditional forms of Judaism, as reflected in earlier Jewish sources. This new interest in themes related to artificial anthropoids is shared also by Christian authors like Mary Shelley's *Frankenstein*, for example.

All of these treatments, disparate as they are, are contemporaneous and the sources of their inspiration seem to be limited to a relatively small geographical area: traditions found in Central Europe. Even later on into the nineteenth century and the twentieth century, it was this geographical area which would remain the main cultural centre for the development of ideas connected to the golem, including operas, movies, and literary creations like Gustav Meyrink's famous novel, *The Golem*. Just as some European authors found interest in the Jewish topic of the golem in the early-nineteenth century, so too some Jews dealt with this topic in much wider contexts. This can be seen in the traditions of the late eighteenth-century Praguean homelist R. Yedidiah Tia Weill,[77] in the glosses applied by the above-mentioned Ma'aravi when describing the golem, and in R. Pinehas Eliyahu Horowitz's passages – and his lost composition on the topic.[78]

These discussions presumably did not contribute to the creation of a golem in reality. However, what they did craft was a more active vision of man who, though the imitation of God, is predisposed to envision – at least in some circles in Central European Jewry – activity, not contemplation, as the achievement that most expresses human perfection. This activity was the sequel to a previous period of preparation, a contact with the divine: in fact it was a fulfilling of His will, a situation that may inhibit extreme or immoral behavior. The divine men and the divine perfection, mentioned by R. Isaac of Acre, and the possibilities for creating new beings advanced by Emden, reflect a view of humanity that is, in essence, the inverse of the apparent depravity of human nature in its European

---

75 Discussed by Kieval, 'Pursuing the Golem'.
76 See Idel, 'On Astral Golems'.
77 Idel, 'On Astral Golems'.
78 Idel, *Golem*, pp. 237–238, 240.

environment. The magical, like the scientific approach is less religious and less interested in metaphysical speculations, and the surge of the interest in the Golem at the same time when modern science makes its first steps is fascinating case of synchronicity.

It is my opinion that modern science was less influenced by the details of Golem techniques, if at all. Nevertheless scientific developments triggered the interest in the traditions related to the artificial creation, in Jews and gentiles, and thus contributed to the discussions about the Golem, a type of problematic that was characteristic of the patrimony of pre-modern Ashkenazi Jewish culture, and elicited an interest in German authors.[79]

---

79 See Kilcher, *Die Sprachtheorie der Kabbala*, pp. 83–84, 307–317.

Antonis Liakos

The End of History as the Liminality of the Human Condition: From Kojève to Agamben

Commentaries on the *End of History* touch on two aspects: the concept of history and the concept of the human species. The *End of History* is a returning topos in historical thinking, and depends on an understanding of history as a concrete totality, which, having a beginning, should also have an end.[1] The Apocalypse is a controlling end of history, and the end of history comes together with the end of time and cosmos. This *End* introduces into the concept of history a mutual relation between past and future, between *promise* and *fulfilment*. Reality acquires a double dimension. Events become signs, or figures, of other events. The past is not the cause of the future, but figures out the future: Adam prefigured Christ; the Tree of Knowledge, the Cross; the Ark of Noah, the Church, and so on. Human history is in a mutual relationship between the divine project and its realization.[2] At the end of history, the transfiguration of man also awaits. The *City upon the Hill*, the Paradise, will mark not only the new covenant between God and humans, but also a transfiguration of the man. Humans are also subjected to this relationship of *figural realism*.[3] Humankind becomes a sign, between *promise* and *fulfilment*. There is an enigmatic phrase in the First Epistle of Saint John the Evangelist that says: "*Beloved, now we are the sons of God, and it doth not yet appear what we shall be; but we know that, when He shall appear, we shall be like Him; for we shall see Him as He is*".[4] This phrase gave birth to the idea of *Theosis* (Godmanhood), which means the transcendence of human nature in order to attend and participate in the nature of God.[5] In Eastern Orthodox theology, *Theosis* is possible even before the Last Judgment.

---

1 Antonis Liakos, *Αποκάλυψη, Ουτοπία και Ιστορία* [Apocalypse, Utopia and History] (Athens: Πόλις, 2011), pp. 203–221.
2 Liakos, *Αποκάλυψη*, pp. 116–118.
3 On figural realism, see Erich Auerbach, *Mimesis* (Princeton: Princeton University Press, 1953), pp. 194–195; Hayden White, *Figural Realism: Studies in the Mimesis Effect* (Baltimore: Johns Hopkins University Press, 1999), pp. 88–91.
4 1 John 3:2
5 Liakos, *Αποκάλυψη*, p. 398.

In the utopian novels of early-modern Europe (Thomas More, Tommaso Campanella, Francis Bacon, Johannes Andreae), which were written for a literate audience, there is neither an end of history nor a transfiguration of humans. Utopia means another place, and another configuration of time, existing in parallel with the real time. The *End of History* returned in the eighteenth century as the inner plan of history and such a *telos* of history is Immanuel Kant's image of a universal peaceful cosmopolitan society.[6] There are also various references to the *telos*/end of history in Georg Hegel, who nominated Christianity, or modern European civilization, as the *telos*/end of history: he used the concept of *telos* in a way similar to St Paul's reference to the "time of salvation". Salvation would be realized through the presence of God on Earth. But it would not be realized at the same time for all. The 'end' may be realized, but there is a *remaining time* to be completed. For Hegel, as well as for St Paul, the concept of the *remaining time* is crucial because it is the time we live in. But Hegel makes no reference to the end/or transformation of humans. The end of history is the realization of reason.[7] Karl Marx, in *The German Ideology* (following Hegel), refers to the end of history as the end of human 'prehistory'.[8]

Marx also introduces an idea of human transformation, not in biological terms, but as a potentiality of the total development of humans' intellectual capacity. The crafting of humans was not a topic in Marxism until the advent of the Russian Revolution. The Russian Revolution was a utopian experiment intermixed with eschatology. Already at the end of the nineteenth century, Vladimir Soloviev wrote a book on the end of history and the Anti-Christ, in which he advocated a homogeneous world-state and a new covenant with God.[9] In this homogeneous world-state humans would be transformed, mixing their historic knowledge with divine *pansophia* to realize a state of *Theosis*. Such a homogeneous world-state – but this time without a god – was also advocated by the Bolshevik leader Alexander Bogdanov, who was also a science-fiction writer. In his novel *Red Star*, he outlined a society of the future, where the prolongation of life was to be guaranteed through blood transfusions from younger to older people.[10]

---

6 Immanuel Kant, 'Idea for a Universal History with a Cosmopolitan Aim', in *Kant's 'Idea for a Universal History with a Cosmopolitan Aim': A Critical Guide*, ed. by Amélie Rorty and James Schmidt (Cambridge: Cambridge University Press, 2009).
7 Georg Hegel, *The Philosophy of History* (Whitefish, MT: Kessinger Publishing, 2004) passim; See also, Joe McCarney, *Hegel on History* (London: Routledge, 2000); John Grumley, *History and Totality: Radical Historicism from Hegel to Foucault* (Routledge London, 1989).
8 Karl Marx, *The German Ideology* (Moscow: International Publishers Co., 1970).
9 Vladimir Soloviev, *War, Progress and the End of History: Including a Short Story of Anti-Christ. Three Discussions*, trans. Alex Bakshy (London: University of London Press, 1915).
10 Alexander Bogdanov, *Red Star: The First Bolshevik Utopia* (Bloomington, IN: Indianna University Press, 1984).

Another form of crafting humans was the "utopian robotry" during the Bolshevik revolution. Alexei Gastev's proposals for a precise and tough implementation of Tailorism in work, and the robot like change of body movements, were coupled with the strict control of every day timetable proposed by Platon Mikhailovich Kerzhentsev who founded the *League of Time* in 1923, an institution which envisaged individual time as part of the total time of the industrial society. He advocated that humans should be conformed and harmonized with the rhythm of the machinery.[11] More than any other, Leon Trotsky undertook the initiative to figure out what was required for the crafting of humans within a communist society. Combining Marx's ideas about the communist society, with Bacon's vision of the future of science, and with eugenics, Trotsky proposed that not only should human reproduction not be left to chance, but that sexual relations, breathing, and the circulation of blood in the body should all be controlled and planned consciously.[12]

The risk of this unconditional surrender to an extreme belief that technology, science, and the rational planning of society should prevail on any other historical or traditional regulation, be it in Russia or the USA, was denounced in dystopian novels such as Yevgeni Zamyatin's *We* and Aldous Huxley's *Brave New World*, where the crafting of humans is the central issue.[13] At the same time in film, Fritz Lang's *Metropolis* and Charlie Chaplin's *Modern Times* criticized the industrial and mechanical transformation of the human, as advocated by Frederick Taylor and Henry Ford in early twentieth-century America.[14]

In the late 20th century, the end of history came together with the end of man in Francis Fukuyama's book, *The End of History*.[15] His argument drew from the theories of Alexandre Kojève, who, in his lectures in Paris in the 1930s, connected the idea of the End of History to the story of *Man and Slave* in Hegel's *The Phenomenology of the Spirit*.[16] For Kojève, this story depicts *in brevis* the entire dialectic course of human history. Hominids enter into civilization and become human beings, either as slaves or as masters, and human history depicts the

---

11 Richard Stites, *Revolutionary Dreams: Utopian Vision and Experimental Life in the Russian Revolution* (Oxford: Oxford University Press, 1989), pp. 149–159.
12 Leon Trotsky, *Literature and Revolution* (Chicago, IL: Haymarket Books, 2005), pp. 206–207.
13 Yevgeni Zamyatin, *We: New Edition* (London: Penguin Books, 1993); Aldous Huxley, *Brave New World* (New York: Random House, 2008).
14 Fritz Lang, Metropolis (1927); Charlie Chaplin, Modern Times (1936); Henry Ford, *Great Today and Greater Future* (Kila, MT: Kessinger Publishing, 2003 [1926]); Idem, *My Philosophy of Industry* (New York: Forum Publishing Co., 1928); Frederick Taylor, *The Principles of Scientific Management* (New York: Harper Bros, 1911).
15 Francis Fukuyama, *The End of History and the Last Man* (New York: Free Press, 1992).
16 Alexandre Kojève, *Introduction à la Lecture de Hegel (assembled by Raymond Queneau)* (Paris: Gallimard, 1947).

unfolding of this relationship. In the last phase, master and slave recognize each other, and this mutual recognition means the spreading of rights to all. This historical moment marks the end of history.[17]

The end of history means that human society will continue to exist without politics, philosophy, and great art, a situation that will soon lead to a transformation of human nature. Post-historical humans, satisfied with their life, will cease to be human beings and become humanlike animals. At the same time that they enter this post-historical condition, humans also enter a post-human condition. The disappearance of man at the end of history does not entail a biological catastrophe, because humans remain as they were in their historical period, albeit they now they live, not in contradiction with nature, but in harmony with it, like the other animals. The fundamental distinction of subject and object comes to an end, and as a consequence, philosophy and the human sciences vanish. In the post-historical and post-human future, humans will live in harmony with their environment.[18] Culture will not be the opposite of nature. The historical phase of human existence having come to an end, they will traverse the threshold of humanity, being ever since human – like animals.

The contextual counterpart of these ideas on the end of history as being the end of man can be found in the mid-twentieth-century French philosophy which declared the death of the subject and the end of humanism as a category of thought. Claude Lévi-Strauss, Jacques Lacan, Jacques Derrida, and Michel Foucault became the main pillars of anti-humanism in twentieth-century thought.[19] In structuralism and post-structuralism, the human does not constitute an autonomous concept in itself. One of the threads of these theories is related to the Italian philosopher Giorgio Agamben. He reads Kojève's post-human condition as the end of negative action by humans. For Agamben, the human is the *sickness of the animal*, and humanhood is a perversion of the natural condition. Man is a harmful animal, the most ruinous and self-catastrophic, who lives at the expense of other species and nature itself, damaging the foundations of its own existence in the long run. Humans, living in insatiable and acquisitive societies, and mastering nature with science and technology, pave the way, ultimately and without hesitation, to their defeat.[20] In contrast to the positive values, with which the concept of humanism has been endowed, in this line of thinking, the qualities that have transformed *Homo sapiens* into human beings are considered disastrous.

---

17 Kojève, *Introduction à la Lecture de Hegel*, pp. 3–70.
18 Fukuyama, *The End of History*, pp. 310–312.
19 Stefanos Geroulanos, *An Atheism that is not Humanist Emerges in French Thought* (Palo Alto, CA: Stanford University Press, 2010).
20 Giorgio Agamben, *L'aperto: L'uomo e l'animale* (Torino: Bollati Boringhieri, 2002), pp. 12–20.

So far I have presented the philosophical arguments according to which the end of history transforms humans. But there is also a practical aspect of crafting humans, related to techno-science and its projection to the future. In this debate the end of history is the consequence, not the prerequisite of transforming humans into post-historical beings.

The dream of the prolongation of life and the abolition of pain gave a tremendous impetus to the development of medicine and medical technology since the nineteenth century.[21] The new frontiers are the elimination of old age and the prevention of inherited diseases. Both imply forms of crafting humans. If old age is taken as a sum of dysfunction, each one could be eliminated through mechanical and chemical interventions. The result is that the limits of the human body are changing and will expand and coincide with the possibilities of medical technology. Another aspect of this intervention is that the autonomy of the human personality is losing ground to heteronomy and dependence on medical personnel. This is not something which will happen in the distant future. It is happening now, and all of us will probably enter this new phase towards the end of our life. From this point of view, we are living in a temporality of *remaining time*.[22]

The second remark to be made has to do with genes. Genetic engineering is one of the most serious examples of crafting humans because it has to do with the reproduction of the human being on a scale surpassing even the wildest eugenic dream. Although bioethics tries hard to hold it back, the defenders of scientific freedom also strongly reject the raising of ethical arguments. The ethical question behind the opening of new frontiers in the biosciences is whether we should admit that pain and sickness is a natural condition for humans and, therefore, whether we should accept a state of affairs where the imperfectability of human nature becomes its stronghold. Another argument is that reproductive intervention is not a state affair, as during most of the twentieth century, but an individual choice.[23]

Is this another utopia of the End of History? Whatever the accomplishments that projects of genetic intervention will produce in the future, there is a big difference between them and the classic utopias. Transhumanism is not the transformation of social conditions, which seeks to change human behaviour and produce happy societies. It intends to transform the human body, and, as a

---

21 Stephen Katz, 'Imagining the Life-span: From Premodern Miracles to Postmodern Fantasies', in *Images of Aging: Cultural Representations of Later Life*, ed. by Mike Featherstone and Andrew Wernick (London: Routledge, 1995), pp. 61–75.
22 Nikolas Rose, *The Politics of Life Itself: Biomedicine, Power, and Subjectivity in the Twenty-First Century* (Princeton and Oxford: Princeton University Press, 2007).
23 Nicholas Agar, *Liberal Eugenics: In Defence of Human Enhancement* (Oxford: Blackwell, 2004).

consequence, the human personality, without interfering in projects that seek to alter the conditions of social living and society. Such interventions will have diluvial consequences for the future of human society. The distinction between nature and culture will indeed disappear, but not by adapting humans to nature but by intervening in human nature. The concept of evolution will transform into techno-evolution, where the natural process of evolution will be complemented by the nature-like evolution of technology; both will form a new natural reality. If laboratories for the crafting of humans do open, the result will be the emergence of several species of humans with different competences, aspirations to long-living and with asymmetric access to the available natural resources. In such a posthuman Jurassic Park, all the concepts with which we now understand humanity, as well as the norms of social life, art philosophy, and history, will have vanished. The concept of society is a historical term, created to cover the coexistence of autonomous beings who share the same essence, i.e. human nature. Although human nature was always a strongly contested idea, it is the foundation stone of natural law, of human rights, of ethics and morality, of justice and freedom. None of these concepts will keep their value in the new environment of different hybrids of trans- and posthumans. According to Habermas, the instrumentalization of human nature will change the way in which human beings understand themselves and their past.[24] The borders between the human and the nonhuman will disappear.

Apart from the problem of bioethics, which has become more and more central in thinking the future of the humans, it is important to point out that the concept of humanism is now understood in a different way to how it has been in the past. Agamben's distinction between Ζωή, as barren life and Βίος, a life endowed with rights in society, extends the problematic into the future but also projects it into the past.[25] The fabrication of the new life has its equivalent in the fabrication of the end of life, for example, in the industrialized mass extermination in the Nazi extermination camps. As a consequence, this liminality between the human and nonhuman poses again the problem of the basis of human nature. Is human nature a biological or a social event? Can human nature be realized in concentration camps, under humanitarian crises, and in war? From this point of view, the problem of humanism becomes a problem defining the core values of society.

There is also another aspect that gives a negative connotation to the concept of humanism. The encounter with the posthuman future has not only provoked an anticipatory mourning for the eventual loss of the human world, but also, and in

---

24 Jürgen Habermas, *The Future of Human Nature* (Abingdon: Taylor & Francis, 2005), p. 49.
25 Giorgio Agamben, *Homo Sacer: Sovereign Power and Bare Life* (Palo Alto, CA: Stanford University Press, 1998), pp. 19–35.

contrast, a celebratory discourse. Donna Haraway has suggested this approach in her 1985 essay 'A Cyborg Manifesto: Science, Technology, and Socialist-Feminism in the Late Twentieth Century'. She welcomes the hybridization of machine and organism, as forms of living, social experience and cultural imagination. Cyborgs are not only creatures of medical technology and bioscience, but also 'a condensed image of both imagination and material reality, the two joined centres structuring any possibility of historical transformation'.[26] Cyborg culture is the negation of humanist culture and its foundational dichotomies. It transgresses three crucial boundaries: the distinction between culture and nature, the distinction between the grown (physical) and the made (machine), and the distinction between materialism and idealism. Accepting and understanding this new cyborg reality means: a) to consider any universal and totalizing theory as impossible; and, b) declining to surrender to a demonology of science and technology and to a metaphysics of human essence. The new cyborg reality means the unmaking of humanist cultural boundaries and a redefinition of the main categories of thought. Crafting humans presupposes to rethink and refashion humanism.

But there is also a third aspect which poses the problem of rethinking and crafting the human, and humanism, in relation to the environmental crisis. In 2009, Dipesh Chakrabarty published an article, in the form of a manifesto, on the subject of bioclimatic change, in which he writes that human society has became, since the Industrial Revolution, a geological force which forms not only the life on the planet but also the climate of the planet.[27] This force is expanding its impact, through the augmentation of energy consumption and greenhouse gas emissions, with catastrophic results for certain regions and the populations living there. In the future, this fact will reinforce, not diminish, geopolitical inequality and conflict, because, above all, it is a threat to the poor and the unborn.

The problem now is how to consider the philosophical, the techno-science, and the climate approach together, and how to envisage a new role for the humanities, and particularly for history, in this context. The connecting link is that they pose the problem of history at the threshold dividing the human from the non-human. From this point of view, history may be conceived as a discipline bridging the human with the biological and the technological, but also linking the human with the forces which will shape the face of the planet. As a consequence history becomes not the discipline of human deeds, but the discipline

---

26 Donna Haraway, 'A Cyborg Manifesto: Science, Technology, and Socialist-Feminism in the Late Twentieth Century', in *Simians, Cyborgs and Women: The Reinvention of Nature* ed. by *idem* (New York: Routledge, 1991), pp. 149–181 (p. 150).
27 Dipesh Chakrabarty, 'The Climate of History: Four Theses', *Critical Inquiry* 35:2 (2009), 197–222.

of traversing thresholds/boundaries between the human and the non-human. History as a study of liminality considers humans not as something given, but as something to be crafted in society. From this point of view, society in the long run acquires the technological properties of crafting the human or of conceiving what is human.[28] How humans are crafted arises as a question through the study of political, social, and cultural changes in history, especially those during the 20th century. Yet, this is an issue of the deep history, comprising the making of the human brain and comportment.[29]

---

28 Joanna Bourke, *What it Means to be Human, Reflections from 1791 to the Present* (London: Virago, 2011).
29 Daniel Lord Smail, *On Deep History and the Brain* (Berkeley: University of California Press, 2008).

Roger Griffin

Bio-nomic Man (and Woman): Fantasies of Anthropological Revolution as a Reaction to Modernity's Nomic Crisis

In Don DeLillo's premonitory novel about terrorism, *Mao II*, the author asks 'When the Old God leaves the world, what happens to all the unexpended faith?'[1] Looking back on the rise of secular modernity over the last three centuries from the increasingly precarious, ramshackle belvedere of the early twenty first century, it is obvious where vast reserves of faith, no longer channelled into Christian hopes of an afterlife, were spent and often squandered: in ideological projects to create a 'better' world through human agency. In *The Brothers Karamazov*, Dostoevsky describes socialism's scheme for a new humanity as 'the tower of Babel built without God, not to mount to heaven from earth but to set up heaven on earth'.[2]

As Nietzsche's prophecy of the 'death' of God as an existential reality became palpably fulfilled, cultural, social, and scientific space in the West was churned with eddying currents: of secularization and desecularization; of disenchantment and re-enchantment; and, of a disintegrating Christian total world view or *nomos*, which once endowed the world with magic, transcendence, and the numinous, and countervailing renomizing projects, whether private (and hence practically invisible) or collective and revolutionary, erected on rival construction sites for a new Babel. Some projects promised merely momentary escape from anomie and absurdity, while others envisaged the creation of an entirely new social system within which life would once more become self-evidently meaningful and sacralized, even if only in a worldly, temporal sense. Often, at the heart of this latter group of 'totalizing' schemes lay the myth of a 'new man', an anthropological revolution without which the socio-political one could not become a reality.

We have available a sophisticated critical discourse with which to analyse renomizing initiatives within every medium of the arts by talking about them in

---

1 Don DeLillo, *Mao II* (London: Vintage, 1992), p. 7.
2 Fyodor Dostoevsky, *The Brothers Karamazov*, trans. by Constance Garnett (New York: Dover Publications, 2005), p. 19.

terms of one much investigated topic: 'artistic modernism'. However even here, within the flood of publications on the topic, strikingly little attention has been accorded to the need to distinguish modernists who creatively explored the anomic experience of modernity and attempted to achieve, express, and record visionary glimpses of transcendence of a terrestrial kind (e. g. Van Gogh, Kafka), and those who went further by working towards the foundation of an entirely new society altogether, brought about through revolutionary change in the perception of ideal forms and spaces (e.g. Kandinsky, Gropius). Elsewhere, I have suggested that these two types of modernism should be called 'epiphanic' and 'programmatic', though there are obviously porous membranes between them.[3] In the same book, I have argued that the term 'modernism' should be extended far beyond the narrow confines of art to embrace the flood of diverse initiatives to create a new world through social, political, and scientific innovation, which characterized the period 1880–1939. A study of the first five years of the Bolshevik Revolution demonstrates just how absurd it would be not to treat the massive political and economic change the country underwent as connected both to utopian movements in science, technology, and social housing and to the ethos of Russian futurism, science fiction, and constructivism. Their protagonists believed, however naively, they were all contributing to the establishment of the first socialist society as a beacon to the rest of the world, and many idealists and utopians continued to project their ideal future onto Lenin's and Stalin's regime, despite the increase in human suffering, persecution, and death it conspicuously entailed.

It was in the heady climate of the late nineteenth century that programmatic modernism was to have a major impact on one sphere in particular by re-evaluating the importance of the human body, so neglected by Christian and Enlightenment thinkers alike, and casting it as instrumental not just to societal rejuvenation, and a restored relationship with nature, but to renomizing a decadent world. The result might be called 'Corporeal Modernism', a heterogeneous vision of rebirth, of palingenesis, intimately related to the various bids to make human beings healthier and even to craft new types of human being in this period. In identifying as quintessentially Modernist the revolutionary new significance attributed to the body in various quarters, and in particular in the context of projects to create a 'new man', a neglected aspect of Nietzschean philosophy assumes fresh significance: especially given his centrality to so many cultural and political programmes of renewal that emerged in this period. *Also Sprach Zarathustra* (1883–5), the cornerstone of his 'Dionysian modernism', contains the passage:

---

3 Roger Griffin, *Modernism and Fascism: The Sense of a Beginning under Mussolini and Hitler* (London: Palgrave, 2007).

> To the despisers of the body will I say my word. Not that I would have them learn and teach differently, but simply say farewell to their own bodies – and thus become mute. 'Body am I, and soul' – thus talks the child. And why should one not talk like children? But the awakened one, the one who knows, says: Body am I through and through, and nothing besides; and soul is merely a word for something about the body'. The body is a great reason, a manifold with one sense, a war and a peace, a herd and a herdsman. A tool of the body is also your small reason too, my brother, which you call 'spirit' – a small toll and toy of your great reason.[4]

In the context of Nietzschean thought, this emphasis on the body is intended to underline the rigorous materialism that is the premise of his intended revaluation of values. The objective absence of any realm of the spirit or metaphysical other-world (*Hinterwelt*), as a hidden source of values or purpose, demands as an existential imperative that human beings must create their own ethical principles to confer meaning on life without invoking 'higher principles' derived from an imaginary incorporeal realm of 'spirit'. Yet such a passage is also symptomatic of an important shift in European sensibilities, away from idealism of a religious or secular kind, especially the idealism of Kant and Hegel, and towards vitalism, or rather what one German historian of this period calls *Lebensmystik*, an 'immanentist', monistic life mysticism, expressed in a wide range of styles and genres.[5] At the heart of vitalism lay the celebration of life in itself as a source of wonder, transcendence, and value, a sentiment which reached its ultimate religious expression in Haeckel's monistic world-view based on a spiritualized biology. The spiritual currency, no longer expended in worshipping a spiritual 'other-worldliness', is reinvested in a reconfigured 'this-worldliness' now imbued with numinous, auratic significance, producing such typical *fin-de-siècle* masterpieces as: Rilke's *The Duino Elegies*; the decadent sensuality of Klimt's *The Kiss*; Munch's *Frieze of Life*; Bergson's 'discovery' of the *élan vital*; Freud's exploration of the dynamic life of the psyche; and Jung's quest for universal spirituality. It is manifested too in a new importance attached to the human body as a source of transcendent value, and, at its most utopian, in attempts to refashion human beings and craft a 'new man'.

While the European *avant-garde* was intent on purging Western culture of Christian and post-Christian ideas of transcendence by drawing on neo-Romantic, neo-pagan, and symbolist themes, their efforts were being complemented by pioneers working in the human sciences, or in areas of social reform concerned with public health. In an age of spectacular technological and

---

4 Friedrich Nietzsche, *Thus Spoke Zarathustra*, trans. by Graham Parkes (Oxford: Oxford University Press, 2005), p.30.
5 Dietrich Rasch, *Zur deutschen Literatur seit der Jahrhundertwende. Gesammelte Aufsätze* (Stuttgart: Metzler, 1967).

scientific advance, the self-appointed custodians of society in the late nineteenth century were increasingly concerned with the threat posed to the long-term progress of humanity, not just by rapid urbanization and the loss of contact with nature, but also by the rise of the masses and the spectre of degeneration, both moral and physical.[6] It was a concern in which medical alarm at the way modernity was changing the quality of life became conflated with anxiety at the aggressive power of materialism and science to erode not just revealed religion but spirituality. Thus the dire warnings issuing from a generation of "decadent" artists, that spirituality, creativity, and magic were draining from the world under the impact of science and 'progress', mingled with the vociferous calls of social commentators for measures to bring about physical regeneration.

The confluence of these two currents of 'body-centred' longings for a better world can be seen in the painting 'Prayer to Light' (1894), by the German painter Hugo Höppener (Fidus), in which a naked youth ecstatically greets the sun. The painting is the expression of a neo-Romantic and symbolist sensibility, one which has a resonance with the celebration of the life force in the Nordicist, *völkisch*, and occultist circles at the time. But it also touches on scientific concerns with cosmopolitan degeneracy in its attempt to infuse modernity with a lost sense of spirituality, vitalism, awe, and transcendence. It portrays a 'pure', athletic (possibly Aryan) figure standing ecstatically in the mountain air, far removed from crowded, unhygienic city streets, and free, both physically and spiritually. Once the main strands of the disparate body-centric movement of regeneration that emerged in Europe at the height of the *fin-de-siècle* are disentangled, the recurrence of early twentieth century socio-political initiatives to create a new human being, a new phenotype of *homo sapiens* become more intelligible.

Mount Truth and the Body Reform Movement

A glimpse into the new role that the body was assuming by the 1890s is offered by the rum goings-on at Monte Verità, a private estate just above Ascona on the Swiss side of Lago Maggiore. From the 1890s, 'Mount Truth' became a major site for forging a new relationship with the body, simultaneously ancient and ultra-modern, in a spirit of rebellion against societal norms which uncannily presages the key motifs of Hippy counterculture in the 1960s. For over thirty years it attracted spiritual rebels – poets, painters, pacifists, anarchists, self-styled prophets – acting as a 'sacred mountain', where those hungry for a new *nomos*, a

---

6 As suggested by Daniel Pick, *Faces of Degeneration: a European Disorder c. 1848–1918* (Cambridge: Cambridge University Press, 1989).

new sacred canopy to protect them from nihilism and absurdity, could feel at home. Year after year its Bohemian clientele could freely indulge in an alternative vision of morality and civilization based on a *pot-pouri* of spiritual fragrances supplied by Nordic paganism, feminism, Tolstoy, Freud, psychoanalysis, sun-worship and heliotherapy, macrobiotic and vegetarian diets, yoga, free love, lesbianism and homosexuality, expressive dance, or naturism, sprinkled with liberal helpings of Nietzsche. Typical sojourners were Gusto Gräser, Taoist and poet of liberation, and Otto Gross, militant opponent of 'the Goliath of German patriarchy' and advocate of psychoanalysis to free individuals of the repression of a neurotic civilization and allow them to achieve the sacredness of love. More famous creative individuals whose quest for liberation brought them to Lake Maggiore included Rudolf Laban, Mary Wigman, Isadora Duncan, the founders of *Ausdruckstanz* (expressive or expressionist dance), Hermann Hesse, D.H. Lawrence, C.G. Jung, Paul Tillich, as well as two more surprising figures, Max Weber and Franz Kafka.[7] Steven Aschheim confirms that the 'pervasive atmosphere' in Ascona was Nietzschean:

> These were not will-to-power, but Dionysian Nietzscheans who aspired to a kind of ecstatic dynamism. They sought to create beauty in motion and affirm life-creating values – above all that of Eros. The Ascona search for Eros and beauty, *for freeing the body and soul in motion*, found its most dynamic physical expression in the idea and development of modern dance. Here the notions of self-creation and Dionysian community could fuse.[8] (My emphasis)

In particular, Aschheim stresses the relevance to understanding the ethos of the Mount Truth commune of the aphoristic assertion in *Also Sprach Zarathustra* that:

> we should consider every day lost on which we have not danced at least once. *The Birth of Tragedy* conceived of the dancer as one in whom all productive power was contained, and included one godlike dancer who was himself transformed into a work of art.[9]

Building upon this, Laban and Wigman would go on to transform the theory and practice of modern dance, but only because the mood within educated elites resonated with the gospel of kinetic freedom that they brought to a society whose creative energies they saw ossified in classical forms that had become soulless. After all, this was also the age when Sergei Diaghilev and Sergei Prokofiev were transforming ballet through new forms of classical dance which led to the formation of the *Ballets Russes*, and Rudolf Steiner was advocating 'eurhythmics' as

---

7 Martin Green, *Mountain of Truth: The Counterculture Begins: Ascona, 1900–1920* (Lebanon, NH.: University Press of New England, 1986).
8 Steven Aschheim, *The Nietzsche Legacy in Germany, 1890–1990* (Berkeley: University of California Press, 1992), p. 59.
9 Aschheim, *Nietzsche Legacy*, p. 60.

a key component of his alternative education system based on "anthroposophy": a blend of Madame Blavatsky's theosophy with Goethean wisdom. The dancing body was the very embodiment of the Corporeal Modernism that was "in the air" by the outbreak of the First World War. A point that Modris Eksteins make luminously clear in the first chapter of his *Rites Of Spring*, a seminal book for understanding the pervasive atmosphere of longing for renewal, for regeneration which made Germany 'the most modernist nation in Europe'.[10]

Each component of the re-evaluation of the body, undertaken in Ascona for over a generation, had its own complex, tangled story within the history of the early twentieth century. Thus the neo-paganism and cult of nature, so much in evidence there, had affinities with the *völkisch* movement that had arisen in several Nordic countries to celebrate pre-urban national idylls. In Austria and Germany there was also an occultist dimension to such 'anti-modern', pagan (but simultaneously modernist) impulses, which could sometimes assume the form of an esoteric and fanatically anti-Semitic racism, as in the case of the *Germanenorden*, which became a part of the prehistory of the Nazi Party.[11] Even expressive dance would in Germany become absorbed into the Nazi ethos of 'strength through joy', thereby celebrating Aryan vitality, creativity, and eternal youth.[12]

The cult of nature assumed a specifically physical outlet of a less elitist sort in the international emergence of scouting and youth movements through which young city dwellers could go 'back to nature' and have exercise in the open. Within four years of Baden-Powell's publication of *Scouting for Boys* in 1908, which had originally been inspired by fears about the palpable unfitness of so many of British youth for military service, scouting and guiding together already had over 41 million members worldwide. In the German *Wandervögel* the celebration of youth and physical contact with the countryside assumed aspects of a mass protest movement against the evils of an urbanized modernity, with the cult of health acquiring political and nationalistic connotations. In Germany, these developments would be later exploited by the Nazis, but youth groups stressing the need for physical exercise and practical experience of living in nature became a feature of many political movements, from left and right, and religious sects in inter-war Europe and North America.

Naturism was also an international phenomenon, though it was taken up in Germany with singular passion, providing a more populist outlet than just mountain retreats for those who felt driven to escape from the prison of social

---

10 Modris Eksteins, *Rites of Spring* (Boston: Houghton Mifflin, 1989).
11 Nicholas Goodrick-Clarke, *The Occult Roots of Nazism: Secret Aryan Cults and Their Influence on Nazi Ideology* (New York: New York University Press, 1992).
12 Lilian Karina and Marion Kant (ed.), *Hitler's Dancers: German Modern Dance and the Third Reich* (Oxford: Berghahn, 2003).

conformity and repression—one which spontaneously lived out the drive to reconcile id and superego, which animated Freud's psychoanalysis, without recourse to therapy. The virtues of the naked body were preached with religious fervour by evangelists of nudism such as Richard Ungewitter, as the key to the West's salvation. It was also seen as a cure to the spiritual diseases of a tired civilization, and its unhealthy preoccupation with money, as diagnosed by Ungewitter's contemporary Oswald Spengler;[13] again a movement particularly popular in a Weimar Republic awash with palingenetic, modernist energies.[14] For thousands of educated city dwellers, brought up at the height of repressive middle class morality, to join societies in which they encounter each other without hiding themselves under clothes points to more than an urge to throw off the trammels of sexual repression or Victorian moral values. It indicates an even deeper impulse for a more authentic, grounded existence, denied by everyday urbanized living, which already was 'in the air' before the First World War and intensified once the genocidal madness of Western civilization had been exposed by four years of mechanized slaughter.

Both the 'back to nature' movements and naturism were in turn manifestations of what became known as the *Lebensreform* or Life Reform Movement. This is to be thought of not as a cohesive, structured organization, but as a number of diverse initiatives for healthier living that started in the mid-nineteenth century and which came to be loosely grouped under one heading, so that the term refers to a number of largely separate "cultic milieus" rather than a coordinated force for change. Though its epicentre was Germany and Switzerland, activities and projects expressing the yearning for a 're-embedding' and 're-grounding' of a civilization gone awry, for a healthier, more physically and spiritually dynamic, 'undecadent' way of life were encountered all over the West even before the *fin-de-siècle* period. For example, Seventh Day Adventist John Harvey Kellogg, inventor of the cornflake breakfast, opened the Battle Creek Sanitarium (sic!) in 1868, in which exercise, hydrotherapy, and colonic irrigation were treated as the key to a healthy body and soul, while his German contemporary, Sebastian Kneipp, became an ardent advocate of 'naturopathic' medicine. Such widespread concerns with health formed the precondition for the intense international interest in the work of Freud and Jung on mental health and the workings of the psyche.[15]

The urge to reconnect with fundamental human drives that were dangerously

---

13 Karl Toepfer, *Empire of Ecstasy: Nudity and Movement in German Body Culture, 1910–1935* (Berkeley: University of California Press, 1997).
14 Chad Ross, *Naked Germany: Health, Race and the Nation* (Oxford and New York: Berg, 2005).
15 For an excellent overview of the health obsessed counter-culture which acted as a sounding board to Jung's ideas, see Richard Noll, *The Jung Cult* (New York: Simon & Schuster, 1994).

starved and neglected in an over-civilized, over-*cerebral* society also forms the common denominator between movements as diverse as Expressionism, Fauvism, Primitivism, and Futurism. It also informs the work of individual artists: D. H. Lawrence's *Women in Love* (1920), which probes into the relationship between society, erotic drives, and the quest for personal meaning (the dramatic climax of which is played out in the Swiss mountains); Thomas Mann's labyrinthine *Magic Mountain* (1924), which dramatizes the struggle between decadence (*Thanatos*) and life (*Eros*) in a sanatorium in Davos; and, the macabre Expressionist poetry of the German doctor Gottfried Benn. All three are very different reflections and refractions of an age deeply concerned with the body as the locus of psychological and physical health, and sickness, in a decadent age that had just produced the hecatombs of the First World War.

The Life Reform movement itself is identified with a surge of interest in 'alternative medicine' (e.g. herbal remedies, footbaths, massage, homeopathy, hydrotherapy, chiropractics, craniosacral therapy, Alexander technique), and in the growing popularity among the privileged of spas, sanatoria, and mountain walks (especially for tuberculosis, which was still a widespread killer disease at the time). This development was also associated with a movement in Europe and the USA promoting natural clothing, banishing corsets, stays, and constricting or prudish attire for women, wearing sandals instead of shoes, and promoting loose-fitting garments made of linen and wool close to the skin instead of rough cotton, just when the first artificial fibres such as viscose (1894) and rayon (1910) were beginning to make an impact. The late 1800s was also a period of intense counter-cultural interest in nutritional reforms (vegetarianism, veganism, and Sagen Ishizuka's orientalized version of macrobiotics, pioneered in Germany a century earlier), yoga,[16] organic farming (the anthroposophist Rudolf Steiner developed 'bio-dynamic farming' as part of his bid to transform the West).

It was at the turn of the century that muesli was invented by the nutritional reformer Maximilian Bircher-Benner, and Edwardian London alone boasted thirty vegetarian restaurants. It was also the time of the first European spiritual retreats or *ashrams*, of the 'Garden city' movement, and of several communes hosting experiments in physical and psychological health along the lines of Monte Verità, such as the German communes Oneida, Heilerau, and Eden (which produced the homonymous margarine based on vegetable oil still eaten today). The tradition of communal retreats from the anomie of city life established patterns of thought and practice that had a major impact both on the *kibbutz* system pioneered by Zionism and on the *völkisch* Artamanen movement in

---

16 On the enthusiastic uptake of yoga in Europeanized societies of the late 19th century, the age of theosophy, spiritualism, and the occult revival, see Mark Singleton, *Yoga Body* (Oxford: Oxford University Press, 2010), Ch. 2, 'Fakirs, Yogins, Europeans', pp. 35–54.

Germany, which set up Aryan communities along racial lines anticipating the ethos of the Third Reich, especially in the Hitler Youth.[17]

Yet Europe's new body-centeredness was not just confined to cultic communes and health fads. Its mainstream expression was the extraordinary rise of sport as a mass leisure and spectator activity. By the eve of the First World War football and cycling had gained a huge public following, and it was in 1908 that the modern Olympic movement finally gathered momentum to the point where with the 1928 event held in Amsterdam the modern age of international passion for watching sporting events and the creation of vast stadia in which to watch them had finally arrived.

Eugenics and the Cult of the 'New Man'

The cult of mass spectator sport, which was gathering pace by 1914, forms a bridge between counter-cultural, and sometimes esoteric rebellions against the official norms of society, which attached new importance to the body as a vessel of the spirit, and three less spiritually oriented developments from within the very bastions of the existing social order, which also promoted a stress on corporeal strength, youth, health, and athleticism. One was the link, being increasingly made by the end of the nineteenth century, between national strength, demographic growth, and the physical fitness of youth: a link we have already encountered in Baden-Powell's launch of an international scouting movement, against the background of concerns regarding the future quality of the troops needed to garrison the British Empire.[18] This development was complemented by a major shift within education, pioneered in British, Canadian, and US public schools (and even in some private institutions for girls, such as The Cheltenham Ladies' College), to emphasize the value of sport in the moral education of the young. It was a development deeply bound up with both the 'Muscular Christianity' and YMCA movements, which wanted to take Christianity out of the pulpit and Sunday School and into nature, and with the growth of hiking associations in Germany animated by nationalist sentiments of a more pagan, and potentially racist, variety. The youth hostel movement was founded in Germany in 1909 by a schoolteacher and a conservationist and by the 1930s had become an international organization.

But there was an even more powerful, and sinister, force fuelling a health-

---

[17] The classic study of this aspect of German counter-culture is George Mosse, *The Crisis of German Ideology: Intellectual Origins of the Third Reich* (New York: Howard Fertig, 1998).

[18] Joseph A. Mangan, *Militarism, Sport, Europe: War Without Weapons* (London: Routledge, 1966).

oriented and body-centred diagnosis of the state of society within academic and political elites by the eve of the First World War. Several factors had conspired to provide momentum to the emergence of social hygiene and eugenics: the impact of Darwinism and Social Darwinism; rapid strides in the understanding of genetics and the technology of animal breeding; and ruling class alarm that the 'rise of the masses' was bringing about modern civilization's degeneration and collapse. The current of body-centred thinking about combating social decay was intensified by scientistic speculation in all advanced countries that the latent criminality and immorality attributed to the increasing population of urban poor was the product not of desperate poverty and social deprivation, but of 'dysgenic' inherited physiological and mental properties.[19] The resulting programmes for enhancing society's health could focus on ways of promoting physical strength and agility (positive eugenics) or ways of purging it of disease through sterilization and even more drastic methods (negative eugenics). The fact that the first exponents of eugenics saw the new science not just in technocratic terms of social engineering, but as a solution to the spiritual crisis of civilization is underscored by Francis Galton's argument that the science, whose name he had coined, should become the religion of modern society:

> [Eugenics] must be introduced into the national conscience, like a new religion. It has, indeed, strong claims to become an orthodox religious, tenet of the future, for eugenics co-operate with the workings of nature by securing that humanity shall be represented by the fittest races. What nature does blindly, slowly, and ruthlessly, man may do providently, quickly, and kindly.[20]

To disseminate his vision among the Edwardian public, at a time when H. G. Wells was getting into his stride as a popular fiction writer, he even worked on a (for him) utopian novel, *Kantsaywhere* (1910) about a society run by a new breed of benign scientists, eugenicists. In short, eugenics is yet another example of programmatic modernism which arose as a response to the deepening nomic crisis of the West.[21]

---

19 See Marius Turda and Paul Weindling (ed.), *Blood and Homeland: Eugenics and Racial Nationalism in Central and Southeast Europe 1900–1940* (Budapest: Central European University, 2007).
20 Francis Galton, 'Eugenics: Its Definition, Scope, and Aims', in *idem, Essays in Eugenics* (London: The Eugenics Education Society, 1909), p. 42.
21 Marius Turda, *Modernism and Eugenics* (London: Palgrave, 2010).

Crafting Humans as renomization

The visionary belief in eugenics, as the orthodox religion of the future, which Galton propounds in what purports to be a scientific article, has a direct bearing on the themes discussed in this chapter. It reminds us that, even when it emanates from milieus far removed from the counter-culture whose cultic millenarianism is so typical of all New Ageists, past and present, the concern with a body-centred regeneration in the early-twentieth century also had both a metaphysical and metapolitical agenda. Metaphysical because underpinning the overt concern with health lay the subliminal longing to heal the West *spiritually* now that its *nomos*, its sacred canopy,[22] had been eroded by the forces of modernity, thus halting what various commentators have called the disenchanting, disembedding, de-centring, or 'de-souling' (*Entseelung*) impact that was making modern human beings spiritually anomic, 'homeless', and 'disinherited'.[23] Metapolitical, because politics, instead of being a purely party-political force or a matter of deciding how the power to govern society was achieved and deployed, acquired a transcendental rationale and purpose: to restore health, spirituality, and meaning to the lives of modern human beings. The late nineteenth and early twentieth-century initiatives of *Lebensreform*, in all their highly variegated anti-establishment and pro-establishment forms, were thus ultimately all manifestations of a spontaneous revitalization movement, a movement to renomize the West. One product of 1970s TV science fiction in the US of the space race and the Cold War was bionic man and woman. The new species of human beings at the heart of various brands of early twentieth century utopianism were 'bio-nomic', fusing a regenerated body with a restored spirituality to produce a complete human being uniquely tailored to the modern age.

It is with the advent of totalitarian experiments to transform society and history after the First World War that these bio-nomic fantasies became integrated into state policy.[24] Indeed, the historian Emilio Gentile sees as one of the definitional features of totalitarianism the aspiration to bring about an 'anthropological revolution'.[25] Such an aspiration is typical of what Zygmunt Bauman describes as 'the gardening state', which sees its task to root out weeds, dig and plant, and force a garden to emerge from the anarchic wilderness of

---

22 Peter Berger, *The Sacred Canopy: Elements of a Sociological Theory of Religion* (London: Doubleday, 1967).
23 See Griffin, *Modernism and Fascism* for a detailed exposition of this thesis.
24 David Roberts, *The Totalitarian Experiment in the Twentieth-Century* (New York: Routledge, 2006).
25 Emilio Gentile, 'The Sacralisation of Politics: Definitions, Interpretations and Reflections on the Question of Secular Religion and Totalitarianism', *Totalitarian Movements and Political Religion*, 1:1 (2000), 18–55.

liberal society using the maximum force of the state, and so conquer the ambivalence that is the hallmark of modernity.[26]

Yet while Soviet Russia and fascist regimes and movements drew heavily on currents of 'Corporeal Modernism' in their efforts to create either: the 'New Soviet Man and Woman'; the *uomo fascista*; the new Aryan; the Romanian *omul nou*; or, the Vichy *homme nouveau*;[27] along with their various counterparts in other movements of national regeneration, it should not be forgotten that, long before this concern with the West's decline, revolutionary movements in Europe had pursued the myth of an anthropological revolution. It is a myth which draws on an archetype of the palingenetic imagination at the heart of all religions concerned with the spiritual transformation of human beings or the apocalyptic metamorphosis of history. Thus, the early French Revolutionaries were obsessed with the regeneration of 'Man',[28] and already in 1811 the gymnastics instructor and patriot Friedrich Jahn was setting up a network of gymnastic clubs that would be the crucible of the new German, as a response to the threat posed by Napoleon to the latent German nation, earning him the title 'Turnvater Jahn', and the dubious distinction of a hagiography written by one of he leading intellectuals of the Third Reich.[29]

By the late 1800s, when militaristic and imperialistic nationalism were reaching their apogee, the 'Scramble for Africa' was in full swing, racist myths of national purity or uniqueness were gaining strength, the total politicization and biologization of crafting humans was underway. Nor was this a development confined to the milieus that generated Aryanism and anti-Semitism. Todd Presner has explored the extraordinary process that led Max Nordau, the scourge of cultural decadence in his bestselling *Degeneration* (1892), to become the advocate of 'a muscular Judaism' designed to create a new type of 'warrior Jew', able to realize the Zionist goal of a new homeland in Palestine. The project drew on historical episodes where Jews produced the *Sicarii*, a terrorist militia of the first century AD, but also on currents of modernist and eugenic thinking common at the time. It also involved setting up a nation-wide network of gymnasia for hardening Jews in body and soul.[30] The development of projects to re-craft Jews demonstrates just how widespread the simultaneous metapoliti-

---

26 Zygmunt Bauman, *Modernity and Ambivalence* (Cambridge: Polity, 1991).
27 Limore Yagil, *L'Homme Nouveau' et la Revolution Nationale de Vichy, 1940–1944* (Villeneuve d'Ascq: Presses Universitaires du Septentrion, 1977).
28 Mona Ozouf, *L'Homme régénéré. Essai sur la Révolution française* (Paris: Gallimard, 1989).
29 Alfred Baeumler, *Friedrich Ludwig Jahns Stellung in der deutschen Geistesgeschichte* (Leipzig: H. Eichblatt, 1940).
30 Todd Presner, '"Clear Heads, Solid Stomachs, and Hard Muscles." Max Nordau and the Aesthetics of Jewish Regeneration', *Modernism/Modernity*, 10:2 (2003), 269–96; and, *idem*, *Muscular Judaism: The Jewish Body and the Politics of Regeneration* (London and New York: Routledge Press, 2007).

cization and biologization of politics had gone at time of deep nomic crisis in which a whole generation felt history was reaching a turning point from decadence to regeneration.

By the mid-1930s the Bolshevik and fascist regimes had embarked on vast programmes of social and anthropological engineering through organizations 'shaping' the leisure time of the masses so as to coerce their participation in gymnastics, sport, trekking, and callisthenics, while exposing them to a continuous state propaganda campaign of images and speeches, designed to create a collective feeling that a new race was being born. The key agency of social engineering in this field was, of course, the youth organization, and a study of Fascist efforts in this area leave no doubt that, even if negative eugenics and myths of racial purity were absent, in marked contrast to the Third Reich, there was a eugenic myth that animated the education of Italians under Mussolini, practically from infancy.[31] Sport too became a major arena of biosocial transformation under fascism, attempting to turn the body into an icon of the total revolution in the nature of modernity being realized.[32]

The mood of the times is captured in a remarkable passage of 'Notes to Understand the Century' by the French fascist intellectual, Pierre Drieu la Rochelle, who believed he was witnessing 'the rebirth of European man', and saw in the cult of the body the essence of the revolutionary nature of the times:

> The new man has appeared in uncompromised fullness in Italy and Germany. He first appeared mutilated and compromised in Russia, because the 'barbarians' who are 'primitives' affected and thrown into disarray by the decadence of their neighbours, like dogs without masters, rummage for scraps in dustbins; they are forced to digest rotting filth.
>
> The first task of the new man is to restore the values of the body. He starts out from the demands and attributes of the body. This is the great revolution of the twentieth century which a section of French intellectuals have dimly sensed but which they have not been able to grasp clearly and communicate to the nation: the revolution of the body, restoration of the body [...] The new man starts with the body, he knows that the body is the articulation of the soul, and that the soul can only express itself, reveal itself, acquire substance in the body. There is nothing more spiritual than this recognition of the body. It is the soul that calls, that demands salvation, that saves itself by rediscovering the body.
>
> Nothing is less materialist than this movement. The pathetic mistake of the last generation of rationalists, one which summed up all the dissolution, all the bastardization

---

31 Tracy Koon, *Believe, Obey, Fight: Political Socialization of Youth in Fascist Italy, 1922–1943* (Chapel Hill: University of North Carolina Press, 1985).

32 Joseph Mangan (ed.), *Superman Supreme: Fascist Body as Political Icon – Global Fascism* (Portland, OR: Frank Cass, 1999).

of their pseudo-humanism, was to accuse of materialism a revolution which salvages and restores the sources and mainstays of the spirit.[33]

Such a text, with its vitriolic attack on humanism, provides a context for Nazi attempts not merely to bring about the physical regeneration of the Aryans weakened and made 'soft' by urban civilization and liberal values, but to breed a new elite in the training academies of the SS, the *Ordensburgen*, where hundreds of years of decadent education would be undone and a new type of man would be fashioned. Hence Hitler's declaration during one of his conversations in the presence of Hermann Rauschning:

> In my Ordensburgen a youth will grow up before which the world will shrink back. A violently active, dominating, intrepid, brutal youth [...] indifferent to pain. There must be no weakness or tenderness in it. I want to see more in its eyes the gleam of pride and independence of the beast of prey.[34]

On another occasion he told his table-companions:

> Do you now appreciate the depth of our National Socialist Movement? Can there be anything greater and more all comprehending? Those who see in National Socialism nothing more than a political movement know scarcely anything of it. It is more even than religion; it is the will to create mankind anew.[35]

The dark side of the anthropological revolution

There is clearly something chilling (at least for all non-Nazis) in the conception which Hitler divulged to his inner circle: that of the Third Reich not as a political system, but as what Bauman called a 'gardening state'. Under him the new Germany would devote itself to carrying out, at all costs, an anthropological revolution, to remove all traces of weakness, decadence, and degeneracy in every cultural, political, and biological sphere and establish a total *nomos* for all 'true' human beings, namely the Aryans. It is in this spirit that he declares in chapter two of *Mein Kampf:*

> And thus because the people whom it concerns are vacillating, they are timid and half-hearted in putting into effect even the measures which are indispensable for self-preservation. When the individual is no longer burdened with his own consciousness of blame in this regard, then and only then will he have that inner tranquillity and outer

---

33 Pierre Drieu la Rochelle, 'Renaissance de l'homme européen', in *idem*, *Notes pour comprendre le siècle* (Gallimard, Paris, 1941), pp. 149–154.
34 Hermann Rauschning, *The Voice of Destruction* (New York: G.P. Putnam's Sons, 1940), p. 252.
35 Rauschning, *The Voice of Destruction*, p. 234.

force to cut off drastically and ruthlessly all the parasite growth and root out the weeds.³⁶

Once revolutionary vanguards and political rulers have decided that the task of crafting new human beings demands the root and branch removal of all enemies of the great mission they have undertaken, then persecution and eventually mass murder inevitably ensue. Such crimes against humanity are carried out by individuals whose sense of duty to the leader or the cause frees them of the 'burden' of personal moral guilt, and of the compassion that might otherwise interfere with their heroic task on behalf of their people or the new order. The resulting state of mind is a travesty of the (deeply humanistic) Nietzschean concept of being 'beyond good and evil', and is the mainspring of the ruthlessness of all revolutionaries, convinced that the purging of an ailing old order of its unhealthy elements is a precondition to the creation of the new society.

Nor is this mindset peculiar to the twentieth century. At the end of the eighteenth century Maximilien Robespierre showed in his speech of February 1794 his lucid conviction that the regeneration of 'Man' demanded the use of terror and the guillotine, so as to tailor the French population to the Procrustean bed of the Republic of Virtue that was replacing the *ancien regime:*

> If the driving force of popular government in peacetime is virtue, that of popular government during a revolution is both virtue and terror: virtue, without which terror is destructive; terror, without which virtue is impotent.³⁷

Following this revolutionary, *palingenetic* moral logic, systemic mass murder for a healthy revolutionary ceases to be destructive, and is rebranded as creative, or, according to that terrifying modern oxymoron of Nietzschean coinage, as 'creative destruction'. A similar logic informed Stalin's Great Purge of 1937–8, in which over 700,000 people were executed in order to crush not even the reality but the possibility of (revisionist or fascist) dissent from the Party line he imposed. To push the socialist revolution through to its logical conclusion in the face of liberal and fascist forms of capitalist opposition, those left were to be turned into the ideal Soviet citizen, the 'New Soviet Man' entirely stripped of individualism through an exquisite blend of education and social engineering with the propaganda and coercion of an intensely secular form of religious politics. Likewise, under Pol Pot's *Khmer Rouge*, those who lived in the cities were assumed to be contaminated by contact with bourgeois capitalist education, and hence the natural enemies of the new regime. Those pursuing a liberal

---

36 Adolf Hitler, *Mein Kampf*, trans. by James Murphy, www.greatwar.nl/books/meinkampf/meinkampf.pdf p. 32 (accessed 12/01/2012).
37 http://teachers.sduhsd.k12.ca.us/tpsocialsciences/world_history/dem_ideals/robespierre.htm (accessed 12/01/2012).

profession were seen as 'new people', and hence as 'weeds', to be annihilated physically along with the entire Cambodian cultural tradition. The purge would leave only uneducated peasants and children (i. e. 'healthy' Cambodians) as the raw material of the new *Khmer,* whose founding ideology was a curious blend of nationalism and communism. The result would be a Year Zero after which the nation's history would start again from scratch, practically *ex nihilo,* the ultimate logic of millenarian thinking applied to a rigorously secular project of renewal.[38]

It is well known that the re-crafting of human beings under the Nazis was, in stark contrast to Fascist Italy, pursued with the ruthless application of both positive and negative eugenics, both growing new plants and rooting out human weeds. The ultimate result was the mass sterilization and euthanasia programmes, and the purge of allegedly asocial and dysgenic human beings as well as ideological enemies.[39] However it has become increasingly clear that the precondition for this dark chapter in modern history was not the rise of German nationalism, but the development of negative eugenic thinking in many places in the Europeanized world of the nineteenth century, especially in non-Catholic countries.[40] Ground for this development had been prepared by Cesare Lambroso's pioneering (but ultimately abortive) research into the physiology of 'criminal types', and elements of negative eugenics became explicit policy in the US and Scandinavia before Hitler's election as Chancellor. Indeed, a law was introduced in Indiana in 1907 mandating the compulsory sterilization of 'degenerates', and in 1924 the State of Virginia introduced a Racial Integration Act which permitted the sterilization of some prison inmates. Elsewhere, attempts by US racial scientists were being made to classify allegedly dysgenic human beings scientifically.

Nor did revelations of the many millions of atrocities committed in the name of a master race before 1945 kill the negative eugenic dream of crafting new human beings in the extreme right-wing *imaginaire.* Palingenetic fantasies of a new man live on in William Pierce's *Turner Diaries,* whose climax describes the Armageddon which breaks out between Aryans and 'dysgenic' Whites, and the use of nuclear and chemical weapons to purge the planet of inferior races and finally inaugurate, on a global scale, the age of White Supremacy dreamt of by Adolf Hitler. They also resurface in the context of Anders Breivik's alarm at the

---

38 Ben Kiernan, *The Pol Pot Regime: Race, Power and Genocide in Cambodia under the Khmer Rouge, 1975–1979* (New Haven, CT: Yale University Press, 1996).
39 Michael Burleigh and Wolfgang Wippermann, *The Racial State in Germany: 1933–1945* (Cambridge: Cambridge University Press, 1991).
40 Turda and Weindling (ed.), *Blood and Homeland*; Christian Promitzer, Sevasti Trubeta and Marius Turda (ed.), *Health, Hygiene and Eugenics in Southeastern Europe to 1945* (Budapest: CEU Press, 2011).

implications of "interracial breeding" for the long-term survival of Europeans. In his 1500 page 'compendium', *2083. A Declaration of European Independence*, posted on the Web in July 2011 shortly before his massacre of Labour Party Youth activists (representative of the left-wing politics that he saw as encouraging through multi-culturalism the genocide of true Norwegians) he noted:

> Why is eugenics and reprogenetics so extremely politically incorrect to discuss? The answer is due to the "negative eugenics programs" of Nazi Germany. Forced sterilisation and forceful experimentation of human test subjects are factors used at that time which should never have occurred. Many European countries used to forcefully sterilise Gypsies/Rom up to approx. 1972 to prevent them from breeding because they used to be considered "sub-human" etc. These programs are today referred to as "negative eugenics" due to these and other factors. In any case, we need to get over this taboo as soon as possible because it is estimated that the Nordic genotypes will be extinct completely within 200 years.[41]

Yet despite the admixture of genetic science, the re-crafting of human beings through social engineering, whether for religious or secular ends, is inevitably a failure, rendering all totalitarianisms a chimera despite the heady palingenetic fervour that may seize broad swathes of the masses at the prospect of the end of repression and a new dawn. Aleksandr Zinoviev's *The Yawning Heights*, *The Radiant Future*, and *Homo Sovieticus* relentlessly expose the black farce into which the Marxist Leninist utopia of the Soviet New Man had degenerated by the 1970s, and now presage the imminent demise of the Soviet Union itself. Fascism's anthropological revolution, so much less costly in human lives, fared no better. The regime's massive ship of state, so impressive while still in the sheltered straights of domestic politics, had capsized immediately it entered the international waters of history. In the end even Giuseppe Bottai, the tireless technocrat of Fascism's social and anthropological revolution and the political religion that was intended to bring it about, had to resign himself to the fact that the project to Fascistize Italians, and so create an artificial new *nomos* for them to live by, had run aground on the stubborn obduracy of human nature, and perhaps its need for authentic, not state-manipulated faith:

> The failure of every official religion of the State, or State art and the like, like all attempts to revive religion (and not only revealed religion) on scientific and rational grounds, stems from the inability to appreciate the intrinsic and irreplaceable character of every genuine belief and faith.[42]

And all humanists, whether secular or religious, can only say, 'Halleluja'!

---

41 Andres Breivik, *2083. A Declaration of European independence* (London, 2011) *unitednations.ispnw.org/archives/breivik-manifesto-2011.pdf* (accessed 12/01/2012), p. 1180.
42 Giuseppe Bottai, 'I miti moderni', *Primato* (15 Feb., 1942), reprinted in *'Prospettive', 'Primato' (Antologia)*, ed. by L. Polato (Treviso: Canova, 1978), pp. 183–187.

Merryn Ekberg

Eugenics: Past, Present, and Future

Introduction

The aim of this chapter is to compare eugenic policies of the past with re-progenetic policies of the present, and to speculate on genetic enhancement technologies of the near future. The discussion is divided into three sections. Section one offers a review and discussion on the diverse origins and many definitions of eugenics, giving particular emphasis to how these are shaped by social values, political ideas, and cultural norms. Section two offers a comparison between the (old) eugenic policies and practices of the early to mid-twentieth century and the (new) genetic policies and practices of the late twentieth to early twenty-first century. The primary focus in this section will be on explaining how the shift from 'old' eugenics to 'new' genetics coincided with the shift from Mendelian to molecular genetics, and at the same time, with the transition from the 'old public health', where the emphasis was on the control of infectious diseases to the 'new public health', where the emphasis is on the prevention of inherited genetic diseases and acquired lifestyle illness. Section three offers a discussion on the imaginary eugenics policies and practices of the future. This section includes a critical evaluation of somatic cell nuclear transfer (also known as reproductive cloning) and genetic enhancement technologies. Cloning and genetic enhancement technologies will be described as the eugenic policies and practices of the future. The chapter concludes with a discussion on the core theme of all eugenic policies, that is, the theme of *Crafting Humans*. At the core of all past, present, and future eugenic policies is the theme of crafting stronger, faster, healthier, happier, or smarter human beings. The three eras of eugenics discussed in this chapter have all used very different techniques, but all with the common aim of influencing the direction of human evolution and crafting the future of human populations.

'Old' Eugenics: Origins

The term 'eugenics' was introduced into the English language at the end of the nineteenth century by Sir Francis Galton (1822–1911). The origins of the word can be traced to the two classical Greek terms 'eu' meaning 'well' and 'genos' meaning 'birth' and is generally translated to mean 'well-born'. Galton defined eugenics as the 'science which deals with all the influences that improve and develop the inborn qualities of a race'.[1] From this original idea, the term "eugenics" has diversified and now includes many variants, which have been given different labels to emphasise their different orientations. Historians of eugenics refer to racial and class eugenics; positive and negative eugenics;[2] coercive and non-coercive eugenics;[3] state directed and privatised eugenics, or authoritarian and liberal eugenics;[4] strong and weak eugenics;[5] and, finally, utopian and dystopian eugenics.[6] Some authors have written about eugenics as a transnational or global social movement,[7] while others have described the distinct national and cultural variations in the history of eugenic thought. For example, MacKenzie and Stone have written about British eugenics,[8] McLaren has examined eugenics in Canada,[9] Proctor has given an account of eugenics in Nazi Germany,[10] Turda has contextualised Central and South-eastern European eugenics,[11] Scandinavian eugenics has been described by Broberg and Roll-Han-

---

1 Francis Galton, 'Eugenics: Its Definition, Scope, and Aims', in *idem, Essays in Eugenics* (London: The Eugenics Education Society, 1909), p. 35.
2 Daniel J. Kevles, 'Eugenics, the Genome and Human Rights', *Medicine Studies*, I:2 (2009), 85–93.
3 Allen Buchanan, 'Institutions, Beliefs and Ethics: Eugenics as a Case Study', *The Journal of Political Philosophy*, 15:1 (2007), 22–45.
4 Nicholas Agar, *Liberal Eugenics: In Defence of Human Enhancement* (Oxford: Blackwell, 2004).
5 Tom Shakespeare, 'Choices and Rights: Eugenics, Genetics and Disability', *Disability and Society*, 13:5 (1998), 665–681.
6 Aviad E. Raz, 'Eugenic Utopias/Dystopias, Reprogenetics and Community Genetics', *Sociology of Health and Illness*, 31:4 (2009), 602–616.
7 Deborah Barrett and Charles Kurzman, 'Globalizing Social Movement Theory: The Case of Eugenics', *Theory and Society*, 33:5 (2004), 487–527; Paul Weindling, 'International Eugenics: Swedish Sterilization in Context', *Scandinavian Journal of History*, 24:2 (1999), 179–197; Alison Bashford and Philippa Levine (ed.) *The Oxford Handbook of the History of Eugenics* (New York: Oxford University Press, 2010).
8 Donald MacKenzie, 'Eugenics in Britain', *Social Studies of Science*, 6:3–4 (Dec., 1976), 499–532; and, Dan Stone, *Breeding Superman: Nietzsche, Race and Eugenics in Edwardian and Interwar Britain* (Liverpool: Liverpool University Press, 2002).
9 Angus McLaren, *Our Own Master Race: Eugenics in Canada 1885–1945* (Toronto: McClelland and Stewart, 1990).
10 Robert Proctor, *Racial Hygiene: Medicine under the Nazis* (Cambridge, Ma.: Harvard University Press, 1988).
11 Marius Turda and Paul Weindling (ed.), *Blood and Homeland: Eugenics and Racial Natio-*

sen,[12] and the idiosyncratic features of American eugenics have been discussed by Lombardo.[13]

Common to all these definitions or interpretations, is the quest to enhance the health of the population and to prevent what was then perceived to be a decline, degeneration or crisis in the human condition. The 'old' eugenics was fundamentally based on a utilitarian ethos, that is, it required some sacrifice of individual liberty in order to achieve the greater good of society. Reproductive liberty was subordinate to the higher goal of improving the health and vitality of the population.

The scientific basis and core ideology of eugenics was gradually transformed into policies designed to address social problems. Old eugenic social policies included: restrictive immigration, restrictive marriage, and anti-miscegenation laws; the sexual segregation of individuals with physical or mental disabilities; tax benefits and family allowance schemes to encourage reproduction within the 'fittest' members of society; compulsory sterilization for people with mental or physical disabilities; eugenic euthanasia; and, in its most extreme form, systematic genocide.

'Old' eugenics was heavily influenced by the utopian ideals of the Enlightenment and the progressive ethos of modernity. It emerged during an era when there was a strong belief in progress, the advance of science and technology, and mastery over nature including human nature. The vision was to improve the health of the population by encouraging people with good or desirable characteristics to reproduce and by discouraging people with 'inferior' or 'defective' characteristics from reproducing. Whilst eugenic euthanasia and genocide clearly had an immediate effect on individuals, the primary goal of eugenic policies was to achieve changes in patterns of reproduction the ultimately, changes in the composition of the population. Thus, in order to succeed, eugenic programmes relied on a strong belief and firm commitment to the ideals of utilitarianism and intergenerational justice, that is, a sacrifice of individual liberties in the present generation for the greater collective good of future generations.

After the Second Word War, and after the world learned about the atrocities of the Nazi regime, the term eugenics fell out of favour and there was a shift in

---

nalism in Central and Southeast Europe 1900–1940 (Budapest: Central European University, 2007) and, Christian Promitzer, Sevasti Trubeta and Marius Turda (ed.), *Health, Hygiene and Eugenics in Southeastern Europe to 1945* (Budapest: CEU Press, 2011).

12 Gunnar Broberg and Nils Roll-Hansen (ed.), *Eugenics and the Welfare State: Sterilization Policy in Denmark, Sweden, Norway, and Finland* (East Lansing, MI: Michigan State University, 2005 [1997]).

13 Paul A. Lombardo (ed.), *A Century of Eugenics in America: From the Indiana Experiment to the Human Genome Era* (Bloomington, IN: Indiana University Press, 2011).

emphasis away from genetic determinism and towards social and environmental explanations of human behaviour. The idea of changing patterns of reproduction and changing genetics as a solution to endemic social problems went into recession. However, with the discovery of the helical structure of DNA in 1953 the new era of molecular genetics (often described as 'the new genetics') was born.[14] Along with this revolution in the science of human genetics came a rebirth in the ideals of eugenics, thus marking the entry into stage two in the history of eugenics.

'New' eugenics: genetics and assisted reproductive technologies

This era of 'new' eugenics (which is a combination of advances in molecular genetics and the emergence of assisted reproductive technologies), is based on the same philosophy as the 'old' eugenics, but uses very different techniques. The core idea is the benevolent desire to reduce the incidence and prevalence of genetic diseases in the population. One crucial difference is that while 'old' eugenics was primarily focused on what we now perceive as complex, polygenic, and multifactorial behavioural traits, such as alcoholism, addiction, feeblemindedness, prostitution, insanity, and criminality, 'new' eugenics is primarily focused on diseases caused by chromosomal disorders or single gene mutations.

With our current knowledge of human genetics, and with the current availability of clinical genetic tests, we are limited to the diagnosis of aneuploidies such as trisomy 21 and Turner's syndrome and single gene disorders such as cystic fibrosis, Duchene muscular dystrophy, sickle cell disease, thalassaemia, and haemophilia. In the future we may also have effective genetic diagnostic and susceptibility tests for more common and more complex multifactorial diseases such as cancer, cardiovascular disease, and diabetes, and for personality and behavioural traits such as aggression, depression, anxiety disorder, and impulsivity.

This 'new' version of eugenics includes four common practices that were not available to the 'old' eugenicists. The first is premarital carrier testing and presymptomatic testing, which occurs within communities that have a high incidence of inherited diseases such as haemophilia, thalaseaemia, and Tay-Sachs disease.[15] The second is pre-implantation genetic testing, followed by

---

14 James D. Watson and Francis Crick, 'Molecular Structure of Nucleic Acids', *Nature*, 171:4356 (25 April 1953), 737–738.
15 Barbara Prainsack and Gil Siegal, 'The Rise of Genetic Couplehood?: A Comparative View of Premarital Genetic Testing', *BioSocieties*, 1 (2006), 17–36.

embryo selection and artificial insemination. The third is prenatal genetic testing following by the selective abortion (or eugenic abortion) of any embryo or foetus that is found to have a disease causing mutation. The final practice is the use of donor gametes, in donor-assisted IVF conception, and in some cases, the positive selection of gamete donors that have the physical, moral, intellectual, or emotional characteristics that the prospective parents may desire.

'New' eugenic practices also include public health policies that apply our better understanding of the conditions required to achieve a healthy pregnancy, such as: recommendations for optimal maternal nutrition; recommendations for an increased intake of folic acid to prevent spina bifida; campaigns to encourage pregnant women to avoid tobacco and alcohol and other teratogens that are harmful to the developing foetus; campaigns to warn older women about the risks of having children in later life due to the increased risk of genetic damage or chromosomal abnormalities; and, programmes to vaccinate all young women against rubella, because of the increased risk of congenital rubella syndrome if a woman develops rubella during pregnancy. Since the aim of all these programmes is to encourage a healthy pregnancy and to improve the health of the resulting child, they may be described as eugenic, even though they may not fit the classical definition of eugenics as altering reproductive practices and thereby influencing the transmission of hereditary traits.

As with 'old' eugenics, there are many social, cultural, and contextual influences that have combined to influence the emergence, direction and shape of the 'new' eugenics. The first is the emergence of a period of genetic optimism, and the accompanying process of geneticization. The second is the new ethos of public health with its emphasis on prevention rather than diagnosis and treatment. The third is the era of individualism and the formal recognition of inalienable human rights in national laws and international declarations. The fourth is the increasing involvement of the private sector in the delivery of healthcare and in the conduct of biomedical research, along with the concomitant rise of a consumer society. The final social and contextual factor is the establishment of a network of formal processes for assessing, evaluating, and monitoring the ethical acceptability of clinical genetic services and genetics research. Each of these contextual factors will be discussed in turn beginning with the emergence of a new era of genetic optimism.

The recent revival of interest in eugenics has been largely shaped by a climate of genetic optimism and the accompanying (or driving) process of geneticization. The latter is an extension of the earlier thesis on the medicalization of society or 'the transformation of human conditions into medical disorders'.[16]

---

16 Peter Conrad, *The Medicalization of Society: On the Transformation of Human Conditions into Treatable Disorders* (Baltimore, Md.: The John Hopkins University Press, 2007).

Building on the former concept of medicalization, geneticization has been defined as the tendency to describe more and more human problems as having a genetic origin and, thereby, as amenable to a genetic solution.[17] This process of geneticization is largely fuelled by the enthusiastic press coverage of new genetic discoveries and a consequent increase in public interest and awareness of advances in human genetics.[18] This increasing geneticization is also fuelled by the activities of commercial biotechnology and pharmaceutical companies, which develop genetic tests, create a consumer demand for these tests, and, in some cases, sell genetic tests direct to the public through mail order internet sites.[19]

Critics of 'new' eugenics are concerned that the pendulum has swung back towards excessive genetic explanations of human traits, which was one of the characteristics of eugenics in its original form. These critics fear that, once again, we will diminish or ignore the role of the environment in shaping an individual. Such that, the consequence of this excessive geneticization, genetic determinism, genetic essentialism, or genetic reductionism, is that the individual who develops an illness, or who acts in an antisocial manner, is blamed for inheriting 'bad' genes, rather than being seen as a potential victim of an oppressive, antagonistic, or hostile social environment.[20] The aim of eugenic policies is to change the individual rather than change the social environment. For example, to reduce or eliminate the problem of heightism (defined as discrimination against short people), the 'new' eugenic solution would be to use pre-implantation or prenatal genetic diagnosis to negatively select out embryos or foetuses that have a deficient copy of the growth hormone gene or to positively select for embryos or foetuses that contain a 'normal' copy of the growth hormone gene. In contrast, the social solution would be to change the environment in which tall people enjoy a social advantage and to change social attitudes to ensure that both short and tall people are viewed equally and have the same opportunities.[21] Similarly, to address the current epidemic of childhood obesity, the eugenic solution would be to medicalize (or geneticize) obesity and thereby to define obesity as a disease that requires medical treatment, to channel more resources into biomedical research that seeks to understand the role of genetics in the aetiology of obesity, to develop a prenatal genetic test for the 'obesity

---

17 See H.A. ten Have, 'Genetics and Culture: The Geneticization Thesis', *Medicine, Health Care and Philosophy*, 4:3 (2001), 295–304.
18 Jose van Dijck, *Imagenation: Popular Images of Genetics* (New York: New York University Press, 1998).
19 Paul Martin and Robert Frost, 'Regulating the Commercial Development of Genetic Testing in the UK: Problems, Possibilities and Policy', *Critical Social Policy*, 23:2 (2003), 186–207.
20 Evan Willis, 'Public Health and the "New" Genetics: Balancing Individuals and Collective Outcomes', *Critical Public Health*, 12:2 (2002), 139–151.
21 Thomas H. Murray, 'Enhancement', in *The Oxford Handbook of Bioethics*, ed. by Bonnie Steinbock (Oxford: Oxford University Press, 2007), pp. 491–515.

susceptibility gene' and to abort any foetus that is found to inherit this 'obesity susceptibility gene'. The alternative would be to encourage a change in the way modern society is structured so that there are more opportunities for people to select healthy food and to be physically active.

The second contextual factor influencing the shape of "new" eugenics is the changing ethos within public health. In this 'new' public health, the emphasis is on the prevention and early detection (rather than treatment and cure) of chronic lifestyle diseases such as cancer and cardiovascular disease and on the prevention of lifelong genetic diseases. One of the major strategies used in this new public health is to encourage individual responsibility for avoiding health risks.[22] In contrast, the 'old' public health was more focused on the prevention and treatment of acute infectious diseases such as smallpox, cholera, poliomyelitis, and tuberculosis, and the strategies used were largely government-initiated measures such as vaccination, isolation, quarantine, sanitation, and water purification. Within the discourse of the 'new public genetic health' responsible individuals are encouraged to seek genetic counselling and to engage in pre-conception, pre-implantation, or pre-natal genetic testing in order to prevent the birth of a child with a genetic condition.[23]

The third contextual factor shaping the current eugenic environment is a unique combination of the ascendance of an ideology of liberal individualism, the rise to dominance of bioethical principles of autonomy, and the global emphasis on promoting and protecting inalienable human rights. While the 'old' eugenics was largely enacted through coercive state policy, the new eugenics is largely based on the principles of non-directive counselling, respect for autonomy, and the promotion of individual choice.[24] There are no compulsory eugenic abortion laws today, which would be analogous to the compulsory sterilization laws of 'old' eugenics. Pre-1945 eugenics has been strongly criticised for being a violation of human rights and in particular, a violation of the right to procreative liberty.[25] In an attempt to distance itself from older coercive eugenic policies, 'new' eugenics has been given the term *liberal* or *voluntary eugenics*.[26] In this new 'liberal' eugenics there is far more emphasis on promoting

---

22 Alan Petersen and Deborah Lupton, *The New Public Health: Health and Self in the Age of Risk* (London: Sage, 1996).
23 Alan Petersen and Robin Bunton, *The New Genetics and the Public's Health* (London and New York: Routledge, 2002) and Anne Kerr, 'Rights and Responsibilities in the New Genetics Era', *Critical Social Policy*, 23:2 (2003), 208–226.
24 Merryn Ekberg, 'The Old Eugenics and the New Genetics', *Social History of Medicine*, 20:3 (2007), 581–593.
25 Kevles, 'Eugenics, the Genome and Human Rights'.
26 Agar, *Liberal Eugenics*.

and protecting an individual's right to have access to genetic information, genetic counselling, and genetic testing services.[27]

The emphasis on promoting individual choice and protecting human rights has been challenged by disability rights activists. Shakespeare for example, argues that the 'search and destroy' ethos that underpins pre-implantation and prenatal genetic testing is an affront to the rights and dignity of people living with a disability.[28] The use of pre-implantation or prenatal testing to select out any embryo or foetus that is diagnosed with a disability, according to Shakespeare, sends a clear message that society does not value the lives of disabled people. Furthermore, some people with disabilities claim that not only do they have an equal right to life (that is, to not have their lives terminated *in utero*), but also, that they have a right to positively select for an embryo that contains a disability causing gene. In essence, these individuals are claiming a right to reproduce disability. Deaf couples, for example, have claimed a right to select for a child with heredity deafness.[29]

This emphasis on promoting individual choice and protecting human rights has also been challenged by some feminist writers.[30] Whilst generally supportive of a woman's right to abortion, many feminists see the new reprogenetic technologies as placing an additional obligation on women, rather than as promoting reproductive autonomy and free choice. Women are being pressured by the expectations of society, by healthcare professionals, and by the lack of social support for disabled children, to undergo reprogenetic testing and selective abortion, rather than making a free choice. As Farhot Moazam states: 'there can be subtle pressures on a woman to make use of this technology with an in-built assumption that if she rejects amniocentesis, she must bear the responsibility of bringing a handicapped child into the world'.[31]

The fourth contextual factor influencing the shape of 'new' eugenics is the greater involvement from the private sector, especially from the biotechnology and pharmaceutical companies that develop and market 'direct to the consumer' genetic testing kits.[32] 'New' eugenics is taking shape within the context of a "biocapitalist consumer society", in which private companies market to in-

---

27 Kerr, 'Rights and Responsibilities'.
28 Shakespeare, 'Choices and Rights'.
29 Julian Savulescu, 'Deaf Lesbians, "Designer Disability", and the Future of Medicine', *British Medical Journal,* 325:7367 (5 October 2002), 771–773.
30 Lori Andrews, *Future Perfect: Confronting Decisions About Genetics* (New York: Columbia University Press, 2001) and Jyotsna Agnihotri Gupta, 'Towards Transnational Feminisms: Some Reflections and Concerns in Relation to the Globalisation of Reproductive Technologies', *European Journal of Women's Studies,* 13:1 (2006), 23–38.
31 Farhat Moazam, 'Feminist Discourse on Sex Selection and Selective Abortion of Female Foetuses', *Bioethics,* 18:3 (2004), 205–220 (p. 213).
32 Martin and Frost, 'Regulating the Commercial Development of Genetic Testing'.

dividual health consumers either over the counter or by mail order from an internet site. Critics of this system warn that the marketing of genetic testing through private sources is a subtle source of coercion. These critics fear that the risk of covert coercion, coming from private companies seeking to maximise profits, may be greater than the risk of overt coercion emanating from the authoritarian and interventionist state, which was a defining feature of 'old' eugenics. The coercive element, therefore, is still present in eugenics, but it now comes from more diffuse and more insidious sources. Coercion in the 'new' eugenic environment, according to Troy Duster, comes through the invisible backdoor of private enterprise, rather than the visible front door of the State.[33]

The rise of bioethics as an interdisciplinary academic discipline and the emergence of formal processes of clinical and research governance is the final contextual factor contributing to current debates on the resurgence of eugenics. Contemporary eugenic policies are enacted in an era in which there is a far greater awareness of research ethics and clinical ethics amongst researchers and clinicians. This is evidenced by the existence of an integrated system of formal processes for: evaluating the ethical impact of any proposal to conduct an empirical study in human genetics; and, for ensuring that ethical standards are maintained in all clinics that offer reprogenetic services. Most countries now have well established ethical guidelines and codes of practice, and most operate specialist clinical and research ethics committees for monitoring the activities of researchers, and for making decisions about the complex or controversial ethical dilemmas that may arise in clinical practice.[34] The origins of this ethical regulation can be traced to the post World War II Nuremberg trials and the subsequent development of the Nuremberg Code in 1947.[35] At around the same time, bioethics emerged as an autonomous academic discipline dedicated to the study of the ethical, legal, and social impact of the biosciences and biotechnologies.[36] In contrast, the 'old' eugenics policies took place before the birth of bioethics and before clinical and research ethics committees were established, the only control mechanism was professional self-regulation.[37]

To conclude this section, at the level of ideology, 'new' eugenics has much in

---

33 Troy Duster, *Backdoor to Eugenics*, 2nd edition (New York and London: Routledge, 2003).
34 Elvi Whittaker, 'Adjudicating Entitlements: The Emerging Discourses of Research Ethics Boards', *Health*, 9:4 (2005), 513–535.
35 Paul Weindling, 'The Origins of Informed Consent: The International Scientific Commission on Medical War Crimes and the Nuremberg Code', *Bulletin of the History of Medicine*, 75:1 (2001), 37–71.
36 Albert R. Jonsen, *The Birth of Bioethics* (Oxford and New York: Oxford University Press, 1998).
37 Kathleen Montgomery and Amalya L. Oliver, 'Shifts in Guidelines for Ethical Scientific Conduct: How Public and Private Organizations Create and Change Norms of Research Integrity', *Social Studies of Science*, 39:1 (2009), 137–155.

common with 'old' eugenics; both share a common vision of reducing the incidence and prevalence of genetic disease in the population. In practice, however, there are important differences between them, and many of these can be explained by the different social, historical, and contextual factors in which eugenic thought is located. Contextual factors such as genetic optimism and geneticization; the preventative ethos of the 'new public health'; the age of individualism and human rights; the rise of the private sector as a major player in the delivery of personalized genomic medicine; and, the birth of bioethics and bioethics committees as independent regulators, have played an important role in shaping the policies and practices of the 'new' eugenics.

'New' eugenics has many supporters, but it also has its critics and one of the concerns raised is that genetic engineering puts us on a slippery slope towards the next stage of future eugenics. Critics fear that once all the policies and practices of 'new' eugenics become routine and normalized, then the stage is set for entry into the more powerful era of future eugenics. This future eugenics involves the more advanced biotechnologies of reproductive cloning and germ line genetic modification.

Future eugenics: reproductive cloning and genetic enhancement technologies

In 1997, the first cloned mammal was produced through somatic cell nuclear transfer by Ian Wilmut and colleagues at the Roslin Institute in Scotland.[38] This has led to the possibility of human reproductive cloning and, when combined with genetic enhancement technologies, this development marks the beginning of a 'third' era of eugenics and a further development in the crafting of humans. This third era of "future" eugenics applies the same philosophy as the first and second era, but using very different biotechniques. The core aim remains that of strengthening, enhancing, or elevating the physical, emotional, moral, and cognitive powers of human beings.

If the ultimate goal of eugenics is to breed fitter, stronger, smarter, healthier, happier, more compassionate, cooperative, and virtuous humans, then the supporters of reproductive cloning argue that the technique could be used to achieve this goal. Reproductive cloning could ostensibly be used to *re*-create multiple copies of the most talented, innovative and inspirational individuals in society. Cells from university professors, Olympic athletes, inspirational leaders, creative scientists, and great composers or musicians could be used to clone

---

38 Ian Wilmut, *et al.*, 'Viable Offspring Derived from Fetal and Adult Mammalian Cells', *Nature*, 385:6619 (27 February 1997), 810–813.

future individuals. Whilst this may appeal to future eugenicists, the idea is fundamentally flawed since these cloned individuals will not be identical to their creator because they will grow and develop in a different social and political environment. They will have the same genotype, but a different phenotype.

The proponents of reproductive cloning also argue that cloning is beneficial and should be permitted because it offers a technological solution for some forms of infertility (including medical and social infertility) and because it offers couples at risk of transmitting a gene mutation to their progeny the opportunity to avoid the birth of a child with a genetic disease. Thus, cloning has the potential to contribute to the eugenic goal of reducing the incidence and prevalence of genetic diseases in the population.

The critics of reproductive cloning argue that the technique should not be permitted because of the risk of causing physical and psychological harm to the cloned individual and because of the harm caused to our current social norms, values, customs, and beliefs. David Gurnham, for example, argues that the knowledge required to clone a human is sacred or forbidden knowledge and should not be permitted because humans should not tamper with the wisdom of nature. He insists that we should leave the mystery of human reproduction to the superior forces of Mother Nature. Gurnham believes that there are 'certain things about human life that should always remain mysterious.' He states that: 'at the core of human life there remains a mysterious element that cannot and should not be explained or explainable.'[39]

A second objection to human reproductive cloning is based on the principle of non-maleficence, or the obligation to do no harm. Although limited, the empirical evidence suggests that cloned animals have a higher incidence of developmental problems and a shorter life expectancy than animals born from natural conception. Cloning, therefore, may reduce the survival and longevity of offspring and therefore, would be dysgenic.

A third objection is that cloning disrupts our traditional beliefs about the heterosexual, nuclear family and creates ambiguous and confused familial relationships.[40] It is unclear for example, whether the nuclear donor is the parent or twin sibling of the cloned individual.[41] By enabling single women, single men, and same sex couples to become parents, cloning goes against the original eugenic idea of encouraging the 'perfect' heterosexual, monogamous, nuclear family.

Reproductive cloning is currently illegal in the UK under the *Human Re-*

---

39 David Gurnham, 'The Mysteries of Human Dignity and the Brave New World of Human Cloning', *Social and Legal Studies*, 14:2 (2005), 197–214.
40 Onora O'Neill, *Autonomy and Trust in Bioethics* (Cambridge: Cambridge University Press, 2001).
41 Immaculada de Melo-Martin, 'On Cloning Human Beings', *Bioethics*, 16:3 (2002), 246–265.

productive Cloning Act 2004, but even if social attitudes change, and if it were to become legal, it is unlikely to ever be used on such as scale as to change the gene frequencies in the population. The eugenic (or dysgenic) potential of reproductive cloning is, therefore, limited. Germ line genetic modification however has greater eugenic potential and is already used in agriculture to generate bigger, stronger, faster growing, nutritionally enhanced, pest-resistant, and disease-resistant transgenic plants and animals.[42] To date, germ line genetic modification has never been used to create transgenic humans, however, its close cousin, somatic cell genetic modification, is used to treat a small number of medical conditions including cystic fibrosis and severe combined immune deficiency (SCID).[43] Somatic cell genetic modification, however, is not inherited and, therefore, is not eugenic.

A number of well-reasoned arguments have been advanced to support the development and use of intentional genetic modification or enhancement technologies in humans. The first is the moral obligation of parents to their children argument, or what Julian Savulescu calls the obligation of 'procreative beneficence'.[44] Julian Savulescu argues that we have a moral obligation to produce the best children we can, and an obligation to use the best biotechnologies available to achieve this. He suggests that if we have the technology to biologically enhance children and thereby, to give children a better opportunity to live a happy, healthy and fulfilling life, then it would be unethical not to use it.

Extending this first argument to a higher level, the second argument is the wider moral obligation of the present generation to future generations, or the intergenerational justice argument. As Harris suggests: 'to decide not to intervene to enhance where we can do so is to condemn future generations to life without the advantages we might have bestowed'.[45] Like Harris, many argue that since the current generation enjoys the many benefits that are a product of the labour of previous generations of bioscientists, we have an obligation to ensure that future generations benefit from our social investment in positive enhancement technology.

A third argument in favour of eugenic enhancement is the continuation of past practices or the 'precedent already exists' argument. According to this argument, there is no difference between giving a child a vaccine to enhance

---

42 Merryn Ekberg, 'Genetic Expectations', *International Journal of Science and Research*, 2:1 (2006), 41–48.
43 LeRoy Walters and Julie Gage Palmer, *The Ethics of Gene Therapy* (Oxford: Oxford University Press, 1997).
44 Julian Savulescu, 'Procreative Beneficence: Why we Should Select the Best Children', *Bioethics*, 15:5–6 (2001), 413–426.
45 John Harris, *Enhancing Evolution: The Ethical Case for Making Better People* (Princeton: Princeton University Press, 2007), p. 139.

their immune system, or giving a child music lessons to enhance their musical skills (both of which are given to increase the child's opportunities in life), and giving a child a genetic enhancement to improve their resistance to infection and, thereby, increase their opportunities in life.[46] If we allow, encourage or facilitate the first type of intervention, then by comparison, and for consistency, we should allow the second. Enhancement is simply a continuation of past practices, which are socially acceptable.

Promoting and protecting reproductive autonomy, reproductive choice and reproductive liberty is the fourth argument supporting the future eugenic era of human enhancement. The essence of this argument is that while people should never be forced to use enhancement technology, people should have the choice and should be free to use the technology if it is safe and if they so choose. The State should not interfere in the very intimate and personal choices made by individuals including choices about reproduction. This libertarian argument is based on the 'harm principle' first articulated by the nineteenth-century English utilitarian philosopher John Stuart Mill. Mill insisted that the only legitimate place for the state to intervene in private affairs was to prevent harm to others.[47] In a society based on liberal democratic values, freedom and individual choice is always preferable to restriction and state prohibition. The state may provide the services for people to exercise their reproductive liberty, the state may regulate these services to ensure compliance with minimum safety standards, and the state may provide the information that people need to make informed choices, but the ultimate decision about whether to use these services, or not, should be made by those individuals whose lives will be directly affected by the consequences.

The final argument in favour of 'future' eugenics is the idea that it advances transhumanist values and moves us along the evolutionary trajectory to the transhuman condition. The essence of this argument is that throughout history, humans have sought inventive ways to extend longevity, augment natural talents, and to improve the human condition.[48] Using the new science of genetic enhancement to improve human lives and to better the human condition is simply a continuation of this eternal quest to perfect the human condition and, as such, it should be used to overcome some of the obstacles to realizing the unlimited

---

46 Russell Powell and Allen Buchanan, 'Breaking Evolution's Chains: The Prospect of Deliberate Genetic Modification in Humans', *Journal of Medicine and Philosophy*, 36:1 (2011), 6–27; Allen Buchanan, et al., *From Chance to Choice: Genetics and Justice* (Cambridge: Cambridge University Press, 2000); and Murray, 'Enhancement'.
47 John Stuart Mill, *On Liberty* (London: J. M. Dent, 1910).
48 Nick Bostrom, 'A History of Transhumanist Thought', *Journal of Evolution and Technology*, 14:1 (2005), 1–25.

human powers, and to further extend the vast range of unrealized human possibilities.[49]

Alongside the positive arguments in support of genetic modification in humans, a number of ethical arguments have been made against 'future' eugenics, or against the development and use of enhancement technologies. The first objection is that of social justice and social equity. Critics fear that biological enhancements will only be available to the wealthy, thereby creating an inequality both within and between nations. The fear is that society will become divided between the 'enhanced' and the 'normal', or, as Silver suggests, between the 'gene-rich' and the 'gene-poor'.[50] The counter argument is that this is true for all new technologies from motor cars to personal computers to laser surgery. Initially, the technology is only available to the affluent, but over time, the cost falls and more people gain access. Ironically, being the first to access a technology is not always an advantage. By having early access to a new technology, the affluent are exposed to the higher risks that accompany any new innovation. By the time the technology reaches the wider consumer market and becomes 'normalized' the initial risks or flaws have usually been identified and the product has been modified. The product is then judged to be 'safe' because it has been 'tried and tested' over time. Another counter argument is that human enhancement could be used to raise the prospects for the disabled and disadvantaged, and thus could be used to reduce the gap between the advantaged and disadvantaged.[51] Human enhancement would thereby promote social equity and diminish health inequalities.[52]

The second argument concerns the 'welfare of the child'. The essence of this argument is that children have a right to inherit a genome that is not manipulated. Feinberg describes this as a child's right to an open future.[53] The counter argument is that children have a right *not* to inherit a disease causing gene and indeed, to be free from an inherited disease is to promote the child's right to an open future, because to have a chronic illness is to have a restriction on life opportunities. A second child-based argument is that the unborn child cannot give voluntary and informed consent to the enhancement. The counter argument

---

49 Nick Bostrom, 'Human Genetic Enhancements: A Transhumanist Perspective', *The Journal of Value Inquiry*, 37:4 (2003), 493–506.
50 Lee M. Silver, *Remaking Eden: Cloning and Beyond in a Brave New World* (New York: Avon books, 1997).
51 President's Council on Bioethics, *Beyond Therapy: Biotechnology and the Pursuit of Happiness* (Washington: National Bioethics Advisory Commission, 2003).
52 Michael H. Shapiro, 'The Impact of Genetic Enhancement on Equality', *Wake Forest Law Review*, 34:3 (1999), 561–637.
53 Joel Feinberg, 'The Child's Right to an Open Future', in *Whose Child?: Parental rights, Parental Authority and State Power*, ed. by William Aiken and Hugh LaFollette (Totowa, NJ: Rowman and Littlefield, 1980), pp. 124–153.

is that although the unborn child cannot give explicit consent, there are alternative forms of consent that are ethically and legally acceptable and, if sought, can make the consent process legitimate. One of these alternatives is the notion of 'presumed consent', the idea that most people would want to be born without a genetic disease rather than with, and the second is the notion of 'proxy consent', which in the case of minors, is consent from the parents or a legal guardian. Arguing in favour of allowing treatment for minors, Harris has suggested that: 'if consent were required before we could do things for or to children, few children would survive long enough to grow to adulthood and the consequent cruelty to children would reach unprecedented proportions'.[54] By analogy, childhood vaccinations are given without the consent of the child, but are ethically acceptable because of the *presumed* consent that the child would want to be protected against infectious disease and because of the legitimacy of the *proxy* consent received from the responsible parents.

A third argument against human enhancement is that parents should not impose their own preferences on their child, thereby setting up expectations that may not be realized. In essence, critics warn that enhancement would be harmful to the emerging parent-child relationship.[55] The counter argument is that many parents already impose certain expectations on their children. For example, there is often an expectation that the child will provide emotional care and financial support for his or her parents when the parents reach older age, or that they will take over the management of a family farm or family business when the parents retire, and/or there is an expectation that sons (and perhaps unmarried daughters) will carry on the family name and *re*produce the next generation. With or without enhancement technologies, parents always have, and probably always will have, certain expectations for their children and, with or without enhancement technology, the parent-child relationship is already in a process of change in line with prevalent social norms, values, traditions and expectations. A ban on enhancement technology will do little to reverse this trend towards the formation of new familial and kinship relations in what Anthony Giddens describes as a post-traditional society.[56]

The fourth argument is that we should not interfere with the higher Laws of Mother Nature and should not interfere with the grand master plan of evolution.

---

54 Harris, *Enhancing Evolution*, p. 139.
55 Leon Kass, *Life, Liberty and Defence of Dignity: The Challenge for Bioethics* (San Francisco: Encounter Books, 2002); Michael J. Sandel, 'The Case Against Perfection: What's Wrong with Designing Children, Bionic Athletes and Genetic Engineering', *Atlantic Monthly*, 292:3 (2004), 50–62; and, Michael J. Selgelid, 'Ethics and Eugenic Enhancement', *Poiesis & Praxis*, 1:4 (2003), 239–261.
56 Anthony Giddens, 'Living in a Post-traditional Society', in *Reflexive Modernization*, ed. by Ulrich Beck, Anthony Giddens and Scott Lash (Cambridge: Polity Press, 1994), pp. 56–109.

According to Sandel, genetic enhancement 'threatens to banish our appreciation of life as a gift'.[57] The counter argument is that the entire medical profession is an interference with nature, so should we ban the entire enterprise of modern medicine? Should we stop giving insulin to diabetics, and stop giving dialysis to patients with kidney disease? Critics fear that if we intervene with the human genome and upset the natural balance, then ultimately, nature will take revenge. Adding to this, we do not know what the form of this revenge will be, or when it will come into play, which leads to the next argument about unpredictability.[58]

The "certainty of uncertainty" principle, or the concern that there will always be unanticipated, unanticipated, or unforeseen side effects, is the fifth argument against future eugenic enhancement. To offer an example, bioscientists caution that there is a risk that an exogenous gene introduced into a cell nucleus during gene therapy could insert in the wrong place and switch off a vital gene or alternatively, it could switch on a harmful gene such as an oncogene leading to over-expression of the gene and overproduction of the gene product. This is an example of the type of 'manufactured risk' described in Ulrich Beck's *Risk Society*.[59] The counter argument is that if we never took any risks, in science, in business, or in the Arts, society would stagnate. The challenge is to find an acceptable level of risk and an acceptable balance between risk and benefit.

Distributive justice is the sixth argument against future eugenics. This is based on the belief that the money allocated to genetic enhancement research and development could be better spent on funding research and treatment for more life threatening conditions. However, this assumes that we can draw a line between therapy and enhancement, which is not always the case. Enhancement can also be therapy if it is used to prevent the onset or severity of an illness. Enhanced immunity to infectious agents, enhanced resistance to cardiovascular disease, and enhanced tumor-supressor genes to protect the body against cancer are all examples of enhancements that are simultaneously therapeutic. These few examples suggest that enhancement may well constitute an ethical distribution of research funds and ethical use of clinical resources as it may save many lives and considerable sums of money in the longer term.

The seventh argument is that giving people a positional advantage through enhancement will ultimately be futile. As Bostrom and Roache explain, some enhancements are only advantageous because other people do not have them.[60]

---

57 Sandel, 'The Case Against Perfection'.
58 For an excellent review, discussion and critique of the MEA, see Powell and Bucannan, 'Breaking Evolution's Chains'.
59 Ulrich Beck, *Risk Society: Towards a New Modernity* (London: Sage, 1992).
60 Nick Bostrom and Rebecca Roache, 'Ethical Issues in Human Enhancement', in *New Waves in Applied Ethics*, ed. by Jesper Ryberg, Thomas S. Petersen and Clark Wolf (Basingstoke: Palgrave, 2007), pp. 120–152.

For example, if one person is enhanced to be able to faultlessly play Rachmaninov's second piano concerto in C minor, and if very few others have this talent, then this musically enhanced person may enjoy a social advantage. But, once everyone has been enhanced to play Rachmaninov, then there will be no positional advantage for this musically enhanced individual. The counter argument is that many enhancements are not relative or positional. For example, an enhancement that confers greater protection against cardiovascular disease, or greater resistance to cancer will make every individual better off and society as a whole better off.

The final argument is that while people may agree on the idea of producing 'better' children, there is no consensus on what 'better' means.[61] Does it mean being more conservative or more radical? Does it mean being better at music, or sport, or philosophy? Or, does better mean being taller, or more petite? The concept of "better" is highly subjective and will inevitably change with changes in culture and fashion.

Whilst it is essential to continue these ethical debates on the rights and wrongs of genetic enhancement, or what Powell and Buchanan call the 'deliberate genetic modification in humans',[62] some authors conclude that the debate is essentially redundant because, like most new technologies, enhancement is inevitable. This idea was initially advanced by Winner who suggested that technology becomes autonomous and cannot be stopped.[63] Essentially, what this means is that once the techno-genie is out of the bottle, there is no putting her back. More recently, the idea has been discussed by who offer three arguments to suggest that genetic enhancement is inevitable.[64] The first is because it is embedded within a capitalist society that encourages the pursuit of activities that are profitable. The second is because it is embedded within a liberal society, which values the rights and freedoms of individuals to pursue their freely chosen aesthetic, academic or entrepreneurial pursuits with minimal interference from the state. And the third is because humans are essentially inquisitive and creative beings and, as such, will always seek to understand the mysteries of life and the world we live in.

---

61 President's Council on Bioethics, *Beyond Therapy*.
62 Powell, and Buchanan, 'Breaking Evolution's Chains'.
63 Langdon Winner, *Autonomous Technology: Technics-out-of-Control* (Cambridge, MA.: MIT Press, 1978).
64 Francoise Baylis and Jason Scott Robert, 'The Inevitability of Genetic Enhancement Technologies', *Bioethics*, 18:1 (2004), 1–26.

Conclusion

This chapter has described three historical periods of eugenics: the past, present and future. The 'old' eugenics of the early to mid-twentieth century was often characterized by coercive policies restricting immigration and marriage, compulsory sterilization for the insane and feebleminded, and, ultimately, by the totally unethical and unacceptable policy of systematic genocide. 'Old' eugenics was inspired by Darwin's theory of evolution and was shaped by the Enlightenment, the scientific revolution, and the optimistic ethos of modernity. It included a belief that through the use of science, technology, and reason humans would achieve mastery over the forces of nature and would continue to achieve progress towards total liberation from the perils and constraints of nature. The horrific events and barbaric nature of the Second World War lead to a dramatic critique of the ethos of Modernity, and from this critique came a warning and a recognition of the perilous downside of excessive science and technology.[65] This ultimately led to our entry into, what Ulrich Beck has described as, a 'Risk Society', or a society characterised by manufactured, socially constructed, or technological risks. Thus, the fall of the 'old' eugenic regime coincided with a much wider critique of Modernity and with a wholesale shift from optimism to pessimism.

The 'new' eugenics of the late twentieth century to early twenty-first century is characterized by the combination of molecular genetic techniques and assisted reproductive technologies, including premarital, pre-implantation, and prenatal genetic testing. Historically, this era of eugenics emerged alongside new reproductive technologies and is shaped by the ethos of late modernity or reflexive modernity. This is the era of human rights, ratified by the post war *Universal Declaration on Human Rights 1948* and other international documents, such as the *Nuremberg Code 1947*, the *Belmont Report 1979*, and the *Declaration of Helsinki 1964; 2008*. The 'new' eugenics also coincides with the shift from 'old public health' to 'new public health', the birth of bioethics as an autonomous discipline, and the emergence of formal ethics committees as the governors and regulators of minimal ethical standards.

'Future' eugenics will most probably be characterized by the futuristic (but not fictitious) technologies of reproductive cloning and germ-line genetic modification. Unlike its previous incarnations, 'future' eugenics will no longer be constrained by what already exists in the human gene pool. This 'future' eugenics could go beyond the natural limits of the human gene pool by crossing both the species-boundary and the boundary between the natural and the ar-

---

65 Max Horkheimer and Theodor W. Adorno, *Dialectic of Enlightenment* (New York: Continuum, 1972).

tificial. It has been predicted that the future eugenics will create new beings named 'superhumans,' 'transhumans,' 'posthumans,' 'cyborgs', or 'human-animal hybrids'.⁶⁶ As we enter the age of "future" eugenics, we will become the architects and authors of our future. As Buchanan *et al.* suggest, our evolutionary future will no longer be left to *chance*; it will become a product of our own *choice*.⁶⁷

These three historical periods in the history of eugenics share the same goal of crafting better humans. The techniques and policies differ, but the core ideology is the same: to select out undesirable human traits and to select in (or artificially create) desirable ones. Eugenics appeals to a fundamental human desire to achieve better health, greater resistance to infectious disease, longer lives, happier lives, more empathy, compassion, cooperation and altruism, to avoid the degenerative diseases of old age, to increase quality of life and well-being, to lower the incidence and prevalence of genetic disease in the population, and ultimately, to reduce the total amount of suffering in the population. Eugenics in the past, in the present and in the future, is ultimately a utilitarian enterprise.

---

66 Donna Haraway, *Modest_Witness@Second_Millenium.FemaleMan©_Meets_OncoMouse™: Feminism and Technoscience* (New York and London: Routledge, 1997) and Francis Fukuyama, *Our Posthuman Future: Consequences of the Biotechnology Revolution* (London: Profile, 2003).
67 Buchanan, *From Chance to Choice*.

Marius Turda

Crafting a Healthy Nation: European Eugenics in Historical Context

The scholarship on eugenics has long been fragmented: until recently there has been relatively little cross-fertilization between work in the history of science, sociology, anthropology and other disciplines in the humanities. Research has also been fragmented along geographical lines: with relatively little comparative work undertaken and little awareness shown of the regional variations in understandings and configurations that characterized the reception of eugenic ideas in Europe and beyond. The last two decades have, however, seen an increasing number of attempts to redress these omissions.[1] Such that, even those scholars of eugenics who are not comparativists, *per se,* have become increasingly aware of the broad spectrum of variations, in social, national, and gendered organizations, as well as cultural settings and political expressions, that can be encompassed within the field. This awareness, in turn, has informed the ways in which they describe eugenics, pose questions, and formulate answers.

This growing body of scholarship has reframed the study of eugenics in broader and more integrated terms, generating a new direction of research that is interdisciplinary and multi-factorial. The historiography on eugenics is finally 'catching up' with the main problems addressed by current debates, not only in the medical humanities and bioethics, but also in broad historical fields like sexuality, inequality, and disability. What is now emerging is a synthetic and critical perspective, which, on the one hand, assesses the relationship between eugenics and various political ideologies and cultural regimes, while, on the other, shows how eugenics has provided some of the practical and conceptual tools necessary for constructing the bio-technologically informed worldview and ethics cultivated today. But, a crucial question remains unanswered: how

---

* Work supported by the Wellcome Trust's Strategic Award (Project: Health Care in Public and Private. Grant no. 082808). All translations are mine unless otherwise indicated.
1 The most recent collective and comparative work is Alison Bashford and Philippa Levine (ed.), *The Oxford Handbook of the History of Eugenics* (New York: Oxford University Press, 2010); for earlier attempts see Mark B. Adams (ed.), *The Wellborn Science: Eugenics in Germany, France, Brazil, and Russia* (New York: Oxford University Press, 1990).

can this geographical and conceptual diversity be brought together into a normative historical reading of both national and international histories of eugenics?

From its birth at the end of the nineteenth century, and wedded to the emergent 'truths' about human nature being uncovered in disciplines such as sociology, statistics, anthropology, and medicine, eugenics blended opposing visions of human improvement into a new form of scientific knowledge, one based on theories of evolution and heredity as well as population control. Reflecting this wide variety of social and cultural experiences, eugenics often had shifting and fluid, rather than fixed, meanings in different national and international contexts.

In this chapter, I hope to convey something of the historical complexities that eugenicists experienced during the first half of the twentieth century, a period considered by most historians to be the 'golden age' of eugenics. This period and its main features, including the relationship between the state and the individual; race and class; nature and nurture, all remain an active matter of debate in current scholarship. What is now needed is an epistemologically informed account of our eugenic past, present, and future. Here, of greatest importance is interdisciplinary research towards a nuanced history of eugenics that balances the various elements of continuity and discontinuity, of idiosyncrasy and similarity. To this end, my ambition is to situate eugenics within the authentic and symbiotic relationship it once had with its own object of study: the nation in its historical context.

The case for new approaches in the history of eugenics has been laid out before, whether when scholars critiqued assumptions about the unbroken continuity from Weimar to Nazi eugenics,[2] or when they opened the field up to feminism,[3] ethnic minorities,[4] fictional writing, art and theatre,[5] social an-

---

2 See Sheila F. Weiss, *Race Hygiene and National Efficiency: The Eugenics of Wilhelm Schallmayer* (Berkeley: University of California Press, 1987); *idem*, *The Nazi Symbiosis: Human Genetics and Politics During the Third Reich* (Chicago: University of Chicago Press, 2010); Paul J. Weindling, *Health, Race and German Politics between National Unification and Nazism, 1870–1945* (Cambridge: Cambridge University Press, 1989); Hans-Walter Schmuhl, *The Kaiser Wilhelm Institute for Anthropology, Human Heredity and Eugenics, 1927–1945: Crossing Boundaries* (Dordrecht: Springer, 2010); and, Jakob Tanner, 'Eugenics before 1945', *Journal of Modern European History*, 10:4 (2012), 458–79.
3 Eugenic discourses generally describe women as reproductive bodies that ought to be subjected to male control. See Gisela Bock, 'Racism and Sexism in Nazi Germany: Motherhood, Compulsory Sterilization, and the State', *Signs*, 8:3 (1983), 400–421; Ann Taylor Allen, 'Feminism and Eugenics in Germany and Britain, 1900–1940: A Comparative Perspective', *German Studies Review*, 23:3 (2000), 477–505; and, Lesley Hall, 'Women, Feminism and Eugenics', in *Essays in the History of Eugenics*, ed. by Robert A. Peel (London: Galton Institute, 1998), pp. 36–51.
4 Tudor Georgescu, 'Ethnic Minorities and the Eugenic Promise: The Transylvanian Saxon

thropology,⁶ and urban welfare.⁷ In what follows, I want to contribute my own views to this growing scholarship, by concentrating on a core component of eugenic discourse and policy: the ideal of the healthy nation. This ideal was not confined to the domains of identity and nationalism only, but – with eugenics' growing credibility as a science after 1900 – came to influence various theories of social and biological improvement developed during the interwar period.

Perhaps unexpectedly, it was the 'founder of the faith', Francis Galton himself, who initially elaborated the agenda for a national eugenics. In 1904, Galton wrote a letter to the Principal of the University of London, Sir Arthur Rücker, in which he proposed the creation of a research fellowship in 'national eugenics'. It is in this letter that Galton introduced the adjective 'national', even if he did not explain his terminology. It was only when the University appointed a committee to consider the offer, and discuss the terms of the fellowship, that Galton spelled out his definition: 'The term National Eugenics is here defined as the study of the agencies under social control that may improve or impair the racial qualities of future generations either physically or mentally.'⁸ This is the definition of eugenics most people use, both then and now, albeit in a slightly abbreviated form. 'National' was simply excised from subsequent quotations.

In its broadest sense, eugenics is indeed the science of human improvement, but Galton – as Karl Pearson explained in a 1925 editorial for his new journal *Annals of Eugenics* – prefixed eugenics with the adjective 'national' because 'he [Galton] conceived that the nation, not the family nor the individual, was the

---

Experiment with National Renewal in Inter-War Romania,' *European Review of History* 17: 6 (2010), 861–880; and Ben Thorne, 'Assimilation, Invisibility, and the Eugenic Turn in the "Gypsy Question" in Romanian Society, 1938–1942', *Romani Studies*, 21: 2 (2011), 177–205.

5 See Donald J. Childs, *Modernism and Eugenics: Woolf, Eliot, Yeats, and the Culture of Degeneration* (Cambridge: Cambridge University Press, 2001); Angelique Richardson, *Love and Eugenics in the Late Nineteenth Century: Rational Reproduction and the New Woman* (Oxford: Oxford University Press, 2003); Fae Brauer and Anthea Callen (ed.), *Art, Sex and Eugenics* (London: Ashgate, 2008); Alison Sinclair, 'Social Imaginaries: The Literature of Eugenics', *Studies in History and Philosophy of Biological and Biomedical Sciences*, 39 (2008), 240–246; Tamsen Wolff, *Mendel's Theatre: Heredity, Eugenics and Early Twentieth-Century American Drama* (Basingstoke: Palgrave Macmillan, 2009); and, Devon Stillwell, 'Eugenics Visualised: The Exhibit of the Third International Congress of Eugenics, 1932', *Bulletin of the History of Medicine*, 86:2 (2012), 206–36.

6 David G. Horn, 'Constructing the Sterile City: Pronatalism and Social Sciences in Interwar Italy', *American Ethnologist,* 18:3 (1991), 581–601.

7 Wolfgang Voigt, 'The Garden City as Eugenic Utopia', *Planning Perspectives,* 4 (1989), 295–312; Gisela Hauss and Béatrice Ziegler, 'City Welfare in the Sway of Eugenics: A Swiss Case Study', *The British Journal of Social Work,* 38:4 (2008), 751–770; and, Britta I. McEwen, 'Welfare and Eugenics: Julius Tandler's *Rassenhygienische* Vision for Interwar Vienna', *Austrian History Yearbook,* 51 (2010), 170–190.

8 Karl Pearson (ed.), *The Life, Letters and Labours of Francis Galton*, vol. 3 (London: Cambridge University Press, 1930), 222.

proper unit for study'.⁹ It was this reading of Galton's theory that Pearson codified in his 1911 text, *The Academic Aspect of the Science of National Eugenics.* 'Every nation', according to Pearson:

> has in certain sense its own study of eugenics, and what is true of one nation is not necessarily true of the second. The ranges of thought and of habit are so diverse among nations that what might be at once or in a short time under the social control of one nation, would be practically impossible to control in a second. Eugenics must from this aspect be *essentially national* [my emphasis], and eugenics as a practical policy will vary widely according as you deal with Frenchmen or Japanese, with Englishmen or Jews.¹⁰

Most eugenicists emphasised national specificity even when aiming to identify those desirable traits embedded by nature in all humanity. To be sure, not all of this heightened collective consciousness prompted eugenic speculation about the nation; if anything, particularly in Britain, class and race – an awareness of social and biological divisions within the nation – recur more frequently.¹¹ Yet there is no doubt that by the time Galton proposed his eugenic theories, the nation was the dominant analytical category of the cultural and political discourses on human improvement.¹² Even socialists and liberals – for whom a biologized definition of national belonging was less attractive – found the seductive promises of a healthy nation compelling.¹³

In Europe, it was during the Great War, and especially during the interwar period, that programmes of national eugenics fully developed. The Great War

---

9 Karl Pearson, 'Editorial', *Annals of Eugenics,* 1:1–2 (1925), 3–4.
10 Karl Pearson, *The Academic Aspect of the Science of National Eugenics* (London: Dulau, 1911), p. 4.
11 See Pauline Mazumdar, *Eugenics, Human Genetics and Human Failings: The Eugenics Society, Its Sources and Its Critics in Britain* (London: Routledge, 1992); Elazar Barkan, *The Retreat of Scientific Racism: Changing Concepts of Race in Britain and the United States* (Cambridge: Cambridge University Press, 1992); and, Dan Stone, *Breeding Superman: Nietzsche, Race and Eugenics in Edwardian and Interwar Britain* (Liverpool: Liverpool University Press, 2002).
12 Already in the 1970s, Ruth Schwartz Cowan highlighted the need to understand Galton's theories of heredity as part of a broader concern with the future of the nation in Victorian Britain. See Ruth Schwartz Cowan, 'Nature and Nurture: The Interplay of Biology and Politics in the Work of Francis Galton', *Studies in the History of Biology,* 1 (1977): 133–208. For a recent discussion see Chris Renwick, 'From Political Economy to Sociology: Francis Galton and the Social-Scientific Origins of Eugenics', *The British Journal for the History of Science,* 44:3 (2011), 343–369.
13 After World War II, as Matthew Connelly suggests, the nation would gradually cease to be the fundamental unit of analysis. Rather, it was the population as a biological category that provided the appropriate locus of action. See Matthew Connelly, 'Seeing Beyond the State: The Population Control Movement and the Problem of Sovereignty', *Past & Present,* 193:1 (2006), 197–233. Also, Matthew Connelly, *Fatal Misconception: The Struggle to Control World Population* (Cambridge, MA.: Harvard University Press, 2008).

became a catalyst for a number of new eugenic approaches to imagining both the state and the nation. The Spanish eugenicist Antonio Vallejo-Nágera, for instance, compared the nations emerging from the war to a phoenix: these nations 'have been reborn from the ashes and have been able to stand up to the whole world in order to maintain their racial personality'.[14] The state became the embodiment of the agencies and institutions concerned with the population's health, while the nation was seen and valued as biologically adaptable and flexible to the point where it was open to disintegration under degenerative influences, or conversely, to improvement through eugenic technologies of social and biological selection. The reconfiguration of the traditional private sphere and of individual, gender, and religious rights was one important consequence of this transformation. Essentially, the boundary between private and public spheres was blurred by the idea of public responsibility for the nation, which came to dominate both. As a result, it became possible to connect notions of collective welfare with individual responsibility towards the nation.[15]

As well as bringing the nation and the state together, indeed synthesising them in many cases, the Great War also vindicated eugenics as a philosophy of social and biological regeneration across the political spectrum. Both the right and the left, if seemingly for different reasons, sought to exorcise the 'unfit' for the salvation of a healthy majority.[16] National eugenics societies were established in most European countries, and international congresses provided the necessary *fora* for eugenicists to meet and share their ideas.

The Second International Eugenics Congress, held in New York in 1921, for example, welcomed participants from Europe, North and Latin America, as well as Japan and India. This was an impressive scientific meeting, one at which many participants nurtured the idea that eugenics could resolve some of the terrible problems originating from the Great War and the subsequent disintegration of the nineteenth-century international order. For many attending, the congress was also a proud moment, as – for the first time – they were representing their own nations. Vladislav Růžička, a prominent member of the Czech delegation, spelled out this sentiment in his paper, while, at the same time, acknowledging the great challenges facing the newly created states in Eastern Europe.[17] Like

---

14 Antonio Vallejo-Nágera, 'A New Breeding of Spaniards', quoted in *Fascism,* ed. by Roger Griffin (Oxford: Oxford University Press, 1995), p. 190.
15 See Petteri Pietikainen, *Neurosis and Modernity: The Age of Nervousness in Sweden* (Leiden/Boston, MA: Brill, 2007).
16 Essential studies in this respect are Michael Freeden, 'Eugenics and Progressive Thought: A Study in Ideological Affinity', *The Historical Journal,* 22:3 (1979), 645–671; Greta Jones, 'Eugenics and Social Policy between the Wars', *The Historical Journal,* 25:3 (1982), 717–728; and, Diane Paul, 'Eugenics and the Left', *Journal of the History of Ideas,* 45:4 (1984), 567–590.
17 Vladislav Růžička, 'A Motion for the Organization of Eugenical Research', in *Scientific Papers*

other heralds of a new cultural and political landscape, emerging from the trenches of war and revolutions, Růžička affirmed his commitment to the ideal of a nation that was both racially healthy and morally powerful. At the same time, eugenicists recognised that the historical circumstances of the 1920s required different solutions to the ones imaged by the 'founding fathers' of eugenics in the 1890s. Whether expressing a majority or minority point of view, eugenicists strove to grasp the world's dynamic changes and appropriate them for their own particular national purposes.

In particular, Eastern and South-eastern Europe offers an apt insight into how thinking, researching, and writing about the nation had a significant impact upon eugenics.[18] In these regions, a persistent intellectual tradition, running alongside the association of eugenics with modernity, was that of rural idealism.[19] In countries like Britain, the peasantry had all but disappeared by the end of the nineteenth century.[20] However, in Eastern and South-eastern European countries the peasantry survived as a significant segment of the population. As a result, in these rural societies, eugenicists valued the peasantry as an embodiment of racial fertility and national strength. And, similar to their counterparts in Sweden and Norway, many social hygienists and health reformers in Yugoslavia, Romania, and Bulgaria endorsed a form of eugenic pastoralism,[21] praising

---

of the Second International Congress of Eugenics, vol. 2 (Baltimore: Williams & Wilkins, 1923), pp. 452–455.

18 Christian Promitzer, Sevasti Trubeta, and Marius Turda (ed.), *Health, Hygiene and Eugenics in Southeastern Europe to 1945* (Budapest: Central European University Press, 2011).

19 This was not a phenomenon specific to Central and Eastern Europe. American, British and German eugenicists also appealed to an idealised image of the rural community, recasting the countryside in eugenic terms. See Laura L. Lovett, *Conceiving the Future: Pronatalism, Reproduction, and the Family in the United States, 1890–1938* (Chapel Hill: The University of North Carolina Press, 2007); Christopher Lawrence and Anna-K. Mayer (ed.), *Regenerating England: Science, Medicine and Culture in Inter-War Britain* (Amsterdam: Rodopi, 2000); and, Franz-Josef Brüggemeier, Mark Cioc and Thomas Zeller (ed.), *How Green Were the Nazis?: Nature, Environment, and Nation in the Third Reich* (Athens, OH: Ohio University Press, 2005). For a general discussion of ideas of national specificity, see Balázs Trencsényi, *The Politics of "National Character": A Study in Interwar East European Thought* (Abingdon: Routledge, 2012).

20 This is not to say, of course, that debates on national character and 'Englishness' were lacking in intensity because of the disappearance of the peasantry. Nostalgic visions of rural regeneration abounded in Victorian and Edwardian periods. For a critical assessment, see Peter Mandler, 'Against "Englishness": English Culture and the Limits to Rural Nostalgia, 1850–1940', *Transactions of the Royal Historical Society*, Sixth Series, 7 (1997), 155–175. See also Julia Stapleton, *Englishness and the Study of Politics: The Social and Political Thought of Ernest Baker* (Cambridge: Cambridge University Press, 1994).

21 The Romanian eugenicist G. Banu glosses over this form of "rural eugenics" in his 'Critical and Synthetical Examination of the Rural Health Problems', in *Problemele sanitare ale populației rurale din România*, ed. by G. Banu (Bucharest: Tip. F. Göbl, 1940), pp. 1407–1409. Engaging with a similar theme, but looking at a more recent historical context, Irena

rural communities while denigrating the city and urban spaces as degenerate and damaging to the racial health of the nation.[22]

During the interwar period, the eugenic project of rewriting the nation was thus coloured by competing historical, geographical, and ethnic factors. Countries like Britain and Germany displayed a far higher degree of industrialisation and urbanisation than the largely rural and agrarian countries of Greece and Turkey, for example.[23] While, in some national cases, such as Romania and Finland, the size of their ethnic minority populations prompted the state to act aggressively on behalf of the ethnic majority.[24] This commitment to national regeneration after the Great War, moreover, was felt in every European country. Eugenics appropriated this craving for change, melding it into an astonishing array of national programmes for social and biological improvement. This was widely disseminated through a specifically modern form of scientific knowledge. Indeed, the entire infrastructure of this emerging ontology of the eugenic nation in the interwar period was based as much upon the commodification of state power over individual and society as upon achievements in the medical, biological and social sciences.[25] Eugenics, in short, offered a new epistemology of the human body, emphasising its central importance to the life of the individual and the national community.

Eugenics emerged from the Great War as a persuasive strategy of how to protect the nation from a disappointing present and how to guide it into a rewarding future. In addition to offering scientific remedies to the alleged decline in the general population's health, eugenics further provided a defensive biological strategy for particular social, gender, and ethnic groups. Prompted by the need to generate a powerful sense of cohesion and shared identity, in the

---

Rožman suggested the term 'eugénisme archaïque' to describe rural practices of prenatal screening for disabilities in Slovenia. See Irena Rožman, 'Eugénisme et croyances populaires: le dépistages des infirmités dans le passé', *Ethnologie française*, 42:2 (2012), 301–312.

22 Such views were part of a broader depiction of the city as problematic and immoral. See Andrew Lees, *Cities Perceived: Urban Society in European and American Thought, 1820–1940* (Manchester: Manchester University Press, 1985).

23 Despina Karakatsani and Vassiliki Theodoru, *'Hygiene Imperatives': Medical Supervision and Child Welfare in Greece in the first decades of the 20th century* (Athens: Dionikos, 2010) (in Greek); and, Sanem Güvenç Salgirli, 'Eugenics for the Doctors: Medicine and Social Control in 1930s Turkey', *Journal of the History of Medicine and Allied Sciences*, 66:3 (2011), 281–312.

24 Marius Turda, *Modernism and Eugenics* (Basingstoke: Palgrave Macmillan, 2010), pp. 107–110.

25 For a persuasive discussion of this complementary relation, see Mitchell G. Ash, 'Wissenschaft und Politik als Ressourcen für einander', in *Wissenschaften und Wissenschaftspolitik: Bestandaufnahmen zu Formationen, Brüchen, und Kontinuitäten im Deutschland des 20. Jahrhunderts*, ed. by Rüdiger vom Bruch and Brigitte Kaderas (Stuttgart: Franz Steiner Verlag, 2002), pp. 32–51.

wake of profound socio-political changes, eugenicists often employed discriminatory arguments in order to justify their visions of national improvement. On the one hand, a nation's identity was to be determined by biological, social, and cultural boundaries, separating those who belonged to the community from foreigners and outsiders, who were viewed as aliens or potential enemies. While on the other hand, eugenics created a complementary system of 'internal cleansing', according to which those members of society deemed 'unhealthy', 'diseased', and 'anti-social' were separated from the 'healthy' majority.[26] This 'inferior Other' was often segregated, and, in some cases, like Nazi Germany, subjected to radical measures such as sterilization and euthanasia.[27]

Usually purporting to be progressive, eugenics was, however, not necessarily democratic.[28] That is, most eugenicists sought to take reproductive power away from the individual, in an attempt to centralise and control it.[29] In this light, the principle around which eugenics fashioned itself, as a philosophy of national renewal, was the exclusion of those deemed socially and biologically 'unworthy' of reproduction. The corollary of this transformation was that the state increasingly adopted eugenic language, even though most of it was not based on proven scientific arguments, but rather upon speculations about social norms and racial worth. Ideas of economic and social productivity also flowed readily from eugenic arguments, since if an individual was to be socially 'unfit', it was appropriate, the eugenicists argued, for he, or she, to be 'weeded out'. The 'unfit' had thus become the metonymy for those members of society deemed 'pathological', 'criminal', and 'asocial'.[30] The British sexual reformer Havelock Ellis was well-aware of the contested nature of eugenic engineering, when he declared in 1911:

> If in our efforts to better social conditions and to raise the level of the race we seek to cultivate the sense of order, to encourage sympathy and foresight, to pull up racial weeds by the roots, it is not that we may kill freedom and joy, but rather that we may

---

26 See, for example, C. W. Armstrong, *The Survival of the Unfittest* (London: C. W. Daniel, 1927).
27 See Gisela Bock, *Zwangssterilisation im Nationalsozialismus: Studien zur Rassenpolitik und Frauenpolitik* (Opladen: Westdeutscher Verlag, 1986); Michael Burleigh, *Death and Deliverance: Euthanasia in Germany, 1900–1945* (Cambridge: Cambridge University Press, 1994); and, Claudia Andrea Spring, *Zwischen Krieg und Euthanasie: Zwangssterilisationen in Wien, 1940–1945* (Vienna: Böhlau Verlag, 2009).
28 See A. L. Simonnot, 'Un enjeu éthique du XXe siècle: la question de l'eugénisme', *Annales Médico-psychologiques*, 159 (2001), 23–26 and Liza Ireni-Saban and Alberto Spekorowski, 'From "Race Hygiene" to "National-Productivist Hygiene', *Journal of Political Ideologies*, 16:2 (2011), 169–193.
29 Maria A. Wolf, *Eugenische Vernunft: Eingriffe in die reproductive Kultur durch die Medizin, 1900–2000* (Vienna: Böhlau Verlag, 2008).
30 See Richard D. Walter, 'What became of the Degenerate? A Brief History of the Concept', *Journal of the History of Medicine and Allied Sciences*, 11:4 (1956), 422–429.

introduce the conditions for securing and increasing freedom and joy. In these matters, indeed, the gardener in his garden is our symbol and our guide.[31]

Other eugenicists voiced similar arguments in favour of extending the acceptable frontiers of science and social intervention. The Austrian sociologist Rudolf Goldscheid, for example, developed a fully-fledged theory on 'the economy of human beings' (*Menschen-Ökonomie*).[32] Yet it was Karl Pearson who put it most succinctly: 'eugenics as a doctrine of national welfare is a brand of national economy.'[33]

With its objectifying scientific gaze, eugenics contributed to this ideal of a healthy national community, one in which those individuals and ethnic groups who were deemed dangerous to the nation were relegated to institutions and marginal social spaces, traditionally reserved for the elderly and the infirm. Whether individual eugenicists thought in terms of purifying society from 'defective genes', or of protecting it from mixing with 'racially inferior' elements, there was widespread agreement that one of the main functions of the modern state was to pursue the nation's racial enrichment and physical regeneration. This, in turn, was simultaneously a biological and a political project. In the name of science, eugenicists fused hereditarian and cultural determinism with modern visions of a 'new society' and a 'new man', insisting that both pursued the same goal: to heal off the societal wounds torn open by the Great War and the subsequent revolutions. This was the prevalent theory. Certainly, willingness to accept it varied considerably across countries; but even the Bolsheviks, who consistently affirmed the primacy of 'nurture over nature', never abandoned their fundamental commitment to the project of reshaping human society and transforming it ontologically.[34]

Eugenicists persistently campaigned for the nation's health. To some, like Sir William Beveridge, one of the main founders of the National Health Service (NHS) in the UK,[35] or Andrija Štampar in interwar Yugoslavia,[36] this was to be

---

31 Havelock Ellis, *The Problem of Race-Regeneration* (London: Cassell, 1911), p. 71.
32 See Rudolf Goldscheid, *Höherentwicklung und Menschenökonomie. Grundlegung der sozialbiologie* (Leipzig: W. Klinkhardt, 1911).
33 Karl Pearson, *The Problem of Practical Eugenics* (London: Dulau and Co., 1912), p. 25.
34 See Yvonne Howell, 'Eugenics, Rejuvenation, and Bulgakov's Journey into the Heart of Dogness', *Slavic Review*, 65:3 (2006), 544–562; Mark Bassin, 'Nurture *is* Nature: Lev Gumilev and the Ecology of Ethnicity', *Slavic Review*, 68:4 (2009), 872–897; and, Nikolai Krementsov, 'From "Beastly Philosophy" to Medical Genetics: Eugenics in Russia and the Soviet Union', *Annals of Science*, 68:1 (2011), 61–92.
35 Sir William Beveridge's is one of the most successful attempts to incorporate eugenic ideas into a nation-wide programme of health care. See 'The Beveridge Plan' (11 February 1943), The National Archives, War Cabinet, W.P. (43) 28.
36 See Željko Dugac and Marko Pećina, *Andrija Štampar – dnevnik s putovanja, 1931–1938* (Zagreb: Srednja Europa, 2008).

achieved by establishing a modern system of health care, able to detect recurrent social and biological problems. These influential public figures used both conceptions of health and eugenic techniques as strategies for the construction of a modern nation. In the 1920s, however, programmes of national health were often supportive of punitive eugenic strategies. Those afflicted with hereditary illnesses were correspondingly deemed a biological liability, and purveyors of various racial maladies; their biological future was to be determined by normative ideas of health envisioned by biological experts. 'We cannot forget', declared the German Social Democrat Alfred Grotjahn in 1917, that:

> of every 100,000 German citizens roughly 300 are insane or idiotic, 150 epileptic, 200 alcoholic, 60 blind, 30 deaf and dumb, 260 crippled, and 500 are tubercular and in the last stage of the disease. But if we include all the smaller defects, the visual defects and other widespread sickness then it is surely not an exaggeration if one were to estimate the number of all citizens who are in one way or the other physically or mentally inferior as one full third of the whole population.[37]

This dual discourse defining what is a healthy individual and a healthy society percolates into more general themes characterising twentieth century history. Fusing medicine with biopolitical projects of social and biological engineering required the use of historical, linguistic, anthropological, and semiotic tools as well as medical knowledge. Medicine, like history, is knowledge created not only by experimentation, but also by the social and intellectual practices that inform it. Moreover, while medicine is guided by its internal principles, scientists are frequently enveloped by their social and political existence, and often adhere to dominant social and political practices. Scientific discoveries are thus not separated from the culture they inhabit, and the questions scientists ask about the world, as well as the interpretations they extract from their empirical data and experiments, are often shaped by cultural attitudes, social needs, and political possibilities. It is important to note that, with the advent of eugenics, notions of biological decline became entangled with new definitions of social pathology. The corollary to this development was a distinctly modern ethos that viewed the body and mind of individuals in decidedly more negative terms.[38] Sterilization of the so-called 'undesirable' and even euthanasia hence became viable means in the quest to protect the nation's biological core.

Although several European states showed reluctance to introduce negative

---

37 Alfred Alfred Grotjahn, *Die hygienische Forderung* (Leipzig: Tannus, 1917), quoted in Voigt, 'The Garden City as Eugenic Utopia', p. 300.
38 See Laura Otis, *Organic Memory: History and Body in the Late Nineteenth and Early Twentieth Centuries* (Lincoln, NE.: University of Nebraska Press, 1994) and Harold B. Segel, *Body Ascendant: Modernism and Physical Imperative* (Baltimore, MD.: The Johns Hopkins University Press, 1998).

eugenic policies, eugenicists were not discouraged. When presenting his ideas to an American audience in 1920, the Hungarian eugenicist, Géza von Hoffmann, lamented that, too 'much stress is laid upon the positive side of the question, i. e. the propagation of the fit, and no steps have yet been taken to cut off the propagation of the unfit'.[39] Supporters of negative eugenic measures, like Grotjahn and Hoffmann, maintained that these radical methods ultimately rendered society the greatest service: namely, the protection of future generations from social and biological decline.

If eugenics was the science of improving the population's hereditary health, and fostering the nation's social and biological transformation, it was obvious to eugenicists that the state, itself, was central to their project. Entrusting the state with additional powers meant enhancing the eugenicists' crafting mission. In a eugenic state thus defined, the eugenicists' self-styled social and political responsibilities would fundamentally change their professional relationship with society at large. This was to be achieved by insisting on their scientific expertise and, hence, justifying their claim to decide which members of the population were biologically and socially valuable and which were not.[40] As the Swedish eugenicist Herman Lundborg remarked, as early as 1904:

> I dare hope that the time is not far distant, when one will be inclined, in public affairs, to allow the word of the biologically educated physician to have as much weight at least as that of the lawyer and soldier, and when sociologists and statesmen awake to the significance of heredity-hygiene for the future of mankind.[41]

The eugenic empowerment of the state can be said to have contributed in turn to the health expert's rise to national prominence, particularly in Central and South-eastern Europe.[42] 'The physician', the Romanian health reformer Iuliu Hațieganu wrote in 1925, 'is the most useful and important social agent of the state'.[43] It was not only the physician, however, who underwent a radical conversion; medicine itself was seen as a national science serving the state's mission to improve population's health.[44] In crafting the nation's eugenic body, medicine

---

39 Géza von Hoffmann quoted in 'New Eugenics Society in Hungary,' *The Journal of Heredity*, 11:1 (1920), 41.
40 On this process, albeit in a broader context, see Reiner Grundmann and Nico Stehr, *Experts: The Knowledge and Power of Expertise* (Abingdon: Routledge, 2011).
41 Quoted in Hjalmar Anderson, 'The Swedish State Institute for Race-Biological Investigation: An Account of its Origination', in *The Swedish Nation in Word and Picture*, ed. by H. Lundborg and J. Runnström (Stockholm: Hasse W. Tullberg, 1921), p. 49.
42 In Western Europe this process of professionalisation occurred in the nineteenth century. See Noel and José Parry, *The Rise of Medical Profession: A Study of Collective Social Mobility* (London: Croom Helm, 1976).
43 Iuliu Hațieganu, 'Rolul social al medicului în opera de consolidare a statului național', *Transilvania*, 54 (1925), 588.
44 For a very useful discussion of the idea of 'national science' see Carol Harrison and Ann

boldly asserted its authority over the most private of human activities. The priest of the new scientific religion – the eugenicist – was, as a result, depicted as a guardian committed to the protection of the individual and the nation. As János Bársony claimed, in his 1922 address to the Medical Faculty at the University of Budapest: 'the medical profession can no longer confine itself to the mere implementation of scientific knowledge. It must become the midwife in the birth of a new political mentality, which will serve the true interests of the nation.'[45] This was the theory. In practice, social and biological engineering on this scale proved to be beyond the resources of any Central and South-eastern Europe state during this period.

The story I have just sketched pivots during the 1930s and 1940s, when the political project of crafting 'new nations' dovetailed perfectly with the eugenic project of biological improvement, for both were centred on the ideal of a healthy national community. This ideal is as unmistakably represented in the discursive and practical construction of the 'new man' by Soviet, fascist and Nazi propagandists[46] as in the Kemalist discourse in republican Turkey.[47] Constructing the quasi-mythical "new man" was one ambition that eugenics shared with modern political ideologies like communism and fascism; the ideal of a healthy nation was another.[48] For example, in 1929, the director of the Kaiser Wilhelm Institute for Anthropology, Human Heredity and Eugenics, Eugen Fischer, extolled Mussolini as the architect of the first eugenic state, committed to the rejuvenation of the Italian nation. In 1931, another prominent German eugenicist, Fritz Lenz, described Adolf Hitler as 'the first politician of truly effective influence to make race hygiene a central goal of all politics, and set himself to put that powerfully into effect'.[49] While the British eugenicist, Karl Pearson, similarly, praised Hitler for his attempts to regenerate racially the German nation.[50]

Johnson (ed.), *National Identity: The Role of Science and Technology.* Special Issue *Osiris* (2009). For a recent discussion, see Mark Walker, 'The "National" in International and Transnational Science', *The British Journal for the History of Science*, 45:2 (2012), 1–18.

45 Quoted in Mária M. Kovács, *Liberal Professions & Illiberal Politics: Hungary from the Habsburgs to the Holocaust* (Washington, DC: Woodrow Wilson Center Press, 1994), p. 67.
46 See Roger Griffin, *Modernism and Fascism: The Sense of a Beginning under Mussolini and Hitler* (Basingstoke: Palgrave, 2007).
47 See Esra Osyurek, *Nostalgia for the Modern: State Secularism and Every Day Politics in Turkey* (Durham, NC: Duke University Press, 2006).
48 Lion Murard and Patrick Zylberman, 'L'ordre et la règle. L'hygiénisme en France dans l'entre-deux-guerres', *Les cahiers de la recherché architecturale*, 15–17 (1985), 42–53.
49 Fritz Lenz, 'The Position of National Socialism on Race Hygiene', in *The Eugenics Movement: An International Perspective*, vol. 4, ed. by Pauline M. H. Mazumdar (New York: Routledge, 2007), p. 19.
50 Karl Pearson, 'Prof. Karl Pearson's Reply', in *Speeches delivered at a dinner held in University College, London in Honour of Professor Karl Pearson, 23 April 1934* (Cambridge: The University Press, 1934), p. 23. See also Carolyn Burdett, 'From *The New Werther* to Number and

Yet the empowerment of the state to act eugenically was not restricted to Nazi Germany or Fascist Italy. Demand for a eugenically-predisposed state was vast and extensive, colouring the outlook of eugenicists of various political orientations, such as anarchists in Spain, socialists in Britain, feminists and Social Democrats in Germany and Sweden, and health educators in Turkey. A number of Fabians, including luminaries such as G. B. Shaw and H. G. Wells, believed that an effective and comprehensive eugenic programme could best be pursued in a socialist state. This was also an idea entertained by the American eugenicist Herman J. Muller, who believed that Stalin would be the architect of a new humanity, one in which eugenic rationality would reign supreme. In his 1936 letter to Stalin, Muller declared: 'True eugenics can only be a product of socialism, and will, like advances in physical technique, be one of the means used by the latter in the betterment of life.' If that were to happen, Muller assured Stalin, 'many a mother of tomorrow, freed of the fetters of religious superstitions, will be proud to mingle her germ plasm with that of a Lenin or a Darwin, and to contribute to society a child partaking of his biological attributes'.[51] Yet Stalin was unconvinced that having around a host of Lenins and Darwins would do communism any good and he, therefore, rejected Muller's eugenic utopia.[52] Eugenics became a victim of the Soviet cultural policy of the 1930s, which favoured Lynsenkoism. But this should not obscure the fact that in suppressing Mendelian genetics the Soviet project retained eugenics' own objective: human improvement.[53]

Other eugenicists were, however, more successful. Precisely because biological and social engineering, along with the synthesis of race and nation, were more advanced in some countries than others, some eugenicists were free to explore eugenic ideas and practices more boldly. In 1928, the Swiss canton of Vaud adopted the first eugenic sterilization law in Europe, followed shortly by Denmark.[54] In Germany, the Minister of the Interior, Wilhelm Frick, acknowl-

---

Arguments: Karl Pearson's Eugenics', in *Transactions and Encounters: Science and Culture in the Nineteenth Century*, ed. by Roger Luckhurst and Josephine McDonagh (Manchester: Manchester University Press, 2002), pp. 204–233; and, Bradley W. Hart, 'Watching the "Eugenic Experiment" Unfold: The Mixed Views of British Eugenicists Towards Nazi Germany in the Early 1930s', *Journal of the History of Biology*, 45:1 (2011), 33–63.

51 John Glad, 'Hermann J. Muller's 1936 Letter to Stalin', *The Mankind Quarterly*, 43:3 (2003), 305–319, (pp. 308 and 315).
52 The story is certainly more intricate than the simplified version offered above. For a good discussion, see Nikolai Krementsov, *Stalinist Science* (Princeton: Princeton University Press, 1997).
53 Loren R. Graham, *Science, Philosophy, and Human Behavior in the Soviet Union* (New York: Columbia University Press, 1987).
54 Gunnar Broberg and Nils Roll-Hansen (ed.), *Eugenics and the Welfare State. Sterilization Policy in Denmark, Sweden, Norway, and Finland* (East Lansing, MI: Michigan State University, 2005 [1997]); and, Leo Lucassen, 'A Brave New World: The Left, Social Engineering,

edged in June 1933 the importance bestowed upon eugenics by the newly-established Third Reich. 'The scientific study of heredity (based on the progress of the last decade)', he declared, 'has enabled us clearly to recognize the rules of heredity and selection as well as their meaning for the nation and state'.[55] As such, the Law for the Prevention of Offspring with Hereditary Diseases was announced on 14 July 1933 and came into effect on 1 January 1934. In 1935, two additional racial laws were adopted: the Law for the Protection of the German Blood and German Honour, and the Law for the Protection of the Hereditary Health of the German People. If the former was meant to secure the "purity" of the race, the latter made marriage counselling mandatory and stipulated the introduction of pre-marital health certificates.[56]

In an age as intensely nationalistic as this period was, eugenicists of all persuasions were obsessed with the nation's health.[57] Yet, great and earnest as the eugenic promises held out by a resurgent nation manifestly were, they were promises doomed to collide with two great religious and social forces of the time: the Church and individualism. In Catholic countries, the Church openly condemned eugenic sterilization in its *Casti Connubii* issued in December 1930.[58] As for individualism, many eugenicists agreed with Georges Schreiber, the vice-president of the French Eugenics Society. In a 1932 speech, he raised the issue of state interference in the private life of the individual and questioned the right of 'the State [...] to impose an obstacle to the integrity of the body for the good of the nation'. Schreiber further believed that: '[a] nation whose sentiment resents the power of the state to interfere with the individual will not be con-

---

and Eugenics in Twentieth-Century Europe', *International Review of Social History*, 55:2 (2010), 265–296.
55 Wilhelm Frick, 'German Population and Race Politics. An Address by Dr Frick, Reich Minister for the Interior, before the First Meeting of the Expert Council for Population- and Race-Politics in Berlin, June 28, 1933', *Eugenical News*, 19:2 (1934), 36.
56 Nazi *Gleichschaltung* in the field of eugenics and racial anthropology did not happened immediately after Hitler came to power. A very interesting example is provided by the Jewish anthropologist, Wilhelm (William) Nussbaum, who as late as 1933 established an *Arbeitsgemeinschaft für Judische Erbforschung und Erbpflege* (it survived until 1935). See Veronika Lipphardt, *Biologie der Juden: Jüdische Wissenschaftler über 'Rasse' und Vererbung 1900 – 1935* (Göttingen: Vandenhoeck & Ruprecht, 2008).
57 For a more generalised obsession with health during this period, see Geoffrey Campbell Cocks, *The State of Health: Illness in Nazi Germany* (Oxford: Oxford University Press, 2012).
58 Etienne Lepicard, 'Eugenics and Roman Catholicism: An Encyclical Letter in Context: *Casti connubii*, December 31, 1930', *Science in Context*, 11:3–4 (1998), 527–544; Monika Löscher, *"…der gesunden Vernunft nicht zuwider…": Katholische Eugenik in Österreich vor 1938* (Innsbruck: Studien Verlag, 2009); and, Emmanuel Betta, 'La biopolitica cattolica', in *Storia d'Italia. Annali 26. Scienze e cultura dell'Italia unita*, ed. by F. Cassata and C. Pogliano (Torino: Einaudi, 2011), 949–974.

verted to obligatory sterilization by reasoning of any kind; this is why [eugenic] sterilization will probably never become firmly established in France.'[59]

Some scholars have interpreted this opposition to Nazi eugenics, and similar reactions in Spain, Italy, and Romania, as instances of a non-eliminationist 'Latin eugenics', understood to focus more closely upon improving the nation's social environment and education, which contrasted with an 'Anglo-Saxon eugenics', extant in Germany, the Scandinavian countries, and the USA, which was seemingly preoccupied with negative prevention, selective breeding, and racial protection.[60] Across several different national contexts, debates over whether to introduce negative or positive eugenic policies remained hotly contested, and were never conclusively resolved before 1945. In other countries, an alternative terminology was preferred, like *puériculture* and *biotipologia* though whether the distinctions in question were real and substantial were accepted as doubtful, even at the time. Such differences aside, the various brands of eugenics elaborated during the first half of the twentieth century were all ultimately informed by a similar rationale: servicing the nation's requirement for social and biological engineering.

Let me offer some further examples from two countries I am particularly familiar with: Romania and Hungary. In his 1925, *The Hygiene of the Nation: Eugenics*, the Romanian eugenicist Iuliu Moldovan conceptualised eugenics in exclusively national terms, connecting it to state interventionism and radical measures to regulate the health of individuals. The only eugenic reality, he argued, was to be found in the nation's collective existence. Like other Eastern European eugenicists similarly opposed to biological racism, Moldovan rewrote the contents of the eugenic ideal to reflect his country's specific circumstance. Aiming to narrow the difference between the individual and the collective,

---

59 Georges Schreiber, 'Actual Aspect of the Problem of Eugenical Sterilization in France', *Eugenical News*, 11:5 (1936), 105. For other instances of the relationship between individualism and eugenics in the French context, see Louise Lyle, 'French Perspectives on Eugenics as Seen through Selected Writings of Georges Duhamel', *French Cultural Studies*, 20:3 (2009), 257–272; Dominique Aubert-Marson, 'L'eugénisme: une idéologie scientifique et politique', *Éthique & Santé*, 8:3 (2011), 140–152; and, the special issue of *L'Esprit Créateur*, 52:2 (2012) guest edited by Louise Lyle and Douglas Morrey on 'Genetics and French Culture'.
60 William M. Schneider, *Quality and Quantity. The Quest for Biological Regeneration in Twentieth-Century France* (Cambridge: Cambridge University Press, 1990); Pierre-André Taguieff, 'Eugénisme ou décadence? L'exception française', *Ethnologie Française*, 24:1 (1941), 81–103; Nancy Leys Stepan, *"The Hour of Eugenics": Race, Gender, and Nation in Latin America* (Ithaca: Cornell University Press, 1991); Maria Sophia Quine, *Italy's Social Revolution: Charity and Welfare from Liberalism to Fascism* (Basingstoke: Palgrave, 2002); Francesco Cassata, *Building the New Man. Eugenics, Racial Science and Genetics in Twentieth-Century Italy* (Budapest: Central European University Press, 2011); and, Maria Sophia Quine, 'Racial "Sterility" and "Hyperfecundity" in Fascist Italy: Biological Politics of Sex and Reproduction', *Fascism: Journal of Comparative Fascist Studies*, 1:2 (2012), 92–144.

Moldovan found in national eugenics a theme intended to embrace most – if not all – members of Romanian society. Moldovan tried to *nationalize* eugenics as to better fit with the nation-building project in Romania.[61]

Likewise, the president of the Hungarian Association of Biopolitics, Lajos Antal, supported the idea of social welfare with a eugenic philosophy and called this 'biologism'. The only way to achieve 'biological fullness' for both the individual and the national community was through biologism, Antal claimed in 1940. Correspondingly, Hungarian eugenics was based upon 'the maintenance, care and increase of the biological values of Hungarianness and on the opening of new sources of biological strength'. Antal's vision of a healthy nation was predicated upon 'Hungary's qualitative and quantitative development', one which would ultimately decide 'the future of our nation in the Danube basin'.[62]

Being critical of Nazi ideas of racial superiority, does not make Moldovan and Antal less eugenic in their outlook, nor can they be placed in contrasting eugenic camps, whether considered 'Latin' and 'Anglo-Saxon' (surely as a Hungarian Antal would not have qualified for either category). Both of them, while rejecting the relentless insistence upon race, so characteristic of Nazi ideology, did, nevertheless, promote a nationalist interpretation of eugenics.[63] They too believed in the ideal of a healthy nation, as well as the importance placed upon its racial protection. This was also reinforced by a series of eugenic laws introduced across Europe between 1938 and 1942, in countries as diverse as France, Hungary, Bulgaria, Norway, or the Independent State of Croatia.[64] These laws promoted the social, economic, and political power of the dominant racial group to the exclusion of ethnic minorities, especially Jews. Yet they also, as in the Hungarian, Bulgarian, and French cases, introduced new ideas of public health and hygiene, protection for mothers and children as well as in some cases medical screening and mandatory premarital examinations.[65] These laws further

---

61 Iuliu Moldovan, *Igiena națiunii (eugenia)* (Cluj: Institutul de igienă, 1925). See also Maria Bucur, *Eugenics and Modernization in Interwar Romania* (Pittsburgh: Pittsburgh University Press, 2002). For a general discussion of the relationship between the nation-state and human engineering see James C. Scott, *Seeing Like a State: How Certain Schemes to Improve the Human Conditions Have Failed* (New Haven: Yale University Press, 1998).
62 Lajos Antal, *A biologizmus mint új életszemlélet. A magyar biopolitika* (Budapest: Magyar Egyetemi nymoda, 1940), p. 8.
63 For other cases in Central and Eastern Europe, see Ilija Malović, 'Eugenika kao ideološki sastojak fašizma u Srbiji 1930-ih godina XX veka', *Sociologija,* 50:1 (2008), 79–96; Stella Fatović-Ferenčić, '"Society as an Organism": Metaphor as Departure Point of Andrija Štampar's Health Ideology', *Croatian Medical Journal,* 49 (2009), 709–719; and, Ana Cergol, 'Evgenika na Slovenskem v perspektivi spola', *Zgodovinski časopis,* 63:3–4 (2009), 408–425.
64 Rory Yeomans, *Visions of Annihilation: The Ustasha Regime and the Cultural Politics of Fascism, 1941–1945* (Pittsburgh: University of Pittsburgh Press, 2013).
65 Andrés H. Reggiani, *God's Eugenicist: Alexis Carrel and the Sociology of Decline* (New York:

testify to the changes in eugenic thinking and practice, which occurred during the war-torn 1940s. These changes signalled the creation of a eugenic state in which traditional social and religious distinctions, as well as divisions between the cultural and the political, the individual and the collective would all be eliminated, and where eugenicists would be elevated to the role of defenders of the national community.

For Francis Galton eugenics was both a science and an art; and, it was also to be the foundation of a new secular religion. This exalted principle required a strategy of detecting eugenic signatures in their respective social and biological contexts with the help of precise calculations and predictions derived from mathematical statistics, which could then be applied to the measurement of mental and physical characteristics.

Underpinning Galton's calculations and tables, however, was a Victorian celebration of man's responsibility for his own destiny. This philosophical anthropology hovered not only over Galton's utopian novel *Kantsaywhere* but extended to the entire orthodoxy of the emerging humanist eugenics. By 1936, scientists like Julian Huxley had come around to Galton's vision of eugenics as a secular religion, declaring: 'Once the full implications of evolutionary biology are grasped, eugenics will inevitably become part of the religion of the future, or whatever complex of sentiments may in the future take the place of organised religion'.[66] That which was to be disclosed by this ideal of a new eugenic religion was assumed to be a profound transformation of the individual and the collective. This was a process centred upon protecting hereditary qualities deemed superior, while simultaneously, in some cases, introducing preventive measures against dysgenic individuals or racial groups perceived to be inferior and therefore a biological threat to the nation. The nation, as a result, was reconceived as a modern laboratory of social and biological engineering.

Irrespective of how the various different eugenic movements appeared in practice, eugenicists in Europe and beyond intended that eugenics would bring about a new social, cultural, and political order. From this climate came the special achievements of Galton long-prophesised national eugenics. Only a generation later maintaining the nation's racial potential had become of prime political importance alongside the turn to "negative eugenics" and its deployment of instruments for eliminating 'dysgenic groups'. As it became clear, only too painfully, during World War II, maintaining and improving the nation's health demanded the creation of a society and a state organised by, and for, the chosen members of one nation (and increasingly, one race). Whatever, or

---

Berghahn, 2007) and Svetla Baloutzova, *Demography and Nation: Social Legislation and Population Policy in Bulgaria, 1918–1944* (Budapest: CEU Press, 2011).
66 Julian Huxley, 'Eugenics and Society', *The Eugenics Review*, 28:1 (1936), 11.

whoever, endangered the national community was to be marked as an enemy of the state.

In conclusion, during the first half of the twentieth century, eugenics comprised a wide range of views, from religious fundamentalism to sexual anarchism,[67] and was strikingly diverse, both ideologically and geographically.[68] Although eugenic thought was fluid and sometimes even contradictory, it was also held together by strong elements of continuity and coherence, owing to a commonality of purpose, one which I identified in this chapter as the ideal of a healthy nation. To understand this complex experience, therefore, greater attention needs to be paid, not only to the various scientific arguments about heredity and social selection, but also to the political cultures within which such arguments circulated. *Eugenics*, in this sense, functioned as one of the 'keywords' of culture, described by Raymond Williams as 'binding words in certain activities and in their interpretation' as well as 'indicative words in certain forms of thought'.[69]

The eugenic achievements of the first half of the twentieth century, in the main, derived from the creative rivalry between differing social and biological visions of human improvement. Galton's concept of national eugenics brought these visions together. He offered the possibility of an ultimate and overriding synthesis for eugenic knowledge, one that inspired many succeeding eugenicists in Europe and beyond.[70] Moreover, eugenics assumes an even more compelling character when seen, as sketched out here, from trans-national perspectives. There were certainly idealist elements in this nascent eugenic philosophy after 1918, elements that were – particularly during the 1930s – undermined by a number of factors, including the growing power of the state; an obsession with race; and, finally, the spectre of a second world war. But there was also a complex symmetry underpinning the history of eugenics as reflected by an appreciation that science was the sufficient and necessary foundation for the long-awaited renewal of the nation. Eugenics, in this context, suggested not only the improvement of living conditions and health standards, but also a longing for a new and better life.

---

67 See Richard Cleminson, *Anarchism, Science and Sex: Eugenics in Eastern Spain, 1900–1937* (Oxford: Peter Lang, 2000) and R. Sonn, 'Your Body is Yours: Anarchism, Birth Control, and Eugenics in Interwar France', *Journal of the History of Sexuality*, 14:4 (2005), 415–432.
68 See the contributions to Bashford and Levine (ed.), *The Oxford Handbook in the History of Eugenics*.
69 Raymond Williams, *Keywords. A Vocabulary of Culture and Society*. Revised edition (New York: Oxford University Press, 1985), p. 15.
70 See, for example, James R. Bartholomew and Sumiko Otsubo, 'Eugenics in Japan: Some Ironies of Modernity, 1883–1945', *Science in Context*, 11:3–4 (1998), 545–565; and Yuehtsen Juliette Chung, *Struggle for National Survival: Eugenics in Sino-Japanese Contexts, 1896–1945* (New York: Routledge, 2002).

Maria Sophia Quine

Making Italians: Aryanism and Anthropology in Italy during the *Risorgimento*[*]

'Italy is made; now we must make Italians.'

(Piedmontese Prime Minister, Massimo D'Azeglio, in 1860)

Aryan race theory was one of modern Europe's most famous and pervasive myths of origin and descent. As the Prometheus of modern nations, states, and empires, Aryan Man was European Man personified. The quest to uncover the genealogy of *Homo Europaeus* captivated many people, working in many different European countries, for well over a century. For a long time, one of the *idée-fixes* in the scholarship about European science and culture was that Aryanism had no impact in nineteenth-century Italy. Mythologies about ancestral races emanating from foreign countries simply had no allure for Italians, Léon Poliakov argued in his pioneering work on the subject.[1] Historians have begun to remedy this view in recent years.[2] The primary focus of this new body of literature on Aryanism and racism has been the 1880s–1940s.[3] However, an Italian or "Italo-Aryan" race was not "discovered", or "invented", for the first time at the end of the nineteenth century. Furthermore, Italian Aryanism and racism, under both liberalism and fascism, should not be seen solely as a function of meridionalism, imperialism, or 'othering' (Jews, Africans, or Southerners).

This chapter will focus on the work of three major Italian anthropologists

---

[*] All translations from Italian are mine unless otherwise indicated.
[1] L. Poliakov, *The Aryan Myth: A History of Racist and Nationalist Ideas in Europe*, trans. by E. Howard (London: Chatto & Windus, 1974), pp. 68–69.
[2] Alberto Burgio and Luciano Casali (ed.), *Studi sul razzismo italiano*, (Bologna: CLUEB 1996); Jane Schneider (ed.), *Italy's "Southern Question": Orientalism in One Country* (Oxford and New York: Berg, 1998); Alberto Burgio (ed.), *Nel nome della razza: Il razzismo nella storia d'Italia, 1870–1945* (Bologna: CLUEB, 1999); Aliza S. Wong, *Race and Nation in Liberal Italy, 1861–1911: Meridionalism, Empire, and Diaspora* (Basingstoke: Palgrave Macmillan, 2006); Lucia Re, 'Italians and the Invention of Race: The Poetics and Politics of Difference in the Struggle over Libya, 1890–1913', *California Italian Studies Journal*, 1:1 (2010), 1–58.
[3] Aaron Gillette, *Racial Theory in Fascist Italy* (London and New York: Routledge, 2002), pp. 19–20, 23, 55–56, 87, contends that Aryanism made its first appearance in Italy in 1937–1938; Fabrizio De Donno, '"La Razza Ario-Mediterranea": Ideas of Race and Citizenship in Colonial and Fascist Italy, 1885–1941', *Interventions: International Journal of Postcolonial Studies*, 8:3 (2006), 394–412, which argues that Aryanism first arose in Italy in the 1880s.

Giustiniano Nicolucci (1819–1904), Paolo Mantegazza (1831–1910), and Giuseppe Sergi (1841–1936). The first of them, Nicolucci was a physician, anatomist, pathologist, zoologist, classicist, physiologist, and naturalist. His principal contribution to science, though, came from ethnology, which he founded in Italy during the *Risorgimento* and established as a discipline resting on craniology, physiology, history, and archaeology. Nicolucci was rightly considered by his contemporaries to be the 'forefather' of Italian anthropology, which rose to prominence in the 1870s; importantly too, his lasting influence helped embed ethnology within the nascent field of anthropology, and bequeathed it an epistemological concern with the phenomena of mind and culture as much as with the *concreta* of bones and bodies. In Britain, the distinction between ethnology and anthropology was far more clear-cut than it was in Italy.[4] In Italy, anthropology became an embracing, universal, and synthetic discourse and practice.

Nicolucci was the first to import the Aryan idea into Italy and make 'Aryan Man' into an archetype for all Italians. Nicolucci's work on Italy's Aryan progenitors was a vehicle for him to explore the 'primal' and "essential" constituents of Italian national identity and character. Nicolucci's writings from the 1850s–1860s had no precedent in Italy. They represented a kind of *gestalt* shift in the thinking about nation as race. As such, he devised an entirely new racial framework for Italian nationalism. Through and because of his work, we can see race itself become the scientific paradigm and cultural imperative of the age. Nicolucci can also be considered the 'Italian Gobineau' or the 'father' of Italian racism. He established a scientific tradition of race and ethnic studies that proliferated and flourished in the post-unitary period and, ultimately, provided a rich legacy for fascism. This volume is dedicated to the study of the processes by which, in one form or another, the eugenic imaginary of the bio-technical and bio-medical 'crafting of humans' for the purposes of their individual betterment and for the advancement of society as a whole, first conceptualized in the nineteenth-century, became a reality during the twentieth and into the twenty-first centuries. This chapter endeavours to broaden the perspective of eugenic studies by taking the focus right back to the beginnings, when new ideas about race, nation, and people emerged.

Italy's own brand of Aryanism began in the 1850s, at precisely the same time that it did in other countries. Sometimes curiously described by scholars as a scientific backwater, Italy experienced no time-lag in the reception and adaptation of the Aryan idea and the development of its own racist traditions.[5] Italian

---

4 V. A. S. Careless, 'The Ethnological Society of London, 1843–1871' (unpublished master's thesis, University of British Columbia, 1974).

5 Giuliano Pancaldi, *Darwin in Italy: Science across Cultural Frontiers*, trans. R. Brodine Morelli (Bloomington and Indianapolis: Indiana University Press, 1991), p. xv; and, Giuliano Pancaldi, *Darwin in Italia: the Impresa scientifica e frontieri culturali* (Bologna: Mulino 1983).

science during the *Risorgimento* was very much *au courant* intellectually and deeply engaged politically. Inspired by the ideals of patriotism at this momentous time in the nation's history, Nicolucci's research and writings were conscious attempts to 'create a national past' for the purpose of 'cultivating a national identity'.[6] Nicoluccian Aryanism sought to give Italians the 'primordialist' ties which were necessary to bind them together into a nation.[7] Bismarck famously exhorted the German people to forge their nation 'by blood'. Notions about purity of race and blood ties were problematic in a country such as Italy, which seemed composed of such very different peoples. Nicolucci's ethnology defined nation not just as race, but also as an all-inclusive *ethnos*, and sought to demonstrate that Italians could find unity through diversity.

Scienza and *Patria:* Towards a National Anthropology

Though Nicolucci considered James Cowles Prichard (1786 – 1848) to be the true founder of ethnology, he himself was known by his contemporaries as the 'Dr. Prichard of Italy'.[8] According to Nicolucci, Prichard's work extended ethnology beyond the mere Cuvierian, typological descriptions and classifications of the physical characters of different races.[9] Like Prichard, Nicolucci believed that ethnology should seek to be a genuine 'science of Man' – not just a 'science of Race' – by studying human beings in their different environments and understanding their varying moral, mental, and social attributes. His conception of race was both biological and cultural. Nicolucci paved the way for the formation not just of physical anthropology, but also of cultural anthropology, in Italy in the 1870s. The *razze umane* were much more than skulls and bones. The 'spiritual' or mental make-up of the races comprised their *etnìa* and included such important factors as those shared values, beliefs, and customs which were transmitted through the generations; these formed the foundation for what Nicolucci

---

6 Adrian Lyttelton, 'Creating a National Past: History, Myth, and Image in the *Risorgimento*', in *Making and Remaking Italy: The Cultivation of National Identity around the Risorgimento*, ed. by Albert Russell Ascoli and Kristyna von Henneberg (Oxford and New York: Berg, 2001), pp. 27 – 74.
7 Anthony D. Smith, *Nations and Nationalism in a Global Era* (Cambridge: Polity, 1995), p. 66.
8 Royal College of Surgeons of England (RCSE), Hunterian Museum (HM), MLB, Series 2 (1868 – 1906), Serial No. 5965, letter from J. Barnard Davis to William Henry Flower, 9 February 1870.
9 Nicolucci, who knew German, French, and English, as well as classical languages, cited the fourth edition of James Cowles Prichard, *Researches into the Physical History of Mankind*, 5 vols. (London: Sherwood, Gilbert and Piper, 1837 – 1851) in his *Delle razze umane: Saggio etnologico del Dottor Giustiniano Nicolucci*, 2 vols. (Naples: Stamperia e Cartiere del Fibreno, 1857 – 1858); Prichard's masterpiece was originally published in two volumes in 1813, but then expanded.

called (interchangeably) *civiltà* and *civilizzazione* – meaning for him a highly developed, refined, and complex society.[10]

A country boy from the wilds of the Neapolitan frontier, Nicolucci attended university in Naples, where he studied medicine and first began, as a student, to publish scientific works. Italian science was internationalized long before it was nationalized. Naples had become in the seventeenth century a major scientific and cultural epicentre in Europe.[11] Enlightened rulers provided patronage because they saw science as one of the most important means to promote modernity and enhance their prestige. Opened in 1816, the Laboratory of General and Pathological Anatomy at the university supported the humanistic culture of scientific research and experiment that was the foundation of Neapolitan medicine. Gioacchino Murat had founded the university's Zoological Museum in 1811, as a symbol of the power and grandeur of his kingdom. His appointee as the museum's director, Glosuè Sangiovanni, a student of Lamarck and Cuvier, constructed a monumental building for his collection, which was officially opened in the presence of the King of Naples, Ferdinand II in September 1845. This occasion coincided with the Seventh Congress of Italian Scientists, which took place in the neoclassical great hall. The congress showcased the newest discoveries in the natural sciences and attracted intellectuals from all over Italy, as well as huge crowds (though women were not allowed entry until 1875). Nicolucci had just been graduated in medicine in July, but he made a grand *entrée* by presenting his first paper.[12]

The aspirations that the congress embodied, for a national science within a nation-state, were also Nicolucci's. He believed that Science should serve the cause of Italian unity and that Science and Nation shared a common and noble mission to promote Progress and Modernity. He became embroiled in *Risorgimento* politics as a radical liberal and devoted follower of Mazzini. The Bourbon government considered him to be a dangerous subversive because of his involvement in the 1848 uprising to overthrow the monarchy. After the collapse of the Neapolitan revolution, Nicolucci avoided imprisonment, but fled to Turin,

---

10 Nicolucci's influence extended well into the twentieth century. See M. Sciuti, *La vita e le opera di Giustiniano Nicolucci: Commemorazione letta all'Accademia Pontaniana nella seduta del 9 aprile 1922* (Naples, 1922).
11 Pietro Corsi, 'Le scienze naturali in Italia prima e dopo l'unità', in *Ricerca e Istituzioni Scientifiche in Italia*, ed. by Raffaella Simili (Rome and Bari: Laterza, 1998), pp. 32–45.
12 Giuliano Pancaldi, 'Nuove fonti per la storia dei congressi: Scritti inediti di Charles Babbage, Carlo Luciano Bonaparte, e Lorenz Oken', in *I congressi degli scienziati italiani nell'età del positivismo*, ed. by Giuliano Pancaldi (Bologna: CLUEB, 1983), pp. 181–201. Initially promoted by Carlo Luciano Bonaparte, the zoologist and nephew of Napoleon I, the pre-unitary Congresses of Italian Scientists took place for the first time in 1839 in Pavia and annually thereafter until 1847. There were no further meetings until the post-unitary period: 1862 (Siena) and 1873 (Rome).

before travelling widely throughout Italy conducting research and collecting human remains. In 1852 he returned home once again, where he lived under surveillance for a number of years. He was not permitted to leave the commune without authorization, and he and his family were subjected to repeated house searches by state security forces.[13]

Nicolucci's scientific interests can be seen as an outgrowth of his patriotism. He began to study the problem of racial formation at this time and focused this theme on the prehistoric roots of the Italian people. He became a leading specialist in the field of archaeology, which he called palaeo-ethnology, and considered it to be a "sister" discipline to his beloved ethnology.[14] Nicolucci possessed a vast private holding of significant prehistoric artefacts at a time before these treasures were placed in publicly-funded repositories. His international contacts helped further his scientific interests. He corresponded with Heinrich Schliemann (1822–1890), the discoverer of ancient Troy. Rudolf Virchow (1821–1902), the German anthropologist and biologist, possibly introduced them.[15] Nicolucci amassed one of the greatest osteological collections of the century. Adopting and adapting the craniological approach of Joseph Barnard Davis (1801–1881), vice-president of the Anthropological Society of London, Nicolucci established a methodological basis for the study of skulls and bones in Italy.[16] He expressed envy that Davis had the 'largest and most complete collection that exists anywhere';[17] comprising 1,540 crania and entire skeletons of various indigenous peoples from all over the world, it was bigger and better even than the combined holdings of Samuel George Morton (1799–1851) and Johann Friedrich Blumenbach (1752–1840).

Nicolucci was elected to the fellowship of twenty-seven different scientific societies, including the Royal Society of Naples (*Società Reale di Napoli*), which was founded in 1808, and the Pontanian Academy (*Accademia Pontaniana*),

---

13 Alberto Baldi, 'Giustiniano Nicolucci: Cenni bibliografici', in *Alle origini dell'antropologia italiana: Giustiniano Nicolucci e il suo tempo*, ed. by Francesco G. Fedele and Alberto Baldi (Naples: Guida Editori, 1988), pp. 25–35.
14 Alessandro Guidi, 'Nationalism without a Nation: The Italian Case', in *Nationalism and Archaeology in Europe*, ed. by Margarita Díaz-Andreu and Timothy Champion (London: UCL Press, 1996), pp. 108–118 (p. 111).
15 During these years, Schliemann conducted the excavations at Hissarlik (1871), Mycenae (1876–1878), Ithaca (1878) and Tiryns (1884–1885) which uncovered a previously unknown Greek civilization of the Early Bronze Age. In 1879, Schliemann gave Nicolucci a gift of priceless lithic objects. Francesco G. Fedele, 'I contatti internazionali: Nicolucci e Schleimann', in *Alle origini dell'antropologia italiana*, ed. by Fedele and Baldi, pp. 231–43.
16 Sandra Puccini, 'Institutionnalisation de l'anthropologie italienne au xixe siècle', *Gradhiva*, 9 (1991), 63–76 (p. 66).
17 Giustiniano Nicolucci, *Lettera del Dottore Cav. Giustiniano Nicolucci al Dottore Cav. Antonio Garbiglietti intorno all'opera del Signor Dottore J. B. Davis intitolata: Thesaurus Craniorum* (Turin, 1868), p. 4.

which dated back to the fifteenth century. Furthermore, he received the very highest scientific distinction possible in Italy when he was invited to become one of the *Quaranta* (the 'Forty'): the chosen few of the Italian Society of Sciences (*Società Italiana delle Scienze*), which was founded in 1782 by another patriot and polymath, Antonio Lorgna (1735 – 1796). Lorgna envisaged a "Free Association" of the most outstanding thinkers of the day. Science belonged to no single Italian state, but to all of Italy. His aim was to create a 'united body with patriotism as its only bond' as a symbol of the glorious and forthcoming 'Union of all Italians' in a political nation.[18]

Despite his renown, Nicolucci failed to get Italy's first chair in anthropology. He was an anti-Darwinist at a time when Italian anthropology was becoming a stronghold of Darwinism. The honour, therefore, fell to Paolo Manteggazza (1832 – 1910), Darwin's chief disciple in Italy.[19] Mantegazza captured the aspirational essence of an era of scientific modernity by masterfully branding anthropology as a "total" science that embraced archaeology, history, languages, art, literature, biology, medicine, architecture, linguistics, and psychology, but, above all, ethnology, which he accorded an equal place in the title of his new society. Mantegazza had a hostile relationship with Giuseppe Sergi (1841 – 1936), the other leading nineteenth-century anthropologist. Sergi left the Florentine fold and, after a stint in Bologna, founded his own Roman school of physical anthropology, which built on the craniometric tradition of Nicolucci. By contrast, Mantegazza embraced and advanced the culturalist strain within Nicoluccianism. Mantegazza maintained good relations with Nicolucci, whose influence he recognized. He even suggestively called Nicolucci the 'Saint John' of Italian anthropology.[20] The implication was that it remained for the coming Messiah – Mantegazza himself – to bring anthropology into the modern Darwinian age.

---

18 Giovanni Battista Marini-Bettòlo and Rocco Capasso, *Gli scienziati italiani e le loro riunioni, 1839 – 1847: Attraverso i documenti degli archivi dell'Accademia nazionale delle scienze detta dei XL e della Società italiana per il progresso delle scienze* (Roma: Academia Nazionale delle Scienze detta dei XL, 1991).

19 In 1869, the government established for Mantegazza Italy's first chair in anthropology, based at the Institute of Advanced Studies at the University of Florence (Florence was then the capital of Italy) and the first National Museum of Anthropology, also based at the institute. In 1872, Mantegazza founded there the nation's first Society for Anthropology and Ethnology (*Società italiana di antropologia e di etnologia*); Giovanni Landucci, *Darwinismo a Firenze: Tra scienza e ideologia, 1860 – 1900* (Florence: L. S. Olschki, 1977), pp. 113 – 14.

20 Giovanni Landucci, 'Mantegazza e Nicolucci', in *Alle origini dell'antropologia italiana*, ed. by Fedele and Baldi, pp. 61 – 83 (p. 65). Mantegazza lobbied on Nicolucci's behalf, as did Francesco De Sanctis (1817 – 1883), a scholar of Italian literature, deputy, and minister. Nicolucci was awarded a lectureship in anthropology in Naples in 1880, a position which became a professorship in 1884, the same year that Sergi received his *cattedra* in Rome.

'Arii e Italici'[21]

A central problem of Nicolucci's work was the question of how to define and construct 'Italianness'. Rousseau's notion of 'one nation for one people' seemed to him to be unworkable; Nicolucci's alternative was of one nation of many Italian peoples. Through Aryanism, he found a way to make and legitimize an historic claim to Italian nationality, nationhood, and solidarity based on ties of ancestry, antiquity, continuity, and community – the constituents of what Georges Vacher de Lapouge, the French sociologist and infamous Aryanist, meant by the term *ethnie*, which he coined in 1896. Nicolucci first propounded these views in *On Human Races*, published in two volumes in 1857 and 1858. The work was comparable in scope and breadth to the magisterial, four volumes, *Essai sur l'inegalité des races humaines* (*Essay on the Inequality of Human Races*), by Joseph Arthur de Gobineau (1816–1882), the so-called "Father of Racist Ideology" and one of the great Aryanists of the age.[22]

In *On Human Races*, Nicolucci used the term 'Aryan' in a racial sense.[23] 'Ancient scripture records', he wrote, 'the existence, in the vast regions to the east and west of the Indus River, of two distinct peoples with the same name of Arians [sic], the one who were subject to the code of Manù, and the other who were obedient to the laws of Zoroaster'.[24] The Indian branch of the Aryan racial family invaded and occupied the whole of Hindustan, which was inhabited by 'nomadic hordes, who were probably of the same race as the Arii, but more barbarous, savage, and ferocious'. The ancient Persians, 'Zendi, the Avesta tells us', travelled eastwards towards the Persian Gulf and the Caucasus, where they gave origin to many different peoples. 'A large group of different peoples, which

---

21 Giuseppe Sergi, *Arii e Italici: Attorno all'Italia preistorica, con figure dimostrative* (Turin: Fratelli Bocca, 1898).
22 Politically, however, the two could not have them farther apart. Gobineau was a staunch counter-revolutionary conservative with aristocratic pretensions and monarchist sympathies. See Michael M. Biddiss, *The Father of Racist Ideology: The Social and Political Thought of Count on Gobineau* (New York: Weybright and Talley, 1970), esp. intro. and pt. A.
23 Nicolucci wrote that the term 'Arians' (*Ariani* or even *Arii*), or Aryans, derived from the Sanskrit word (*arya*), which was the name for a person from '*Arya-àvarta*', meaning the land of the Brahmins or noble men. He believed that while the term may have fell into disuse amongst the Indians, it was adopted by ancient Iranians to describe their language and their race. The Persians, he wrote, used the term in reference to Darius, the Great King, who was called 'king of the Persians' and 'sovereign of all Aryan and non-Aryan races'. Inscriptions on public monuments referred to Darius as a 'Persian, son of a Persian, an Aryan, belonging to the Aryan race': *Delle razze umane*, vol. 1, bk 1, p. 55.
24 The writings of Friedrich Max Müller, Franz Bopp, and Adolphe Pictet on Sanskrit influenced him. Christian L. Lassen's studies of Persian inscriptions at Persepolis and Eugène Burnouf's attempts to decipher the original Zend manuscripts, brought to France by Anquetil-Duperron, and compare Avestan to Sanskrit, German, and other languages, formed the basis of his thinking.

had detached itself from its primitive Aryan stock, certainly long before the separation of the Zoroastrians from the Indians, advanced towards the virgin forests of Europe, and in a series of successive migrations occupied Greece, Italy, Iberia, Gaul, Germany and the countries held by the Slavs.'[25]

Nicolucci maintained that either the Persians or the Hindus were the original people and that the cradle of Europe was to be found somewhere in their homelands. Nicolucci focused on the strong resemblance between Zend and Sanskrit as the basis of his acceptance of Aryan race and invasion theory. In keeping with contemporary German linguists, he considered these to be sister-tongues or sub-divisions of the Aryan mother-tongue or family of languages. Nicolucci wrote: 'Philological researches have put in clear light the intimate relationship between the ancient Persian language (*lingua zendica*), Sanskrit (*la samscradanica*), and the different European languages.' In his opinion, this similarity proved beyond any doubt the Asiatic provenance of Europe, and the communal origins of Europeans, Zoroastrians, and Indians. The second branch of the Aryan race comprised the descendents of those marauding bands who advanced into Arabia, Palestine, Phoenicia, Syria, Mesopotamia, and Africa, forming the Semitic branch of the Aryan race.[26]

If European culture had been born in the East, the Italians, like all other Europeans, were descendants of migrant Aryan ancestors.[27] Aryanism could provide its more liberal advocates, like Nicolucci, with a seemingly sound basis for belief in the essential kinship of apparently distinct and widely dispersed peoples. The darkest Bengali and fairest Scandinavian, just like the brown-haired Italian and blue-eyed German, all belonged to a single Indo-Iranian-European linguistic and racial family.[28] Moreover, Nicolucci's assumption that a Jew, an Arab, and a European were all "brothers" in one big Aryan family was quite radical and progressive in its own way and for its time. Along with other Aryanists, however, Nicolucci shared the belief in the racial supremacy of the Aryans. According to him, they were the only human variety that could justifiably be called 'beautiful' (*venusta*). Beauty was not 'a fictional idea', but rather it was 'an absolute reality'. Taste, aesthetics, and sensibility all played a big part in Nicolucci's Aryanism. Influenced by the idealist philosophy of Vincenzo

---

25 Nicolucci, *Delle razze umane*, vol. 1, bk 2, pp. 55–56.
26 Nicolucci, *Delle razze umane*, vol. 1, bk. 1, pp. 57–60; *Delle razze umane*, vol. 2, bk 3, p. 112.
27 Nicolucci, *Delle razze umane*, vol. 1, bk. 2, p. 165 ff. In his discussion of 'other' European Aryans, Nicolucci was just as chauvinistic about the legacy of the Italians as was Gobineau about that of the French and the Germans; Nicolucci asserted boldly that Roman *civiltà* gave to the Germans their love of discipline and order (p. 229).
28 Nicolucci described the upper-caste Brahmins and their ancestors as being pleasing because of their fair skin and European appearance. This Eurocentric view made the theory of the Asiatic provenance of Europeans more palatable: *Delle razze umane*, vol. 2, bk. 4, pp. 62, 64, 78.

Gioberti (1801–1852), which held that God and Truth could be found in nature and form, Nicolucci stated that the harmonious physical characteristics of the Aryan corresponded perfectly to the higher intellectual and spiritual attributes that this noble race possessed. Not all Aryans were equal in beauty, however. He agreed with Gobineau, who argued that the Italian *stirpe* was the most beautiful of all the Aryans.[29]

Even more than beauty, the intellect was 'the most accurate measure of the excellence and superiority of different stirpes'. 'The mental faculty', Nicolucci wrote, 'embraced all those things, which work to improve the material and moral condition of man'. The 'most elevated civilization was and is still today the creation of the Arian [sic] people'. Nonetheless, the two branches of the Aryan family did not share equally 'their love of liberty, indomitable perseverance, warrior spirit and proclivity to science, letters, and the arts'. Those in the Middle East who belonged to the Semitic branch of the Aryans were no less advanced than their Indo-European cousins, but they were different in important respects. Jewish and Arabic Semites did not, for example, have the highly developed aesthetic senses of Indo-European Aryans, who were the 'supreme masters of all the fine arts' and 'took poetry, architecture, painting and sculpture beyond the frontiers of perfection'. Lacking 'artistic genius', he argued, Semitic Aryans also differed in their understanding and construction of morality and religion. While Europeans created God in their own image, and invested in him human traits, Semites believed in a supreme being who was 'separate from the world and was unlike any other'. The 'God of the Sinai, Jerusalem, and Mecca' was 'sublime and perfect' and his laws were absolute. Unlike their western kin, Semitic Aryans were hostage to a religious belief system which disempowered them and, thereby, hampered the advance of civilization. In Nicolucci's opinion, progress could only be made through the effort and imagination of individuals with a strong sense of their own power.[30]

---

29 Nicolucci, *Delle razze umane*, vol. 2, bk. 6, pp. 316–17.
30 Nicolucci, *Delle razze umane*, vol. 2, bk. 6, quotations on pp. 318–319, 320, 322, 330–31.

The Birth of the Italian Race

The Aryan race of nomads, who were masters of the Eurasian steppes, followed the course of the sun from east to west, leaving their Asiatic motherland behind, in order to pursue their destiny and found the nations of Europe. Sometime within a Biblical timeframe, Nicolucci believed, the great racial household of the Aryans began to scatter. Various Aryan clans, such as the Celts, the Teutons, and the Slavs, pushed into Central Europe, before moving into Gaul, Spain, and, eventually, the British Isles. They encountered various indigenous peoples in their path, created settlements which became the nuclei of European nation-states, and spread into the furthest corners of Europe. Chief amongst these Aryan invaders, Nicolucci narrated, were the fabled Pelasgi or Pelasgians, the most distinguished branch of the Aryan family, whose legacy was Graeco-Roman civilization. Nicolucci closely followed Homer's *Iliad* and *Odyssey* and, especially, Herodotus' *The Histories* for his views on the Pelasgians.[31] To these accounts, he added evidence drawn from the Roman authorities, such as Livy, Virgil, Pliny, and Tacitus. According to legend, the Pelasgians were a remotely ancient, sea-faring people who established settlements throughout Asia Minor, the Aegean, the Asiatic Hellespont (Dardanelles), and the Propontis (Sea of Marmara), before travelling to the islands and coasts of the Eastern Mediterranean, where they founded communities in Thrace (Macedonia and Bulgaria), Greece, Illyria (Albania), and Italy. In contrast to the Greek authors on whom he relied, Nicolucci gave these Pelasgian peoples an Aryan history and identity.

Nicolucci defined the Pelasgians of Thessaly and Arcadia (controversially, as some believed the Pelasgians were, unlike the Hellenes, non-Greek) as the 'original Graeco-root-stock' that gave birth to the Hellenic race and civilization. The "Italic branch" of the marauding Aryo-Pelasgian family, comprising *émigrés* from various settlements in Greece, colonized southern Italy, founded *Magna Graecia*, and created the *germi* of a future national culture and society. So, rather than see the Pelasgians as a people with indeterminate origins who settled in Greece before migrating to Italy, Nicolucci invested them with an Aryan pedigree and identity.[32]

The Aryo-Graeco-Pelasgi arrived in Italy before Aeneas (in 1182 B.C.), the exiled Trojan warrior, settled in Latium and founded the city that became

---

31 Nicolucci, *Delle razze umane*, vol. 1, bk. 3, chs. 3–4.
32 Nicolucci, *Delle razze umane*, vol. 1, bk. 2, pp. 116–18. Nicolucci used the term Pelasgic to mean an actual people; he claimed also to possess ancient Pelasgic skulls. Nicolucci's followers continued this tradition; Sergi employed the term in reference to a racial group and skull type too. Giuseppe Sergi, 'Le varietà umane: Principi e metodo di classificazione', *Atti della Società Romana di Antropologia*, 1 (1893), 19–74.

Rome.[33] Herodotus, Thucydides, Strabo, Diodorus Siculus, Dionysius Halicarnassus, Livy, Virgil, and others all knew of their influx between about 1700 B.C. and about 1250 B.C., Nicolucci related. The Pelasgians encountered a motley group of Italic tribes, such as the Ligurians, Umbrians, and the Oscians. The Ligurians dominated huge tracts of land, not just in Italy (occupying modern Liguria as far south as the Tiber), but also in France and Spain too. Amongst what Pliny called the *antiquissimi populi* (most ancient peoples) of Italy were the Umbrians of the eastern lowlands, who were mixed with smaller settlements of scattered Volsci, Samnites, and Sabines. The different branches of the Italic tree also included the Oscians of central Italy, who had driven the Siculi and other kindred tribes into Sicily, and the Latins, who occupied the basin of the Tiber River. The mysterious people called the Tyrrsenes (*Tirseni*) or Tyrrhenes (*Tirreni*) (to denote the Tyrrhenian coast) by the Greeks and the Tuscans (*Tusci*) or Etruscans (*Etrusci*) by the Romans, Nicolucci explained, founded a vast dominion extending from the Alps to the whole of upper and central Italy, up to the Tiber River.

Furthermore, Nicolucci disputed the claim made by foreign anthropologists that some of the tribes which were presumed to be Italic and native were not. The find by his friend, Count Giovanni Gozzadini, in 1865, of a necropolis at Marzabotto near Bologna prompted debate about the ethnicity of the human remains found there. Paul Broca (1824–1880) and Ernest Hamy (1824–1908) argued that the site was a prehistoric Celtic burial ground, but Nicolucci took offence at this suggestion. In Nicolucci's opinion, Pelasgo-Aryans came to mingle with the aboriginal *terrae filii* (native sons). The invaders absorbed indigenous Italics, with the exception of the 'old race' of peoples in Liguria and Piedmont.[34]

Nicolucci depicted the birth of the Italian race as a historical process taking many centuries. An *antico connubio* (ancient union) occurred between the various Italic aboriginals and the migrants of Graeco-Aryan *stirpe* (stock) and this created a new, invigorated Italo-Aryo-Pelasgic mix. Eventually the Aryo-Pelasgians united with the Etruscans of northern Italy and formed a Latin people, which founded city-states throughout central Italy. The Latin states, including Rome, co-existed with the Pelasgian colonies of southern Italy for many centuries until the Romans grew powerful enough to unify all the 'tribes of Italy' and integrate them into a new empire. Despite their diverse background,

---

33 On the enduring appeal of Aeneas and his 'homeland' in the eastern Adriatic (or the so-called 'fifth shore of Italy') to nationalists, see Marta Petricioli, *Archeologia e Mare Nostrum: Le missioni archeologiche nella politica mediterranea dell'Italia, 1898–1943* (Rome: V. Levi, 1990); and, Oliver Gilkes and Lida Miraj, 'The Myth of Aeneas: The Italian Archaeological Mission in Albania, 1924–1943', *Public Archaeology*, 2 (2000), 109–24.

34 Nicolucci, *Delle razze umane*, vol. 1, bk. 2, pp. 119–29.

Italians were, in Nicolucci's opinion, an entirely 'ethnographically unified people' and a 'one and indivisible nation' (*sola and indivisible patria*).³⁵

By the 1880s, the fossil evidence was beginning to accumulate and was forcing a re-formulation of Biblical thinking into geological time. In his *Anthropology of Italy*, a grand summation work, Nicolucci adopted a new "scientific" understanding of when civilization began. In the "Quaternary Period", the Arians introduced agriculture and stock-rearing, thereby causing people to abandon their previous troglodyte existence as anthropoid cave-dwellers.³⁶ Nicolucci saw the discovery in 1872 of Stone-Age artefacts in the Vibrata Valley, located in the province of Naples, as incontrovertible proof of the existence and influence of Aryans. Excavations at the Neapolitan site had uncovered a great variety of domestic implements, as well as the remains of dwellings which were laid out in a uniform village-like formation.

Under the influence of Aryans, who introduced metals, first bronze and then iron, in successive influxes, the early inhabitants of Europe created proper settlements, codified laws, and developed common religious views. In Nicolucci's mytho-romantic vision, the Aryans were tall, muscular, strong-jawed charioteers who brought the sheep and the horse to Europe; they had the rudiments of social organization; they advanced to the stage where the family was considered the main unit of society; the father of the family was master over his household; families united together to form villages governed by a chief "father" or patriarch and a council of elders; and, they evolved a religious belief system based on worship of a single heavenly father. Patriarchal Aryan culture and civilization contained elements which Nicolucci esteemed. The family, father, village and god of the Aryans were the prehistoric building-blocks of the Italian culture and nation of the future.

The presentism of Nicolucci's thinking about prehistory was evident throughout his work. All the Italo-Aryan peoples 'came together under a single pact of unity forged by the noble and supreme command of Rome'. All other Italians submitted to Rome's authority, but the Ligurians, who refused to relinquish their independence to any other. Even when they eventually submitted to Roman rule, Ligurians never lost their uniqueness. The 'Ligurians and Piedmontese of today', Nicolucci stated, 'bear the imprint of their ancestors'. As in the distant past, Ligurians were 'the most vigorous, robust, and industrious' of

---

35 The 'linguistic affinity' which Nicolucci claimed to have observed in ancient tongues indicated that the original Italic tribes were all 'distant cousins' within the same family: *Delle razze umane*, vol. 1, bk. 2, p. 122 ff.
36 Giustiniano Nicolucci, *Antropologia dell'Italia nell'evo antico e nel moderno* (Naples: Tip. dell'Accademia delle Scienze, 1887), pp. 3–4; Jules Desnoyers first used the term 'Quaternary' in 1829 to mean the time period from the end of the Pliocene Epoch (roughly 1.8–1.6 million years ago), when recognizably human beings first appeared.

all Italians. 'Quite different in character from sub-Alpine Italians', Ligurians 'loved order and stability' and were 'a most sober and energetic people'. They, above all others, were the most fit to govern the Italians and become hegemonic over the rest of Italy. Only they, the ancestral Ligurian forebears and their descendants today within the Piedmontese ruling class, were capable of constructing a cohesive Italian *ethnos* and nation.[37]

Their Aryan forebears came together to form the *ceppo italico* (Italic root base or vine stock), thereby creating a strong *stipite* (family line) for all Italians; this was the making of the great "unity of the stirps" that endured through the ages and finally found expression in nationhood. The ties of continuity rather than consanguinity compelled his people to achieve national unity and realize their potential for greatness once more. Nicolucci rendered his Aryan progenitor as the ideal proto-Italian, who embodied all the characteristics of "Italianness" which modern-day Italians possessed.

"Racializing" Italians and "Biologizing" Ethnicity

For Nicolucci, the existence and persistence of ethnicity were incontrovertible facts: products not just of culture, but of "nature" too. One of the most important aspects of his work involved his investigations of the craniological and archaeological evidence pointing to variations in the skull and physical type, as well as the mental make-up and capabilities, of the different "tribes of Italy". He identified not just a distinct Ligurian cranium, but also other national varieties, such as, most famously, the "Etruscan" type – represented in the ancient specimens found in Etrurian sites, such as the sepulchre at Villanova, near Bologna, as well as in the crania and head forms of such luminaries as Francesco Petrarch, Leonardo Da Vinci, and Dante Alighieri. Just like the modern Tuscans, Nicolucci asserted, ancient Etruscans were impressive specimens, with tall, muscular, strong, and perfectly-proportioned bodies. Moreover, they represented the "classic" Italian racial "type", which, in cranial conformation, comprised a broad skull due to a large brain, a prominent forehead, and a full face, with big eyes and a wide, short nose.[38]

Embodying ethnicity in human physiology lent the ethno-nationalism of the *Risorgimento* period an even greater "ineffable importance" than a grounding in

---

37 Nicolucci, *Anthropologia dell'Italia*, pp. 8–9.
38 Antonio Garbiglietti, *Sopra alcuni recenti scritti di craniologia etnografica dei dottori Giustiniano Nicolucci e G. Bernardo Davis: Relazione letta alla R. Accademia di Medicina di Torino nella Tornata del giorno 22 giugno 1866* (Turin: G. Favale, 1866), pp. 35–41 on Nicolucci's discovery of Dante's 'true' Tuscan ethnicity.

culture alone could provide.[39] The primordial bonds making ethnoses resulted from the "givens" of birth, language, religion, territory, and culture, but they were also imprinted on the body, in the bones and brains themselves. A very important development, attributable directly to Nicolucci's early explorations of the plural and integrative nature of Italian ethnicity and nationhood in Italy, was the keen interest that anthropology, from the 1870s, showed in formulating an ethnological map of Italy. Nicolucci had paved the way with his local studies, but Mantegazza carried on the tradition, as part of his attempt both to consolidate anthropology and to make it into a state science.

Mantegazza, like Nicolucci, believed wholeheartedly that Science was the crucible of Progress. Unlike Nicolucci, who had no ambition for ethnology beyond the patriotic aspiration that it serve the Nation, Mantegazza believed that science had a supreme social purpose beyond nationalism, and that it should be the starting-point for government politics and the policies of the future. He furthered this ambitious agenda by using ethnological researches to foster the development of racial anthropometrics and to claim for paleo-ethno-anthropology, under his guardianship in Florence, a key public role within the new unified Italy. In so doing, Mantegazza moved the Italian anthropology of the nineteenth century closer to the Italian eugenics of the twentieth century. For by the 1870s, the conceptual origin, cultural framework, and cognitive foundation of later bio-politics could be found in shifts in the organization, practice, and aims of race science.

Significant changes not just within the configuration of science but also in the orientation of politics took place at this time and amounted to a breakthrough moment in the culture. When Mantegazza was still a professor and physiologist in Pavia, where he founded Europe's first Laboratory of Experimental Pathology, and still a close friend of his pupil, Cesare Lombroso, he also founded *Igea: The Journal of Hygiene and Preventative Medicine*; for many years after 1862, this publication promoted his ideas concerning the strategic importance of matters relating to public health and racial hygiene to a wide readership of intellectuals and professionals. From 1866 to 1905, his series of publications entitled the 'Almanac of Popular Hygiene' and the 'Small Library of the Italian People' produced educational pamphlets and volumes reaching a mass audience of readers in need of sound advice about domestic management and personal maintenance from the self-proclaimed 'doctor in the house'.[40] Mantegazza wished to replace religion in the hearts and minds of his compatriots with a 'new

---

39 Clifford Geertz, 'The Integrative Revolution: Primordial Sentiments and Civil Politics in the New State', in *Old Societies and New States: The Quest for Modernity in Asia and Africa*, ed. by Clifford Geertz (New York: Free Press of Glencoe, 1963), pp. 105–57.
40 Paola Govoni, *Un pubblico per la scienza: La divulgazione scientifica nell'Italia in formazione* (Rome: Carroce Editore, 2002), pp. 214, 232–35.

morality' of scientific modernity proclaiming bodily hygiene and health as the font of national pride and empowerment.

Nation-building, Mantegazza affirmed, had to encompass far more than the creation of a polity. Italians had not just to be 'made' politically into a *polis*, but also to be 're-made' biologically, by science and medicine, into a healthy and vigorous nation capable of progress and prosperity. The liberal project, he firmly believed, had to include plans to improve the sanitary, moral, educational, and social conditions of the masses by means of a state-sponsored programme of racial betterment. He became a deputy for Monza on the liberal Right in 1865, and served four consecutive terms in office. A patriot who had fought at the barricades, and supported Garibaldi, Mantegazza defined himself, as did his contemporaries, as a life-long democrat, radical, troublemaker, and non-conformist. He positioned himself as a moderate conservative out of antipathy for the thuggish Crispi and his 'unquiet gang of men without much culture'.[41] He took his role as a politician seriously and used his position to argue against the immobility of parliamentary politics and in favour of the adoption of his bold and broad programme of action.[42]

Soon after his appointment to the chair in 1869, Mantegazza was elected to the chamber once again, where he served his final term; in 1876, when the liberal Left came to power, he lost his footing as a deputy, but was honoured with a seat for life in the senate. In that year too, he was made a director of the *Consiglio Superiore di Sanità*, the government's high-most public health agency; and, he was also given a leadership role in the *Giunta Centrale di Statistica*, the department responsible for compiling national statistics and the forerunner of ISTAT (the National Institute of Statistics). These were not sinecures, Mantegazza executed his duties responsibly, travelled regularly to Rome for meetings, and completed much paperwork: for example, drafting the nation's first unitary public health code and, similarly, drawing up new national guidelines for state involvement in charitable institutions.[43] Furthermore, in those years, he made inroads into the establishment of what was to become – formally after the turn of the new century – the nation's first official Anthropometric Laboratory.

A racial agenda was a significant aspect of Mantegazza's plan for a sociobiological politics, based on a partnership between science, medicine, and the

---

41 Paolo Mantegazza, *Ricordi politici di un fantaccino del parlamento italiano* (Florence: R. Bemporad, 1896), pp. 1, 38, 248–55.
42 Carlo Reynaudi, *Paolo Mantegazza: Note biografiche* (Milan: Fratelli Treves, 1893), pp. 73–76.
43 Museo Nazionale di Antropologia e Etnologia, Università di Firenze, Fondo Mantegazza: 704, letter from P. M. to G. Omboni, 11 April 1875; 746, letter from Ministro degli Interni to P. M., 4 January 1876; 800, letter from P. M. to G. Omboni, 21 January 1877; 806, letter from Ministero d'agricoltura, industria, e commercio to P. M., 4 March 1877.

state. Nicolucci had measured crania and skeletons for the purposes of comparing ancestral and modern types, and determining racial origins and development. Cesare Lombroso had studied the skulls and facial features of convicted criminals in order to prove the heritability of criminality. Mantegazza's aim was not just to observe and describe physiological differences, but also to use biometric data as the starting point for the planning of new types of government policies. The remedial intent and practical concerns behind Mantegazza's project reoriented science, away from its existing form, as a field of enquiry, and took it into a realm where it claimed social applicability. Based upon a biologistic understanding of social problems, and a belief in the power of science to "fix" them, this endeavour and aspiration encapsulated and prefigured the modernist impulses behind eugenics and biomedicine in the following decades. Years before Francis Galton and Alphonse Bertillon systematized anthropometry, moreover, Mantegazza initiated a national anthropometric study of the effects of race and ethnicity upon the Italians.

Mantegazza exploited his political influence and contacts to advance his cause of building a new empire of and for science. At the second meeting of his Italian Anthropology and Ethnology Society,[44] in 1871, Mantegazza launched a major anthropological project that was being funded generously by his colleagues in MAIC (Ministry of Agriculture). He had devised, along with Arturo Zannetti, a physiologist, Maurizio Schiff, Mantegazza's assistant, and Cesare Lombroso, who was about to leave the Florentine group because of his continuing personal and professional conflicts with Mantegazza, a questionnaire to gather information about the ethnic composition of the Italians. Ten thousand copies of a list of 16 questions were printed and sent to all 8,300 communes in the country in order to collect data about the various *stirpi italiche* (Italic stirps) within the national racial family. Respondents were expected to provide information concerning the following: the height of all females, by age; the height of all males below the age of military service; age at first menstruation; blood pressure, by age, sex, and health of the participant; observations on the diet and nutrition of the locality's poor and rich; observations on the prevalence of overweight or underweight amongst the local population. The remaining questions pertained to those outward physical characteristics which revealed ethnic differences, such as hair and skin colouring and the size and shape of the eyes and body. The survey was based directly upon Virchow's study of the German peoples, which began in 1871.[45]

---

44 The society was re-founded, in 1879, as the Italian Society of Anthropology, Ethnology, and Comparative Psychology – though the journal remained the *Archive of Anthropology and Ethnology*.
45 Andrew Zimmerman, 'Anti-Semitism as Skill: Rudolf Virchow's "*Schulstatistik*" and the Racial Composition of Germany', *Central European History*, 32:4 (1999), 409–29.

In order to succeed, the Italian inquest depended upon the goodwill and cooperation not only of personnel within the nation's mayoral offices, but also of public doctors and school authorities, who were enlisted with the responsibility of collecting information. It was a huge undertaking at a time when the new nation struggled to build a solid infrastructure of government administration. The results, though, could not have been more disappointing; the investigation was no launching pad for anthropology as public science. Only 540 communes actually returned the forms; many of those returned incomplete questionnaires. Virchow had managed to collect millions of pieces of valuable data, because of the high response rate of German officialdom. Mantegazza had at his disposal only a few thousand statistics. Insufficiency of data made any meaningful judgements about the existence and impact of regional and local ethnicity difficult. After eight years of trying to extract information from the localities, Mantegazza's society was forced to terminate the investigation and publish the fragmentary results.

Responsible for reporting the findings, Enrico Raseri, the head of the office of national statistics, could offer only tentative observations. The main purpose of the study was to find support for the idea of ethnic diversity amongst the general population and to gather proof concerning the distinct physical and psychological manifestations of this. The results were mixed, however. Despite attempts to link ethnicity to menstruation, for example, the material relating to this issue showed only the slightest regional or local differences in the average age at the onset of menses. The finding that all women throughout the nation started menstruating at about 14 years of age surprised scientists, who expected to find dramatic evidence of the precocious sexual development of Southern women which would confirm their presumption that Southerners were an especially fecund "race" of people. Data pertaining to height did corroborate their beliefs. Investigators considered pronounced regional differences in stature to be of great importance from a racial point of view. The differences in height which were recorded, Raseri explained, occurred because of the dominant somatic characteristics of the different "ethnic types" prevalent in the regions of Italy.[46] In common with other countries, such as Britain, where height became a focus of early anthropometry, as well as an anxiety for politicians, this issue continued to be of great interest to Mantegazza and his collaborators in Florence.

Based on data supplied by the Ministry of War, Gino Dé Rossi finally pub-

---

46 The average age of the menopause showed greater variety: it was 44 years and 9 months in the North (based on 331 women); 43 years and 6 months in the Centre (based on 208 women); and 47 years in the South and islands (based on 425 women); this was seen as an indication of the greater 'reproductivity' of Southern women. E. Raseri, 'Materiali per l'ethnologia italiana: Raccolti per cura della Società Italiana di Antropologia ed Etnologia', *Archivio per l'Antropologia e la Etnologia*, 9 (1879), 259–288 (p. 276).

lished in 1903 the results of a long-term study which demonstrated that the stature of Italians had steadily increased since unification because of improvements in health and hygiene. Environmental, social, and economic factors were making all Italians taller, he stated, but each of the different types of Italians was enjoying increases that were entirely proportional to their ethnic group. Some degree of geographic diversity in stature would remain even if improvements continued in the future, he concluded. The tallest inhabitants of Italy were found in the Veneto, where the average height of conscripted soldiers in 1855–59 was 1.654 metres, while the shortest lived in Calabria, where the average height of conscripts in 1855–59 was 1.594, and in Sicily (1.611 metres) and Sardinia (1.589 metres).[47]

In the 1850s and 1860s, when faith in the nation-building enterprise was strong, the presumed ethnic differences amongst Italians largely fascinated but did not frighten scientists. In 1869, Mantegazza, who had just returned from a journey through Argentina, published his first major work of a culturalist nature, *Profiles and Passages in Sardinia*, a scientific travelogue. He wanted to discover the secrets of Italy's own hinterland. He described the Sardinians as a nation within a nation. These 'Italians who are born and live in ancient Icnusa' had been isolated from the mainland for centuries, he explained. They had suffered foreign invasions by the Romans, the Phoenicians, the Spanish, and the Moors. Amongst the most singular of all the diverse 'ethnographic types of Sardinia' were the Maurellians (*Maurelli*) of the province of Iglesias and surrounding areas; these strange people had such long and straight skulls that they could hardly be called Dolichocephals. While the true ethnic origins of this people remained a mystery, Mantegazza asserted, he suspected that they were descendants of some distant African colonists, who were, perhaps, Berber in origin.[48]

Mantegazza made no negative associations with the peculiar ethnic attributes of the Sardinians. When disenchantment with the new Italy solidified as a *fin de siècle* crisis, precipitating a full-scale cultural revolt against liberalism and its national project, the 'other' Italians, who inhabited a backward and 'barbarous' world in Sicily, the South, and in Sardinia, came to haunt the scientific imagination. The stereotyping of those who lived in the rural South and islands as 'inferior races' was the product mainly of the Lombrosian school of criminal anthropology. Representative of this highly deterministic and pessimistic branch of anthropology was *Barbarous Italy*, by Alfredo Niceforo (1876–1960). A Sicilian himself, Niceforo lamented the fact that the 'degeneration' of his own

---

47 G. Dé Rossi, 'La statura degli italiani e l'incremento in essa verificatosi nel periodo 1874–1898', *Archivio per l'Antropologia e la Etnologia*, 33 (1903), 17–64, (p. 53).
48 Paolo Mantegazza, *Profili e paesaggi della Sardegna* (Milan: Brigola, 1870), pp. 2–86.

people was largely responsible for Italy's 'social, economic, and anthropological indolence'.⁴⁹ Lombroso and many within his stable commented on the distinct characteristics of the Sardinians, which were defined as 'Negroid'.⁵⁰ Lombroso concluded that the extended palate, and other anomalies and defects, which he observed as features of the Sardinian type, were uncharacteristic of any member of the Aryan race. The tendency to see Sards as non-Aryan, atavistic, and degenerate was very much in evidence in the work of the Lombrosians. Niceforo went so far as to assert confidently that Sardinians had a smaller skull diameter than any other Italian type, including, most surprisingly to him, even other Southerners. He also linked stature to skull shape and called present-day Sardinians the 'pygmies of Italy', or the nation's 'microcephalic idiots', an imbruted, hominid, and bestial type, characterized by a small head, stunted intelligence, and small stature.⁵¹

This kind of negative thinking about ethnicity spawned a whole new science, 'ethnic psychology', a field emanating from Lombrosianism which aimed to study methodically the institutions, customs, and culture of a people, population, or race in order to uncover their psyche. Francesco Del Greco, a physician working in a mental hospital in Nocera, wrote a study of the psychopathology of Southerners. This investigation began with the claim that Southerners suffered, 'with great frequency', from the symptoms of 'mental confusion, hallucinatory fixations, psychomotor asthenia, and impulsive manifestations'.⁵² Traditionally, Del Greco maintained, doctors assumed that these disorders were caused by such factors as chronic exhaustion, alcoholism, hunger, and malnutrition. Increasingly, however – and rightly, in his opinion – experts were coming to the conclusion that all forms of psychopathology were ethnic in origin. Others accounted for Italy's troubles as a "failed nation" by

---

49 Alfredo Niceforo, *L'Italia barbara contemporanea: Studi e appunti* (Milan and Palermo: Remo Sandron, 1898), p. 3.
50 Niceforo donated his collection of Sardinian skulls to Sergi, who used them when writing his book, Giuseppe Sergi, *La Sardegna: Note e commenti di un antropologo* (Turin: Fratelli Bocca Editori, 1907), a work which, because of the depressive influence of his degenerationism, was far darker than Mantegazza's bright and cheery tome.
51 The assumption was that the dolichocephalic skull type was a symptom of degeneration and the brachicephalic type was a reflection of racial superiority. In the Stone Age period, the dolichocephalus dominated, but, by the Bronze Age, the brachicephalus had appeared throughout Europe; the prevalence of this superior type of skull was 40 % in Northern Italy, 36 % in Etruria and Umbria, but only 16 % in the South and Islands. E. Ardu Onnis, 'Le anomalie fisiche e la degenerazione nell'Italia "barbara" contemporanea', *Archivio per l'Antropologia e la Etnologia*, 33 (1903), 447–532.
52 F. Del Greco, 'Elemento etnico e psicopatie negli italiani del mezzogiorno', *Atti della Società Romana di Anthropologia*, 3 (1896), 53–87 (p. 53); see too V. Giuffreda-Ruggeri, 'Appunti di etnologia comparata della Sicilia', *Atti della Società Romana di Anthropologia*, 8 (1902), 241–63.

arguing that some people, like the French and the Germans, had a greater degree of psychological and physical uniformity and could work better as groups towards common goals.[53]

In many respects, though, the racialization and biologization of Italians by anthropologists was a means to construct a positive national identity based on a plural and inclusive model. Alongside the Sergian degenerationists and Lombrosian determinists, a more optimistic tradition of anthropology continued to thrive. This current of anthropological thinking was concerned not with "othering" or classifying some Italians as inferior or backward, but rather with propagating ethno-national and racial ideals for all to follow, such as the archetype of the Aryan, whose characteristics functioned as a stereotype for mimicry. Mantegazza's ethnological endeavours to discover and celebrate the very best of the Italian peoples carried on after the 1871 survey. In 1895, for example, his society held an open competition, asking the winner to draw the best ethnological map and profile of the Italian people. Francesco L. Pullé (1850 – 1934), the Indologist, philologist, and Orientalist, then based at the University of Pisa, won the challenge with a series of four maps charting ethnic origins using data concerning language and dialect, as well as physical and psychological characteristics. His study embraced ethnic diversity as a special and beneficial attribute of the Italian race.[54] Moreover, Pullé brought a progressive, patriotic, and populist dimension to his work which demonstrates just how valuable scientific modernity could be to the liberal enterprise of making a nation. For him, science, in the broad sense, needed to be taken directly to the people and used as a form of enlightenment and liberation. He was a democrat and a patriot who fought as a boy alongside Garibaldi in Trentino, and was then decorated for valour during the First World War. He believed passionately that the moral, mental, and social elevation of the people was the noblest mission of Italian nation-building. Pullé became the leading light behind the pre-war movement for "popular universities". He directed the *Università Popolare Giuseppe Garibaldi* in Bologna and for many years was president of the national federation of popular universities. In Bologna and elsewhere, these institutions sometimes operated through the *Case del Popolo* in order to reach workers directly; they offered courses in serious academic subjects and organized social and cultural outings as part of the plan to 're-craft' the illiterate masses into a modern, educated citizenry. So intrinsic was this organization to socialism and the labour movement that when the fascist squads moved into Bologna in the 'red biennium' of 1919 – 1921, one of the very first buildings that they ransacked during

---

53 V. Vitale, 'Gli Abruzzi', *Atti della Società Romana di Antropologia*, 8 (1902), 214 – 40.
54 F. L. Pullé, 'Profilo antropologico dell'Italia', *Archivio per l'Antropologia e la Etnologia,* 28:1 (1898), 19 – 168.

their campaign of violence against the institutions of working-class politics and culture was Pullé's beloved popular university headquarters.[55]

Nineteenth-Century Aryanism Reconsidered

The consuming desire of the *Risorgimento*, for a communion of all the peoples of Italy, was confronted by a profound cultural malaise that struck at the end of the nineteenth century. The most pessimistic of the great nineteenth-century founders of Italian anthropology, Giuseppe Sergi did not share the belief of his main mentor, Herbert Spencer, in constant, inexorable progress or 'Victorian meliorism'.[56] The Piedmontese political class, he believed, had thrust Italy into a state of perpetual national decline and had failed to create a truly unified nation. Sergi's longing for a regeneration of the principles of political life and a renewal of the bonds of social life caused him to reject the inherited ideals of the *Risorgimento*. The new racial myths that he propagated, however, were built very much on the old.

He came to reject the principles of Aryanism on political grounds. Writing in 1899, he launched a vehement attack in the pages of his journal against 'those anthropologists who are desperately searching for any actual material evidence of the Aryans'. They do so because they consider 'the Germans of today to be descendents of a supposed Aryan Master Race'.[57] These extremists and fanatics mistakenly believed, Sergi continued, that tall, blue-eyed blonds with long heads – the so-called Reihengräber Nordic type – are the epitome of what the ancient Aryan once was. But these scientists were all deluding themselves, Sergi contended, for the Aryans, which they had invented, never really existed. 'Cephalic indexes alone', Sergi argued, 'are not enough' to build big theories of racial difference and hierarchy. The German anthropologists, along with their French counterparts, used minor differences in the size of various skulls as measures of racial differences. What they were doing by their absurd measurements was 'multiplying the number of so-called human races *ad infinitum*'. As yet, Sergi concluded, no one had indisputably identified an ancient Aryan skull or skel-

---

55 Svevo D'Onofrio, 'Il fondo Pullé della Biblioteca dell'Archiginnasio', *L'Archiginnasio*, 52 (2007), 473–87.
56 Robert Young, 'The Development of Herbert Spencer's Concept of Evolution', in *Actes du XIe Congrès International d'Histoire des Sciences* (Warsaw: Ossolineum, 1967), 273–78.
57 Giuseppe Sergi, 'Intorno ai primi abitanti di Europa', *Atti della Società Romana di Anthropologia*, 6 (1900), 67–89 (p. 75); this is an article which also appeared in the Chicago-based scientific journal, *The Monist* in April 1899. Sergi was advancing his own morphological position. His theory of racial classification was based on the notion that the form of the skull did not change over time and should, therefore, be the primary focus of the anthropologist.

eton, let alone determined anything qualitative and substantive about Aryan Man, his civilization, or his descendants.[58]

In reaction to the rise of Aryan supremacism of the Nordic variety, Sergi felt driven in the 1890s to give credence to the new fossil evidence which seemed to endorse an opposing view about the earliest humans. He formulated an alternative vision of the beginnings of Italians and Europeans.[59] In his work on the birth of the Mediterranean Race, Sergi contested the Aryan origin model by positing that the 'primitive populations of Europe, after Neanderthal Man, originated in Africa'.[60] In his opinion, the Mediterranean basin was the 'centre of movement whence the African migrations of Neolithic times reached central and northern Europe'. The three principal varieties of the human species, 'one peculiarly African', 'another Mediterranean', and the third 'Nordic', all originated in Africa. These three varieties, moreover, had 'nothing in common with the so-called Aryan races'. 'It is an error', he wrote, 'to maintain that the Germans and the Scandinavians, blond dolichocephals or long-heads, are Aryans, for they are actually Eurafricans of the Nordic variety'.[61] He conceded that the Aryans probably existed, but, if they did, they were Eurasiatic. Moreover, Aryans were not the blond-haired, charioteered bearers of culture and civilization that many imagined. Rather, in Sergi's blunt appraisal, the Aryans were nothing more than 'savages' when they invaded pre-historic Europe. The Mycenaean civilization, which barbaric Aryans brought to Europe, had nothing in common with the two classical civilizations, the Greek and the Latin, which were Mediterranean, not Aryan in origin. German nationalists were wrong to argue that the original Aryan was German and German-born and that early Germano-Aryans conquered all of Europe, before moving eastward towards Asia and Arabia. The putative Aryan, Sergi argued, was a political construct, rather than a scientific fact.[62]

Sergi had been compelled to rethink the whole issue of racial formation because 'foreigners and extremists, especially the Germans, have written a false prehistory of the Italians'. Niebuhr may have been the first to falsify Etruscan history, he wrote, by alleging that it was not indigenous, but many others have followed in his footsteps by 'deforming history' with their treacherous 'Indo-

---

58 Sergi, 'Intorno ai primi abitanti di Europa', pp. 77, 81.
59 Sergi presented the rudiments of this theory in Guiseppe Sergi, *Origine e diffusione della stirpe mediterranea: Induzioni antropologiche* (Rome: Società Editrice D. Alighieri, 1895); *Africa: Antropologia della stirpe camitica: Specie eurafricana* (Turin: Fratelli Bocca, 1897); and, *Arii e Italici*. He then published his grand summation piece, *Italia – Le origini: Antropologia, cultura, e civiltà* (Milan: Fratelli Bocca, 1919).
60 Guiseppe Sergi, *The Mediterranean Race: A Study of the Origin of European Peoples* (London: Walter Scott, 1901), p. v.
61 Sergi, *The Mediterranean Race*, pp. vi, 17, 38
62 Sergi, *Italia – Le origini*, pp. vii-viii, 104–5, 184, 423 *et passim*.; also see his *Africa*, ch. 1.

Germanism'. The Germans, he charged, have perpetuated lies about the Aryan invasion of Europe, because they see the invaders as Indo-Germans'. They represented Aryan Man as the quintessential *tipo germanico* (German racial type). Sergi also accused French anthropologists of wilfully perpetuating numerous falsehoods about the Aryan race in order to advance their own chauvinistic agenda which demeaned the contribution of the Italians and the Greeks to the creation of European culture and civilization.[63]

Excavations between 1880 and 1889 had led to the discovery of the skeletal remains of 'Castenedolo Man'. Having examined this specimen, which was now exhibited in his Anthropology Museum in Rome, Sergi confidently claimed that it was from the Pliocene Period, that it was the oldest human fossil remains found in Italy, and that it gave a glimpse into the character of early Italians. Comparing this ancient specimen to modern Italian and other European ones, Sergi established to his own satisfaction that the Mediterranean type remained unaltered through the millennia, even where *mescolanze* (racial intermingling) was numerous and continuous.[64] The Aryans who invaded Italy in the prehistoric period, he asserted, 'assimilated the native culture which was Mediterranean in origin, but they imported a language, which has been called Aryan and Indo-European'. This language, which was 'taken up by the indigenous Italians, was also modified by them and turned into a new form, which we find in Latin: this form, I maintain, is an Italic creation, on Italic soil, made by native and indigenous Italics'. These 'indigenous Italics', moreover, were not only the authors of their own language, but also the architects of their own great culture and civilization – a legacy of the Romans and, along with Greek heritage, one of the essential building-blocks of modern European *civiltà*.[65] Sergi masterfully exposed the political underpinnings of one of nineteenth-century anthropology's greatest fictions. He tried to turn belief in the existence of a parent race of Aryans, propagating the seeds of Europe, from a scientific truth into a scientific heresy. Nonetheless, he substituted the Aryan myth with an alternative one about the essential Mediterranean character and identity of Italians and, indeed, of all Europeans.

---

63 Sergi, *Italia – Le origini*, p. xii.
64 Giuseppe Sergi, *The Varieties of Human Species: Principles and Methods of Classification* (Washington, D.C.: Smithsonian Institution, 1894), p. 17.
65 Sergi, *Italia – Le origini*, pp. 15, 20, 104–5, 123, 182.

Conclusion

Italian nationalism and nation-building have largely been seen as a process of 'overcoming' regional and local identities and imposing a homogenizing, "amalgamating", and monolithic national consciousness and culture.[66] But this model of a centralizing state attempting to obliterate historical differences fails to take into account the extent to which the liberal project, conceived as a conscious attempt at "symbolic integration", was motivated by a desire to incorporate the richness of Italy's ethnic diversity into definitions of what was 'national' and 'Italian'. The 'ideal unity' of the Italian nation could be envisaged as a new synthesis – a single nationality and national community framed around distinct locally and regionally based ethnicities.[67] Nicoluccian Aryanism lent its support to this ideal. It located the roots of national identity in ethnicity and kinship and opened up a dialogue about local and regional identities and how they interplayed with the larger nation. Nicolucci's conceptualization of a 'mosaic' nation, in which the achievement of unity rested upon a strong *Heimat* culture, gave stimulus to Italy's own nativist movement of *völkisch* revivalism at the end of the nineteenth century.

From the 1870s, ethnography sought to uncover the different ethnic or folk traditions of the Italian people. Lamberto Loria (1855–1913) conducted the same sorts of ethno-anthropological studies of the way of life of the various *popoli* of Italy as he did of the 'natives' of Turkestan and New Guinea. Along with Aldobrandino Mochi (1874–1931), the anthropologist, Loria went on to found the Museum of Italian Ethnography in Florence in 1906, whose collections formed a central component of the commemorations surrounding the fiftieth anniversary of the unification of Italy in 1911. At the invitation of Ferdinando Martini (1841–1928), the entirety of Loria's material made its way to Rome, where it was destined to become a centrepiece of fascism's Universal Roman Exposition and the nucleus of the Museum of Popular Arts and Traditions, in the new fascist district of EUR (*Esposizione Universale Romana*), built to mark twenty years of fascist rule.[68] A successful nationalist writer, as well as a former

---

66 Lucy Riall, *The Italian Risorgimento: State, Society, and National Unification* (London, and New York: Routledge, 2004); and, idem., *Risorgimento: The History of Italy from Napoleon to Nation State* (Basingstoke: Palgrave Macmillan, 2009), chs. 1–3.
67 Roberto Dainotto, '"Tramonto" and "Risorgimento": Gentile's Dialectics and the Prophecy of Nationhood', in *Making and Remaking Italy: The Cultivation of National Identity around the Risorgimento*, ed. by Albert Russell Ascoli and Kristyna von Henneberg (Oxford and New York: Berg, 2001), pp. 241–255.
68 S. Puccini, 'Evoluzionismo e positivismo nell'antropologia italiana (1869–1911)', in *L'antropologia italiana: Un secolo di storia*, ed. by P. Clemente, A. R. Leone, S. Puccini, C. Rosetti and P. G. Salinas (Rome and Bari: Laterza, 1985), 99–148. The work of building the new museum and the new district of EUR was suspended in 1942. Not until 1953 was the exhi-

minister of the colonies and minister of education, Martini became an early convert to fascism and was rewarded with an appointment to the senate in 1923. He recognized the worth of ethnography to fascism's own project for the nationalization of the masses.

Science should become part of a new paradigm and re-thinking of Italian nationalism. The 'great idea of Italy' and 'love of country', which have formed the basis of new work on the poetry and art of patriotism, animated the scientific imagination no less that they did the artistic one.[69] Nicolucci and *Risorgimento* science, moreover, are the "missing links" in the story of the formative context of eugenics. Mantegazza, on the other hand, first conceptualized a clear bio-political vision of a purposeful anthropology that was the direct antithesis of the Lombrosian worldview. Lombrosianism was always going to be a dead-end because of its non-rehabilitative, non-curative, and non-redemptive stance. That the 'born criminal' was never going to be 're-born' was a cultural and scientific cul-de-sac. The profound cultural pessimism of the Sergian mindset that gave rise directly to eugenics had another side that is often overlooked in the scholarship on degeneration. The other side of degenerationism was regenerationism. Indeed, though Sergi abandoned the positivist faith of Nicolucci's generation, his searing critique of the post-unitary liberal order was premised on a search for workable solutions to Italy's unresolved social problems. And, his timely rejection of Aryanism on political grounds highlights the fact that Italian science was prepared to go its own way. In controversies about Aryanism, which the extremists hijacked, or about such crucial issues as hereditarianism, which lie at the heart of eugenics, Italians would pursue their own path rather than follow the pack, which was marching inexorably 'towards the final solution'. This is not by way of suggesting an Italian *Sonderweg*; rather, the aim is to consider the meaning of some of the significant ideas and impulses within nineteenth-century science that have a direct bearing on the desire for a nation 're-crafted' along eugenic and fascist lines.

The new historiography of the *Risorgimento* should take heed of these for it has a tendency to see Italy as a museum piece and "the nation" as an edifice constructed solely by monuments, idols, and art. In its fixation on the heroic poetry, *bel canto*, pageantry, and painting of the long nineteenth century, the 'new' Risorgimento scholarship has largely ignored a vital part of the history of the 'making' of Italians. If historians wish to operate within rigid 'canons', science should be allowed entry into it and placed alongside the arts in a pan-

---

bition that was planned under fascism actually mounted and the ethnographic collection that it constituted finally given a permanent home.
69 Alberto Mario Banti, *La nazione del Risorgimento: Parentela, santità e onore alle origini dell'Italia unita*, 2nd Edition (Turin: Einaudi, 2002), chs. 1, 9.

theon of patriotism. The 'great' men of Italian nineteenth-century anthropology comprised the triumvirate of Nicolucci, Mantegazza, and Sergi, who all produced 'great' works of fantasy, 'fact', and 'fiction' about the nation. According to the reasoning of some Italianists, however, their works shared more in common with the 'German tradition' of thinking about the nation in racial, biological, and ethnic terms than it did with the more familiar Italian style of nationalism derived from the straight-forwardly political ideas of Mazzini, Cavour, and Cattaneo.[70] Italian ethno-anthropology operated within the domain of the discursive and the mental, which is the prime object of study of the so-called 'cultural constructivists'.[71] But it also became professionalized and institutionalized in the nineteenth-century, as it proffered itself to liberals in government as the premier public science. As it embedded itself in the bourgeois culture of universities and élites, it sought to be a part of the broader process of nation-building. The new ethno-anthropology did not see Italians as museum pieces, forever frozen on the page or the canvas in ritualized Roman salutes or stylized postures of self-sacrifice in battle. Rather, the three racial scientists that comprised the Holy Trinity of Italian anthropology viewed Italians as a work in progress, a living, organic mass of bones, bodies, and brains to be skilfully crafted into a *popolo-nazione*. Furthermore, they were all real patriots whose works aimed to fire the 'hearts and minds' of their fellow Italians. Beginning with Nicolucci, the triumvirs and patriots established scientific disciplines, political agendas, and cultural traditions that can be traced directly to those bio-political aspirations for a New Man, New Woman, and New Italy that constitute the very core of twentieth-century eugenics and fascism.

---

70 Silvana Patriarca and Lucy Riall, 'Introduction: Revisiting the *Risorgimento*', in *The Risorgimento Revisited: Nationalism and Culture in Nineteenth-Century Italy*, ed. by Silvana Patriarca and Lucy Riall (Basingstoke: Palgrave Macmillan, 2012), pp. 1–17 (pp. 2–3).

71 Marnix Beyen and Maarten Van Ginderachter, 'General Introduction: Writing the Mass into a Mass Phenomenon', in *Nationhood from Below: Europe in the Long Nineteenth Century*, ed. by Maarten Van Ginderachter and Marnix Beyen (Basingstoke: Palgrave Macmillan, 2012), pp. 3–22 (p. 6).

Alison Bashford

Julian Huxley's Transhumanism

In the Epilogue to the *Oxford Handbook of the History of Eugenics*, I deemed insufficiently analyzed the trajectory between eugenics and more contemporary projects of human enhancement, imagined and realized as 'transhumanism' and 'posthumanism'.[1] 'Remaking ourselves', is possible, desirable, worthy, and can be socially just, current proponents argue, embracing various levels of technological change that might enhance physical and mental capacity, extend human life and health, and perhaps render 'posthuman' conditions possible.[2] I suggested that 'there is a long-twentieth-century history of enhancement, eugenics, and transhumanism waiting to be written, book-ended by the work of two philosophers, Nietzsche's *Übermensch* and Nicholas Agar's *Liberal Eugenics*'.[3] But posthumanists now seem to be going too far, even for Agar and his defence of human enhancement. He has begun to caution against the trajectory of posthuman possibilities, drawing attention to the costs of such ideas in *Humanity's*

---

1 My thanks to Chris Holdridge for research assistance and to Warwick Anderson for comments. The Woodson Research Center archivists were welcoming and I am grateful for their assistance and interest. This research was enabled by and Australian Research Council grant. Alison Bashford, 'Where Did Eugenics Go?' in *The Oxford Handbook of the History of Eugenics*, ed. by Alison Bashford and Philippa Levine (Oxford and New York: Oxford University Press, 2010), pp. 539–558 (p. 545). For the purposes of this chapter, I won't distinguish between transhumanism and posthumanism, but for proponents' own clarification of the distinction, see 'What is a Posthuman?', http://humanityplus.org/learn/transhumanist-faq/#answer_20 (accessed 1 November 2011).

2 Philip Kitcher, *The Lives to Come: The Genetic Revolution and Human Possibilities* (New York: Simon and Schuster, 1996). See also, Gregory Radick, 'A Critique of Kitcher on Eugenic Reasoning', *Studies in the History and Philosophy of Biology and Biomedical Sciences*, 32:4 (2001), 741–751; Lee M. Silver, 'Reprogenetics: How reprogenetic and genetic technologies will be combined to provide new opportunities for people to reach their reproductive goals', in *Engineering the Human Germline*, ed. by Gregory Stock and John Campbell (New York: Oxford University Press, 2000), pp. 57–71.

3 For Friedrich Nietzsche and *Übermensch*, see Dan Stone, *Breeding Superman: Nietzsche, Race and Eugenics in Edwardian and Interwar Britain* (Liverpool: Liverpool University Press, 2002); Nicholas Agar, *Liberal Eugenics: In Defence of Human Enhancement* (Malden, MA: Blackwell, 2005).

End: Why We Should Reject Radical Enhancement (2010).⁴ It is less Agar than his fellow philosopher, the posthumanist Nick Bostrom who perhaps best captures "overman" for the twenty-first century.⁵ *Übermensch* now materializes as 'Humanity+' or 'H+', as posthumanists sometimes style themselves.⁶

Transhumanism and posthumanism are both future-oriented intellectual projects. This is strange territory for an historian; the future is definitely a foreign country.⁷ Yet, if anything has a past the future does, and accordingly I raise two questions here. How does transhumanism understand its own history? And, more basically, what *is* the history of transhumanism? This chapter is a preliminary answer towards both.

At first glance, future-oriented transhumanists are not interested in the past generally, or their own past specifically. Bostrom's 'Short History of Transhumanist Thought' is one of the very few internalist accounts.⁸ On closer investigation, though, a pattern emerges in the transhumanist self-story. The occasional reference to its own history is typically negatively constructed, stating what transhumanism is not: it is not eugenics. In making this claim, transhumanists seem to mean that any implementation of transhumanist or posthumanist ambition is not, or would not be, coerced. Transhumanism should and does defend "freedoms" and especially individual choices, Bostrom argues, thus avoiding 'last century's government-sponsored coercive eugenics programs [which have been] thoroughly discredited'.⁹ He eschews any 'necessary link with coercive eugenics',¹⁰ and rightly so. The statement is rhetorically and politically useful, but it is also historically and factually spurious since it misunderstands much eugenics in the past. Eugenics functioned as often through liberal governmentalities, as it did through authoritarian coercion, arguably more so, depending of course on national context. Scholars of human enhancement,

---

4 Nicholas Agar, *Humanity's End: Why We Should Reject Radical Enhancement* (Cambridge, MA: MIT Press, 2010).
5 See http://www.nickbostrom.com (accessed 11/11/2011).
6 'Humanity+ is an international nonprofit membership organization which advocates the ethical use of technology to expand human capacities. We support the development of and access to new technologies that enable everyone to enjoy better minds, better bodies and better lives. In other words, we want people to be better than well.' http://humanityplus.org/about/ (accessed 1/11/2011).
7 David Lowenthal, *The Past is a Foreign Country* (Cambridge: Cambridge University Press, 1985).
8 Nick Bostrom, 'A Short History of Transhumanist Thought', *Analysis and Metaphysics*, 5 (2006), 63–9; Nick Bostrom, 'A History of Transhumanism', *Journal of Evolution and Technology*, 14:1 (2005), 1–25.
9 Nick Bostrom, 'In Defense of Posthuman Dignity', *Bioethics*, 19:3 (2005), 202–214 (p. 206).
10 Nick Bostrom and Rebecca Roache, 'Ethical Issues in Human Enhancement,' in *New Waves in Applied Ethics*, ed. by Jesper Ryberg, Thomas S. Petersen and Clark Wolf (Basingstoke: Palgrave, 2007), pp. 120–152.

transhumanism, and posthumanism make the common error of imagining that eugenics only operated through the radical right. They might look again at the history of eugenics, however, where they will find as much talk of "freedom" as they will of 'coercion'. Therein lies the real link.[11] As Diane Paul has pointed out, transhumanists have far less in common with the radical right than with the utopian visions of socialist scientists like J. B. S. Haldane.[12] And, I might add (and perhaps even more to the point), liberal Julian Huxley. My intention here, though, is not to offer an exposé of the eugenics lurking within transhumanism – such exposés are tiresome and historically are often both crude and lazy. Rather, I explore the transhumanism of a mid-twentieth-century biologist and eugenicist who sits squarely in the middle of the long intellectual history from Nietzsche to Bostrom (via Agar): Julian Huxley.

Vital Destinies

When it comes to the Huxleys, authors on transhumanism are far more likely to mention Aldous and *Brave New World,* than his brother Julian.[13] Yet Julian was by far the closer antecedent. He came up with the word:

> The human species can, if it wishes, transcend itself—not just sporadically, an individual here in one way, an individual there in another way, but in its entirety, as humanity. We need a name for this new belief. Perhaps *transhumanism* will serve: man remaining man, but transcending himself, by realizing new possibilities of and for his human nature.[14]

Notwithstanding this critical intervention, Julian Huxley is strangely absent from transhumanist scholarship. He is nowhere, for example, in John Harris's *Enhancing Evolution: The Ethical Case for Making Better People.* An index entry

---

11 Freedom as comprehended and analysed by Nikolas Rose, *Powers of Freedom: Reframing Political Thought* (Cambridge: Cambridge University Press, 1999).
12 Diane B. Paul, 'On Drawing Lessons from the History of Eugenics', in *Reprogenetics: Law, Policy, and Ethical Issues,* ed. by Lori P. Knowles and Gregory E. Kaebnick (Baltimore, MD: Johns Hopkins University Press, 2007), pp. 3–19.
13 For example, Andy Miah, ' A Critical History of Posthumanism', in *Medical Enhancements and Posthumanity*, ed. by Bert Gordijn and Ruth Chadwick (New York: Routledge, 2007), pp. 71–94.
14 Julian Huxley, 'Transhumanism', in *New Bottles for New Wine,* ed. by Julian Huxley (London: Chatto & Windus, 1957), pp. 13–17. Bostrom repeats an incorrect citation to Huxley's 1927 volume of essays *Religion without Revelation* (London: Benn, 1927). While there were certainly some ideas approaching transhumanism in those essays, this quote was not part of that book. Huxley wrote, for example, '[Man] is always not only surmounting what it thought were the limitations of its nature, but, in individual and social development alike, transcending its own nature and emerging in newness of achievement'. (p. 356)

appears for Humpty Dumpty but not Huxley, even though it was the latter not the former who wrote *Evolution: The Modern Synthesis*.[15] Nicholas Agar is one of the few philosophers of human enhancement seriously to recognize the biologist's significance.[16]

Julian Huxley was grandson of Thomas Henry the great defender of Darwin, son of Leonard the publisher, and brother of Aldous the essayist and novelist. This was a family that lived and breathed ideas about humans and nature, science and the future, evolution and social progress. Indeed his entire generational, familial, and scholarly milieu thought and wrote about future humans, not least his co-author H.G. Wells and his colleague the geneticist J.B.S. Haldane. This was a left and progressive political milieu, in Wells' case socialist, in Haldane's case communist, in Huxley's case broadly liberal and latterly strongly anti-communist. Born 1887, died 1975, Huxley's was a twentieth-century life. He was educated at the beginning of the century in zoology at Oxford; taught at Rice University, Texas, just before the First World War; returned to the UK, first as Oxford ornithologist and then at Kings College, London as professor of zoology. Intellectually, he was born into a generation of biologists who were connecting Mendelian genetics to the theory of evolution by natural selection. And he entered a generation of early ecologists, especially at Oxford, who were attempting to bring the new methods and insights of ecology to the understanding of all life, including humans.[17]

By the late 1920s Huxley had abandoned academic life for a future as science writer and popularizer, what would now be called a science communicator or even science journalist. He worked voraciously for decades as a speaker, in print, in broadcasting, and eventually in television. As one of the few books devoted entirely to Huxley is titled, he was also a 'Statesman of Science'.[18] Before the Second World War he was Secretary of the Zoological Society in London. After the war, he was the first Director-General of UNESCO, and a founding member of the World Wildlife Fund. Throughout he was internationalist, conservationist, Malthusian, and eugenicist. He was also, latterly, anti-racist.[19]

---

15 John Harris, *Enhancing Evolution: The Ethical Case for Making Better People* (Princeton and Oxford: Princeton University Press, 2007). Similarly in the essays in *Human Enhancement*, ed. by Julian Savulescu and Nick Bostrom (Oxford University Press, 2009) it is Aldous Huxley not Julian Huxley who is mentioned in passing in the essay by A.J. Coady, 'Playing God', 151– 176. Huxley is not mentioned in *Future Perfect: God, Medicine and Human Identity*, ed. by Celia Deane-Drummond and Peter Manley Scott (London: Continuum, 2006).
16 Agar, *Humanity's End*, p. 3.
17 See, Peder Anker, *Imperial Ecology: Environmental Order in the British Empire, 1895–1945* (Cambridge, MA: Harvard University Press, 2001).
18 C. Kenneth Waters and Albert Van Helden (ed.), *Julian Huxley: Biologist and Statesman of Science* (Houston: Rice University Press, 1992).
19 For Huxley's wider activities, see Alison Bashford, 'Population, Geopolitics and International

In the 1920s – before he abandoned academic and research life to write the monumental *Science of Life* with H.G. Wells – Huxley's biological interests were already circling around radical futures: the radical enhancement of the flatworm. This was experimental work on life extension, reported playfully as 'Long-Sought Elixir of Life is Found: Oxford Savant Experiments Successful. But Alas! With Flatworms'.[20] He explained that the common-sense view of a life cycle – beginning as cells, rapidly growing and differentiating, followed by growth without differentiation, and finally death – might be rethought. This trajectory was not necessarily irreversible and was not inevitable in all organisms. The rate of growth and the length of the period of growth could be modified, by temperature for example. And in the case of mammals, the normal life of rats had been prolonged experimentally by about 40 per cent. He explained the regeneration work of Charles Manning Child, challenging the idea that all somatic cells must die. This was also part of Alexis Carrel's work on tissue culture and Huxley was intrigued by the prospects of prolonging the life of any given organism, by grafting for example. 'We can save any particular part of an old plant from death by taking it for a cutting'. And likewise he reported, in a typescript importantly titled 'Man's Place in the Universe': 'it has been found possible to continue growing the cells of a single original piece of tissue not merely for weeks or months, but for over 7 years'. The cells of the tissue showed no sign of ageing: 'it would seem that tissues cultivated thus outside the body are probably immortal'.[21] But what interested him especially about the flatworm experiments was that they seemed not so much suspended in time, but under certain conditions to look younger rather than older. In concert with numbers of others in the high modern interwar years, it all made Huxley think about the relation between age and time. Age was not a matter of the passage of external time, that is, it was not determined by the lapse of years, but was, more truly, a matter of physiology, which could be independent of external time.

All very well for flatworms, but humans are tricky organisms, Huxley warned. 'We are so constructed that we cannot live upon our own tissues, nor can our temperature be altered'. Humans are delicately balanced, he explained, so the aim must be 'to preserve and to extend this state of balance that we call healthy

---

Organizations in the Mid Twentieth Century', *Journal of World History*, 19 (2008), 327–47; Glenda Sluga, 'Unesco and the (One) World of Julian Huxley', *Journal of World History*, 21:3 (2010), 393–418; and, Paul Weindling, 'Julian Huxley and the Continuity of Eugenics in Twentieth-century Britain', *Journal of Modern European History*, 10:4 (2012), 480–497.

20 Rice University, Texas, Woodson Research Center, Fondren Library, Julian S. Huxley Papers, Box 6, Folder 4, Newsclipping, 1921. Hereafter 'Huxley Papers.'

21 Huxley Papers, Box 63, Folder 7, Julian Huxley, 'Man's Place in the Universe' (1933), typescript.

maturity'.²² Viennese endocrinologist Eugen Steinach was thinking about precisely this in the 1920s; Huxley was thoroughly intrigued and watched his work closely. The so-called rejuvenation work on humans – mainly men – potentially suspended or reversed ageing, independently of time.²³ Various procedures of ligation and grafting made the time of onset of old age appear to not be inevitable at all. 'Are we ever to know enough,' he pondered, 'to be the control of our own vital destinies...for greater growth, for greater vitality, for long life'.²⁴ Vital destinies absorbed Huxley. Like the medical doctors involved in rejuvenation, and entirely like proponents of human enhancement now, Huxley aimed for augmented individual capacity.

At the very end of his own sometimes troubled life, Huxley was engaged in a not dissimilar project. The New York-based Huxley Institute for Biosocial Research was also about ageing, preservation, and extending a state of balance. Established in 1971, the Huxley Institute brochure paraded the family name and line proudly – Thomas Henry, Julian, Aldous – and sought to assist what was called "orthomolecular medicine". Linus Pauling's research, the Huxley Institute claimed, 'can lead to the alleviation of widespread suffering and result in the general enhancement of human life'. Its aim was to 'guarantee the right to optimum health' of every individual, in particular an enhancement of life and health of those suffering from 'schizophrenia, alcoholism, learning disabilities, drug addiction, memory loss, and other diseases of the ageing'.²⁵ This was to bolster the work of Nobel Prize winning molecular geneticist Pauling who himself wrote the book *How to Live Longer and Feel Better*.²⁶

In thinking about future humans, then, Julian Huxley was engaged in changing medical therapeutics at both ends of his life. Some of the projects he was interested in and supported had medical ambitions to increase longevity, and these would simply fall into the domain of standard public health.²⁷ Others – rejuvenation, for instance – were stranger and altogether more ambitious. These were the projects in which current transhumanists might not want to recognize themselves, but should, involving techniques and possibly outcomes that we would now call radical enhancement: rejuvenation, for example. Transhumanism before the fact, this was certainly perceived at the time as radical

---

22 Huxley, 'Man's Place in the Universe'.
23 For a clear rendition of Steinach's procedures, in English, see Norman Haire, *Rejuvenation: the work of Steinach, Voronoff, and others* (London: G. Allen & Unwin, 1924).
24 Huxley, 'Man's Place in the Universe', handwritten note on p. 56.
25 Huxley Papers, Box 113, Folder 1, Pamphlet, The Huxley Institute for Biosocial Research.
26 Linus Pauling, *How to Live Longer and Feel Better* (New York: Avon Books, 1986).
27 For therapy, enhancement, and transhumanism see Ted Peters, 'Perfect Humans or Trans-Humans?' in *Future Perfect*, ed. by Deane-Drummond and Scott, pp. 15–32.

enhancement of individual life, but in ways that raised much larger questions about future humans and future humanism.

Future Human(ist) Populations

As a biologist, Huxley was interested in individual organisms and species. As an ecologist he was interested in populations of organisms in relation to their environment, other species, and their interactions over place and time. He thought through all this in terms of evolution, in terms of Mendelian genetics, and as the neo-Darwinian synthesis in which he was so closely involved.[28] There was always a social and political dimension too, for Huxley. Politically and scientifically, individual humans – even what they might be in the future – were in the end less intriguing, even less important to Huxley, than the social and collective organization of human populations.

When Huxley came to engage with human improvement fully from the 1930s, through the Second World War and into the post-war period, individual enhancement was to some extent irrelevant. He began to think much more in population terms, influenced not least by the population geneticists around him – J.B.S. Haldane and R.A. Fisher in particular. This deeply shaped his eugenics, as well as his anti-racist work in *We, Europeans,* for example. For his eugenics – his plans for human improvement – the mean level of intelligence of any given population needed to be raised. This was the central idea of the 1939 'Geneticists Manifesto' published in *Nature*, of which Huxley was a signatory:

> the raising of the level of the average of the population, nearly to that of the highest now existing in isolated individuals, in regard to physical well-being, intelligence and temperamental qualities, is an achievement that would – so far as purely genetic considerations are concerned – be physically possible within a comparatively small number of generations.[29]

And importantly in terms of tracing the genealogy of transhumanism, the manifesto continued: 'Thus everyone might look upon "genius"...as his birthright'.[30] What doesn't resonate so strongly with current transhumanism, though, is that Huxley's first measure in pursuit of such a goal involved social policy of a very particular mid twentieth-century British welfare kind. Population-level improvement would be achieved in the first instance socially not technologically,

---

28 Julian Huxley, *Evolution: the Modern Synthesis* (New York and London: Harper & Bros., 1942).
29 Julian Huxley, 'Social Biology and Population Improvement', *Nature*, 144:3646 (16 September 1939), 521–522.
30 Huxley, 'Social Biology'.

part of his broadly left politics. Once opportunity for health and education was levelled and levelled up, implementing further improvement or effective eugenic policies would be easier and more effective.[31]

At core, though, it was not particular human populations but the entire human species that were at issue for Huxley. His humanism and even his transhumanism once he started using that term, was always based on what he called evolutionary humanism. 'It related every kind of human activity to the yardstick of desirable evolutionary direction'.[32] Deeply shaped by developments in ecology, Huxley was trained to think in terms of inter-relationships and systems (far more than the current transhumanist focus on the individual). But the system he saw was an apparently open one in which *development* would be species *improvement*. Why? Because humans themselves now directed that evolutionary outcome, that evolutionary improvement.

On the one hand, humans – Man – were part of cosmic nature: 'not only is he made of the same matter and operated by the same energy as all the rest of the cosmos but for all his distinctiveness, he is linked by genetic continuity with all the other living inhabitants of his planet.' Everything was evolution, and evolution was everything. 'Life is in one sense a collective term for all organisms, from bacteria to man.'[33] But on the other hand, he thought the human species was an organism apart, different in kind because of cognition and self-reflection, because of language and culture, all outcomes of the evolutionary process itself. Most importantly, humans had insight into the very process of evolution itself.

Such a view put humans generically into a singular category, compared to all other organic life. But it also reserved an extra-insightful place for those humans who happened to be evolutionary biologists (that is to say Huxley himself). Huxley thought this of his historical moment too. He happened to be living in the third key moment of evolutionary time. The first moment 'at which the process transcended itself' was passage from the inorganic to the biological. The second was passage from the biological to what he called the psychosocial. Now (his present) was the third stage, 'from the psychosocial to the consciously purposive phase of evolution'. And further, this means that 'Man's destiny is to be the sole agent for the future evolution of this planet'.[34] While animal studies theorists now would want to attribute sentience to many organisms, Huxley did not. Sentience was what made humans unique on planet Earth, and if there was other

---

31 D. Hubback, 'Julian Huxley and Eugenics', in *Evolutionary Studies: a Centenary Celebration of the Life of Julian Huxley*, ed. by Milo Keynes and G. Ainsworth Harrison (London: Macmillan, 1989), pp. 194–206 (p. 200).
32 Julian Huxley (ed.), *The Humanist Frame* (London: Allen & Unwin, 1961), preface, p. 6.
33 Huxley Papers, Box 75, Folder 2, Notes on Evolution, 1958–9.
34 Huxley (ed.), *The Humanist Frame*, p. 17.

sentience it was on other planets.[35] Thinking about future humans for him, was, at one level, simply thinking in evolutionary terms, but humans were set apart as the only organisms able to imagine, envisage, and consciously direct the future. The human capacity to imagine the future shifted the total earth environment from 'biosphere' to 'noosphere' he pronounced, borrowing concepts from Russian cosmic Vladimir Vernadsky through French philosopher and Jesuit Pierre Teilhard de Chardin, who was himself busy rethinking Genesis.[36]

The evolved capacity to imagine and direct the future should render evolution the new religion, Huxley claimed, an extension of his claims that eugenics might be the religion of the future.[37] Evolutionary humanism, indeed, was to be "the new world faith". If the editors of this volume write that the most central story in history is that of human perfectibility,[38] Huxley would say that the most central metanarrative in history is evolution. With not a little hubris, Huxley took on much of the responsibility personally for this newly evolved capacity of humans to imagine and shape evolution. Notwithstanding his depressive illness, the whole idea of thinking about possibilities for the future suited him temperamentally and intellectually. Huxley's personal papers show endless folders, notebooks, scraps of papers, and lists on 'possibilities': 'possibilities of Sex'; 'possibilities of biosociety'; 'possibilities of Psycho societies'; 'possibilities of filter feeding'; 'biochemical possibilities'; 'ecological possibilities'. The 'Need for A Science of Human Possibilities' was his special plea and the related idea of university Chairs of the Future was something he was enormously taken by.[39] Huxley would likely be delighted that his own Oxford University now boasts a Future of Humanity Institute. Indeed, we might see Huxley as an antecedent to its Director, Nick Bostrom. Just what were humans and what might they be, Huxley questioned. He even ended up asking, 'What are People For?'[40] In so many ways, Director and Founder Nick Bostrom and Julian Huxley speak as one. Writes the former: 'Not only is this a natural extension of the traditional aims of medicine

---

35 Huxley (ed.), *The Humanist Frame*, p. 18.
36 Julian Huxley, The Future of Man, Evolutionary Aspects, Typescript Lecture, 1963, Box 109, Folder 9. It is significant that it was Huxley who wrote the foreword to Tielhard de Chardin's *The Phenomenon of Man* (New York: Harper, 1959).
37 Julian S. Huxley, 'Eugenics and Society', *The Eugenics Review*, 28:1 (1936), 11.
38 Crafting Humans Conference, Oxford. See http://www.theberendelfoundation.com/node/100 (accessed 7/09/2011).
39 Huxley Papers, Box 75 Folder 2, Evolution, Introduction 1958–59;. Box 63, Folder 7, untitled typescript.
40 Huxley Papers, Box 75, Folder 9, Julian Huxley, Notes and corrected typescript, Lasker Award Address 1959.

and technology, but it is also a great humanitarian opportunity to genuinely improve the human condition'.[41]

The Future of Humanity: Transhumanism Now

If the connections between Bostrom and Huxley are evident and interesting enough, how is current transhumanism (of course quite diverse) different from Julian Huxley's transhumanism? The place of the individual is one key point of difference. Transhumanism in the twenty-first century is so monumentally worried about eugenics that it is intent on distancing itself through liberal individualism, at every turn. It constantly stresses the choice of the free individual to pursue radical enhancement. The Transhumanist Declaration (1998) pronounces:

> We favour allowing individuals wide personal choice over how they enable their lives. This includes use of techniques that may be developed to assist memory, concentration, and mental energy; life extension therapies; reproductive choice technologies; cryonics procedures; and many other possible human modification and enhancement technologies.[42]

The virtue of free individual choice accords with neo-liberalism, but it also serves to distinguish transhumanism from the over-determined history of forced state implementation of population and eugenics policies over the twentieth century.

In pursuing this individualism, transhumanists now espouse a principle of equality of all humans. For some philosophers of human enhancement this is the bedrock of transhumanism. Its non-negotiable. John Harris in 2007, for example, rightly insisted: 'All persons are equal and none are less equal than others. No enhancement however dramatic, no disability however slight, or however severe, implies lesser (or greater) moral, political, or ethical status, worth, or value'.[43] Strangely, though, the individual so important to current transhumanism would be decidedly difficult for Huxley. This was not just because he privileged populations and species, but also because when he *did* think about individuals, he did not actually believe in their equal worth. Like Jan Smuts who invented the term *holism* in an evolutionary context, the parts that made up the privileged whole would and should be different (variation was important) but

---

41 Nick Bostrom, 'Transhumanism: the World's Most Dangerous Idea', http://www.nickbostrom.com/papers/dangerous.html (accessed 7/09/2011).
42 http://humanityplus.org/learn/transhumanist-declaration/ (accessed 11/11/2011).
43 Harris, *Enhancing Evolution*, p. 86.

they would not necessarily be equal.[44] Julian Huxley was quite clear: 'Human beings are not born equal in gifts or potentialities, and human progress stems largely from the very fact of their inequality.' Indeed, he said quite unashamedly, '"Free but unequal" should be our motto', in a book titled *The Humanist Frame*, no less.[45] However, for Huxley, unlike for Smuts, this inequality had nothing to do with racial inequalities, necessarily. He was quite explicit about this too. It concerned the range of ability across any given population, where for him intellectual ability and disability was the most important factor.

Another difference between Huxley's transhumanism and the current field relates to the imagining of the future at a planetary level. For Huxley, planetary-scale thinking was easy: 'a new vision of human destiny ... from the planetary web of world ecology to the individual lives entangled in it, from the dim roots of man's past to the dawning possibilities of his far future'.[46] What a wonderful writer he was. But it all came seamlessly to him because this kind of planetary scale and integrative sensibility was already, in the 1950s, a standard part of the Malthusian repertoire, of which he was a recipient. This is what I call elsewhere the cosmopolitics of population that came out of Malthusian work on earthly limits. In Huxley's register we find something rather more akin to deep ecology than its opposite, transhumanism. Who would have thought they shared an intellectual ancestor?[47]

Given that Huxley talked planetary catastrophe fairly readily, and given that the rest of the twenty-first century planet seems to be talking both globalization and catastrophic climate change, this raises the question of how, precisely, transhumanists now address global issues. The Future of Humanity Institute does, after all, have the brief to address 'big picture questions for humanity'.[48] Recently Nick Bostrom and Milan Cirkovic co-edited *Global Catastrophic Risks*.[49] As formulated in 2008, global catastrophic risks are, or were: astrophysical processes; supervolcanism and geological forces; climate change; plagues and pandemics; nuclear war; and totalitarian threat. It is instructive to line this up with Huxley's catastrophes. 'What future do we contemplate for the human race?' he asked after the apocalypse of the Second World War. In *The*

---

44 For Smuts, see Anker, *Imperial Ecology*. For Huxley on variation, see Diane Paul, 'The Value of Diversity in Huxley's Eugenics', in *Julian Huxley*, ed. by Waters and Van Helden, pp. 223–229.
45 Huxley (ed.), *The Humanist Frame*, p. 23.
46 Huxley (ed.), *The Humanist Frame*, p. 15.
47 For planetary scale of population thought in this period, see Alison Bashford 'Life on Earth: Geopolitics and the World Population Problem' book manuscript in preparation.
48 The Future of Humanity Institute. http://www.fhi.ox.ac.uk/ (accessed 7/09/2011).
49 Nick Bostrom and Milan Cirkovic (ed.), *Global Catastrophic Risks* (Oxford: Oxford University Press, 2008).

Humanist Frame he listed the challenges ahead that would be catastrophic if not addressed. In his words:

> the threat of over-population; the threat of super-scientific war, nuclear, chemical, and biological; the rise and appeal of Communism especially in the under privileged sectors of the world's people; the over-exploitation of natural resources; the erosion of the world's cultural variety; the widening gap between the haves and the have-nots between the rich and poor nations.[50]

Any one of either Huxley's list or Bostrom and Cirkovic's list deserves serious thought. But what interests me most is this: the most pressing item for Huxley is totally absent for current transhumanists (as least as represented here): 'the threat of over-population'. This is not to argue or even necessarily suggest that population growth should be itemized as globally catastrophic. It is, rather, to wonder why transhumanist Huxley's number one issue has fallen off (or more likely has been actively removed from) the current transhumanist agenda at a global level. Most likely, population growth, population control, and eugenics are too closely linked for political comfort.

Huxley was a Malthusian and an active member of early Neo-Malthusian organisations, alongside and as part of his eugenics. This was also where his conservation work sprang from, as well as his cosmopolitan politics and his internationalism.[51] One of his many folders, on the 'Pursuit of Possibilities', shows a small, scribbled qualifier: 'always limitations too'. Although he talked about an open system, possibilities for Huxley did not mean growth. Neither an acceleration in population growth nor acceleration in growth of the consumption of goods and resources was desirable, or ultimately possible, he would say.

Indeed, Huxley's vision of future human improvement positively required a slowing of this growth. For him, thinking at population level again, the acceleration of growth meant an increased threat of war: for this generation population density was almost always comprehended as a cause of war, because it was about land, and this was why population growth on a global scale was considered catastrophic even apocalyptic. But the question was also about 'quality', for Huxley. Slowing population growth he considered a precondition for the levelling-up of population quality. 'The population-explosion…cannot continue much longer….man's destiny is to make possible greater fulfilment for more human beings and fuller achievement by human societies'.[52] Huxley would slip easily from a eugenic use of the idea of quality into what he termed the low 'quality of life', an economic use that referred at one level to standard of living.

---

50 Huxley (ed.), *The Humanist Frame*, p. 21.
51 This is all explained in Bashford, 'Life on Earth'.
52 Huxley (ed.), *The Humanist Frame*, p. 25.

'What future do we contemplate for the human race?', he would often ask. 'Do we just have to put up with more people?'[53] In a speech called 'The Impending Crisis', he described current world culture as 'one in which quantity is threatening quality and also, if you like, one in which the present is threatening the future'.[54] Explosive population increase he said again and again 'prompts us to ask the simple but basic question *what are people for?*'[55] Eugenics returns at this point, where both purpose and worth were being questioned. This was not far, conceptually, from *Lebensunwertes Leben*, 'lives unworthy of life'. But where Nazi policy-makers argued this of already-born humans, neo-Malthusians like Huxley argued it of the not-yet-conceived. The difference, needless to say, is critical.

This was a standard argument for birth control, one that only made sense in the context of high infant mortality rates; those born only to die in infancy or to live with a disability were better not to have been conceived in the first place.[56] It is important to remember that for Huxley's generation, life-span enhancement at a population level was still simply about lowering infant mortality rates: longevity for a population could massively change, demographically, if infant mortality was reduced. Unlike transhumanists now, he would see the benefit accruing to 6 month olds, not 100 year-olds. Low infant mortality is often just presumed or taken for granted by twenty-first century transhumanists (or else is just too mundane), but for Huxley and his generation, achieving this was itself part of the vision for radical human improvement. Huxley's demographic radar was always up, and he would never talk life-extension (controlling death) without also talking reproductive and fertility regulation (controlling birth). Death planning, life planning, and birth planning were necessarily connected enterprises for future humans.

Huxley would align quite easily with the transhumanist tendency to think from the present forwards, rather than to wonder how the present came about, in historical time. For example, one current transhumanist scholar writes with no reference whatsoever to the past, or even to Julian Huxley who said precisely the same thing (and with similar self-enhancing awe):

> This possibility of a new phase of evolution, [is one] in which Darwinian evolution by natural selection, will be replaced by a deliberately chosen process of selection ... This

---

53 Huxley Papers, Box 63, Folder 7. Untitled Typescript.
54 Huxley Papers, Box 75, Folder 5, Julian Huxley, 'The Impending Crisis', Speech Typescript.
55 Huxley (ed.), *The Humanist Frame*, p. 24. This is a phrase and an idea that circulated between Huxley and another zoologist and Eugenics Society General Secretary, Colin Bertram. See G.C.L. Bertram, 'What are People For?' in *The Humanist Frame*, ed. by Huxley, pp. 373–384.
56 See for example Huxley Papers, Box 63, Folder 7, untitled Typescript, Notes and manuscripts, 'Adventures of the Mind, 1958–59'.

new process of evolutionary change will replace *natural selection*, with *deliberate selection, Darwinian evolution with enhancement evolution*.[57]

It is, I suppose, the apparent novelty of this idea that justifies its italicized textual specialness. But of course – and without wanting to diminish the importance of the idea – it is hardly novel to our generation at all. It is eugenics, as the likes of Huxley saw human improvement.

Conclusions and Speculations

The transhumanist self-story involves eugenics disappearing, but really it *wills* eugenics to have disappeared.[58] This does a lot of work for transhumanism's comprehension of its own past. It serves to distinguish current transhumanism from inevitable critique about problematic past practices, and so it can move on to the future untainted. Transhumanism, or Nicholas Agar's more honestly nominated, 'liberal eugenics', is thus redeemed. And yet, through Julian Huxley (at the very least) present-day transhumanism and eugenics are obviously linked. Huxley was a life-long advocate of eugenics, even in the light of the Holocaust, and even though he had authored anti-racist texts like *We, Europeans* and was involved in the UNESCO Statement(s) on Race. He simply didn't perceive eugenics to be necessarily about race at all, nor necessarily about the kind of coercive politics that transhumanist scholars imagine eugenics to have typically or even solely been. Here lies, perhaps, the real usefulness of Huxley for the project of historicizing transhumanism. Huxley's ideas and politics suggest that it's not totalitarian eugenics that needs thinking through; rather, it is the history of eugenics as itself a mode of liberal governmentality. For the likes of Huxley, coercion was the very last mode of governance to be deployed in the pursuit of human perfection and improvement. This is not in the least to suggest that coerced eugenic measures were not also in operation. Nor is it to suggest that the 'freedom' of liberalism is not also problematic. It is rather, to understand that authoritarian, totalitarian, and forced measures were the very opposite of what many eugenics advocates sought in their dreams of future human improvement.[59] Voluntary self-governance, not authoritarian coercion, marked the real

---

57 Harris, *Enhancing Evolution*, pp. 3–4.
58 Bostrom, 'A History of Transhumanist Thought'.
59 See for example, A. M. Carr-Saunders, 'Eugenics in the Light of Population Trends' *Eugenics Review*, 60:1 (1968), 46–56 (p.55). This was originally published, *Eugenics Review*, 27:1 (1935), 11–20. For the significant of voluntary measures, see John Macnicol, 'Eugenics and the Campaign for Voluntary Sterilization in Britain Between the Wars' *Social History of Medicine*, 2:2 (1989), 147–169 (pp.161–62).

biopolitics of eugenics.[60] The irony in the tendency of transhumanists to eschew eugenics (even if it is understandable) is that lifelong eugenics advocate Julian Huxley himself would have been the first to agree with Bostrom's bid for freedoms. Indeed historically he was partly responsible for discrediting the kind of coercion that current transhumanists also have problems with. But in Huxley's own terms and by his own account, this made him rather more than less of a eugenicist. Julian Huxley, then, is the direct link between eugenics and contemporary transhumanism, in ways far more complex and interesting than simply his coining of the term.

Transhumanists are often charged with a kind of hubris with respect to their ambitions for the future. However, that might better be understood with respect to their sense of having arrived in the present *de novo*, either without a history, or at best with a history that is self-serving. Were Huxley alive, and still at Oxford, he would not be talking to zoologists let alone historians. He would be working the corridors of The Future of Humanity Institute and the James Martin Institute for Science and Civilization, talking about tomorrow's technologies, tomorrow's people, and tomorrow's planet, the Institute's own agenda.[61] How he would or would not fit in the twenty-first century conversation is a measure of change over the last 50 years. And it is also a measure of transhumanism's current location in time, in a very specific historically-produced present, not a future at all.

---

60 Far more so, I suggest, than the 'biopolitics' of states. This is the kind of 'freedom' that reforming eugenicists like Frederick Osborn, Carlos Paton Blacker, and Julian Huxley envisaged. See Alison Bashford, *Imperial Hygiene: A Critical History of Colonialism, Nationalism, and Public Health* (Basingstoke: Palgrave, 2004), pp. 172–80 (p. 189); and Nikolas Rose, *The Politics of Life Itself: Biomedicine, Power, and Subjectivity in the Twenty-First Century* (Princeton and Oxford: Princeton University Press, 2007), pp. 54–64.
61 Steve Rayner, 'Foreword', in *Enhancing Evolution*, ed. by Harris, p. x.

List of Contributors

Frank Ankersmit

Frank Ankersmit has held different positions at the History Department of Groningen University, becoming a professor for intellectual history and historical theory at that same University in 1992. His main areas of interest lie with aesthetics, philosophy of history, and political philosophy. He is a member of the Royal Netherlands Academy of the Sciences (KNAW) since 1986, and the Founder and Chief Editor of the *Journal of the Philosophy of History* (since 2007). Ankersmit is a member of the editorial board of a number of journals including *History and Theory* and *Rethinking History*. Ankersmit is also a member of the Berendel Foundation's Advisory Board.

Alison Bashford

Alison Bashford is Professor of Modern History at the University of Sydney. She is the author and editor of numerous books in the history of modern science and medicine, most recently *The Oxford Handbook of the History of Eugenics* (2010, co-edited with Philippa Levine). She is currently completing "Geopolitics and the World Population Problem: Life on Earth in the Global Twentieth Century", a study of the linked biopolitics and geopolitics of population after the First World War. In addition, she is also editing the two volume Cambridge History of Australia.

Merryn Ekberg

Merryn Ekberg is a Senior Lecturer in the School of Health at the University of Northampton. Her teaching areas include medical sociology, public health, health policy, and bioethics. Building on previous research, her current interests explore the ethical, legal and social implications of genetics, embryonic stem cell research, reproductive cloning, genetic enhancement technologies, and assisted reproductive technologies. Her research in bioethics also includes an exploration of the governance of biomedical research and an investigation into the role of research ethics committees.

Roger Griffin

Roger Griffin is Professor in Modern History at Oxford Brookes University. His main publications include *The Nature of Fascism* (Pinter, 1991), and *Modernism and Fascism: The Sense of a Beginning under Mussolini and Hitler* (Palgrave, 2007). He has also edited anthologies of primary and secondary sources relating to fascism, inlcuding: *Fascism* (OUP, 1995), and *International Fascism: Theories, Causes and the New Consensus* (Arnold, 1998). His last book is *Terrorist's Creed: Fanatical Violence and the Human Need for Meaning* (Palgrave, 2012).

Moshe Idel

Moshe Idel is Max Cooper Professor in Jewish Thought, Department of Jewish Thought at Hebrew University, Jerusalem, and Senior Researcher at the Shalom Hartman Institute. Idel has served as visiting Professor at UCLA, Yale, Harvard, Princeton, University of Pennsylvania, and the College de France. Among his publications are *Kabbalah: New Perspectives* (Yale University Press, 1988); *Absorbing Perfections: Kabbalah and Interpretation* (Yale University Press, 2002); and *Old Worlds, New Mirror, On Jewish Mysticism and Twentieth-Century Thought* (Penn University Press, 2010).

Antonis Liakos

Antonis Liakos is Professor of Contemporary History and History of Historiography at the University of Athens. He is also chair of the Board of the International Commission for History and Theory of Historiography (2010–2015) and managing editor of *Historein*. He is the author of *L'Unificazione italiana e la Grande Idea (1859–1871)* (1995) and *Pos stochastikan to ethnos autoi pou ithelan na allaxoun ton kosmo* [*The Nation: How has it been imagined by those who wanted to change the world?*] (2006) [also published in Turkish: *Dünyayi Değiştirmek İsteyenler, Ulusu Nasıl Tasavvur Ettiler?* (2008)].

List of Contributors

Maria Sophia Quine

Maria Sophia Quine held a senior lectureship in modern European history at Queen Mary, University of London before illness forced a lengthy withdrawal from the historical profession and a cessation to the research and writing. She currently holds a research fellowship in modern history at the University of East Anglia and a visiting fellowship in the history of science at the Institute of Germanic and Romance Studies, University of London. Her major publications are in the history of population politics and the Italian fascist welfare state. She is currently bringing a number of projects in the history of Malthusianism, Darwinism, eugenics and fascism to completion. Her most recent article on 'Racial "Sterility" and "Hyperfecundity" in Fascist Italy: The Biological Politics of Sex and Reproduction' was published in *Fascism: The Journal of Comparative Fascist Studies* (2012).

Marius Turda

Marius Turda is Reader in Central and Eastern European Biomedicine, Oxford Brookes University, and director of the Cantemir Institute, at the University of Oxford. His current areas of research are mainly history of ideas and medicine, with a particular focus on eugenics, biopolitics, and race. Recent publications include *Modernism and Eugenics* (Palgrave, 2010), *Health, Hygiene and Eugenics in Southeastern Europe to 1945* (CEU Press, 2011), and *Re-Contextualising East Central European History: Nation, Culture and Minority Groups* (Legenda, 2010). At the moment he is completing a history of Hungarian eugenics to be published by Palgrave and a monograph on race and modernity to be published by Continuum.

Bibliography

Archival Materials

Julian S. Huxley Papers at Rice University, Texas, Woodson Research Center, Fondren Library.
'The Beveridge Plan' (11 February 1943), The National Archives, War Cabinet, W.P. (43).
Museo Nazionale di Antropologia e Etnologia, Università di Firenze, Fondo Mantegazza: 704, letter from P. M. to G. Omboni, 11 April 1875; 746, letter from Ministro degli Interni to P. M., 4 January 1876; 800, letter from P. M. to G. Omboni, 21 January 1877; 806, letter from Ministero d'agricoltura, industria, e commercio to P. M., 4 March 1877.
Royal College of Surgeons of England (RCSE), Hunterian Museum (HM), MLB, Series 2 (1868–1906), Serial No. 5965, letter from J. Barnard Davis to William Henry Flower, 9 February 1870.
Ms. Paris, Biblioteque Nationale 849, fols. 96b, 121b.
'Otzar Hayyim, Ms. Moscow-Guensburg 775, fol. 163ab.
Ms. Cambridge, Genizah, TS. K 12,4.
Ms. Sassoon 919.

Printed Materials

Mark B. Adams (ed.), *The Wellborn Science: Eugenics in Germany, France, Brazil, and Russia* (New York: Oxford University Press, 1990).
Giorgio Agamben, *L'aperto: L'uomo e l'animale* (Torino: Bollati Boringhieri, 2002).
Giorgio Agamben, *Homo Sacer: Sovereign Power and Bare Life* (Palo Alto, CA: Stanford University Press, 1998).
Nicholas Agar, *Humanity's End: Why We Should Reject Radical Enhancement* (Cambridge, MA: MIT Press, 2010).
Nicholas Agar, *Liberal Eugenics: In Defence of Human Enhancement* (Oxford: Blackwell, 2004).
Ann Taylor Allen, 'Feminism and Eugenics in Germany and Britain, 1900–1940: A Comparative Perspective', *German Studies Review*, 23:3 (2000), 477–505.
Hjalmar Anderson, 'The Swedish State Institute for Race-Biological Investigation: An

Account of its Origination', in *The Swedish Nation in Word and Picture*, ed. by H. Lundborg and J. Runnström (Stockholm: Hasse W. Tullberg, 1921).

Lori Andrews, *Future Perfect: Confronting Decisions About Genetics* (New York: Columbia University Press, 2001).

Peder Anker, *Imperial Ecology: Environmental Order in the British Empire, 1895 – 1945* (Cambridge, MA: Harvard University Press, 2001).

Frank Ankersmit, *Meaning, Truth and Reference in Historical Representation* (Ithaca, N.Y.: Cornell University Press, 2012).

Frank Ankersmit, 'The Necessity of Historicism', *Journal of the Philosophy of History*, 4:2 (2010), 226 – 240.

Lajos Antal, *A biologizmus mint új életszemlélet. A magyar biopolitika* (Budapest: Magyar Egyetemi nymoda, 1940).

E. Ardu Onnis, 'Le anomalie fisiche e la degenerazione nell'Italia "barbara" contemporanea', *Archivio per l'Antropologia e la Etnologia*, 33 (1903), 447 – 532.

C. W. Armstrong, *The Survival of the Unfittest* (London: C. W. Daniel, 1927).

Steven Aschheim, *The Nietzsche Legacy in Germany, 1890 – 1990* (Berkeley: University of California Press, 1992).

Mitchell G. Ash, 'Wissenschaft und Politik als Ressourcen für einander', in *Wissenschaften und Wissenschaftspolitik: Bestandaufnahmen zu Formationen, Brüchen, und Kontinuitäten im Deutschland des 20. Jahrhunderts*, ed. by Rüdiger vom Bruch and Brigitte Kaderas (Stuttgart: Franz Steiner Verlag, 2002), pp. 32 – 51.

Dominique Aubert-Marson, 'L'eugénisme: une idéologie scientifique et politique', *Éthique & Santé*, 8:3 (2011), 140 – 152.

Erich Auerbach, *Mimesis* (Princeton: Princeton University Press, 1953).

Johann Jakob Bachofen, *Das Mutterrecht* (Stuttgart: Krais & Hoffman 1861).

Alfred Baeumler, *Friedrich Ludwig Jahns Stellung in der deutschen Geistesgeschichte* (Leipzig: H. Eichblatt, 1940).

Alberto Baldi, 'Giustiniano Nicolucci: Cenni bibliografici', in *Alle origini dell'antropologia italiana: Giustiniano Nicolucci e il suo tempo*, ed. by Francesco G. Fedele and Alberto Baldi (Naples: Guida Editori, 1988), pp. 25 – 35.

Svetla Baloutzova, *Demography and Nation: Social Legislation and Population Policy in Bulgaria, 1918 – 1944* (Budapest: CEU Press, 2011).

Alberto Mario Banti, *La nazione del Risorgimento: Parentela, santità e onore alle origini dell'Italia unita. 2nd Edition* (Turin: Einaudi, 2002).

G. Banu, 'Critical and Synthetical Examination of the Rural Health Problems', in *Problemele sanitare ale populaţiei rurale din România*, ed. by G. Banu (Bucharest: Tip. F. Göbl, 1940), pp. 1407 – 1409.

Meir Bar-Ilan, *Astrology and other Sciences among the Jews of Israel, in the Roman-Hellenistic and Byzantine Periods* (Jerusalem: Mossad Bialik, 2001) (in Hebrew).

Elazar Barkan, *The Retreat of Scientific Racism: Changing Concepts of Race in Britain and the United States* (Cambridge: Cambridge University Press, 1992).

Frederick Barnard, *Herder on Nationality, Humanity and History* (Montreal and London: McGill-Queen's University Press, 2003).

Deborah Barrett and Charles Kurzman, 'Globalizing Social Movement Theory: The Case of Eugenics', *Theory and Society*, 33:5 (2004), 487 – 527.

James R. Bartholomew and Sumiko Otsubo, 'Eugenics in Japan: Some Ironies of Modernity, 1883–1945', *Science in Context*, 11:3–4 (1998), 545–565.
Alison Bashford, 'Life on Earth: Geopolitics and the World Population Problem' (book manuscript in preparation).
Alison Bashford, 'Where Did Eugenics Go?' in *The Oxford Handbook of the History of Eugenics*, ed. by Alison Bashford and Philippa Levine (Oxford and New York: Oxford University Press, 2010), pp. 539–558.
Alison Bashford and Philippa Levine (ed.), *The Oxford Handbook of the History of Eugenics* (Oxford and New York: Oxford University Press, 2010).
Alison Bashford, 'Population, Geopolitics and International Organizations in the Mid Twentieth Century', *Journal of World History*, 19 (2008), 327–347.
Alison Bashford, *Imperial Hygiene: A Critical History of Colonialism, Nationalism, and Public Health* (Basingstoke: Palgrave, 2004).
Mark Bassin, 'Nurture is Nature: Lev Gumilev and the Ecology of Ethnicity', *Slavic Review*, 68:4 (2009), 872–897.
Zygmunt Bauman, *Modernity and Ambivalence* (Cambridge: Polity, 1991).
Francoise Baylis and Jason Scott Robert, 'The Inevitability of Genetic Enhancement Technologies', *Bioethics*, 18:1 (2004), 1–26.
Ulrich Beck, *Risk Society: Towards a New Modernity* (London: Sage, 1992).
Frederick Beiser, *Hegel* (New York and London: Routledge, 2005).
Meir Benayahu, *Kitvei RaMHa"L be-Kabbalah* (Jerusalem, 1979).
Peter Berger, *The Sacred Canopy: Elements of a Sociological Theory of Religion* (London: Doubleday, 1967).
G.C.L. Bertram, 'What are People For?' in *The Humanist Frame*, ed. by Julian Huxley (London: Allen & Unwin, 1961), pp. 373–384.
Emmanuel Betta, 'La biopolitica cattolica', in *Storia d'Italia. Annali 26. Scienze e cultura dell'Italia unita*, ed. by F. Cassata and C. Pogliano (Torino: Einaudi, 2011), pp. 949–974.
Marnix Beyen and Maarten Van Ginderachter, 'General Introduction: Writing the Mass into a Mass Phenomenon', in *Nationhood from Below: Europe in the Long Nineteenth Century*, ed. by Maarten Van Ginderachter and Marnix Beyen (Basingstoke: Palgrave Macmillan, 2012), pp. 3–22.
Michael M. Biddiss, *The Father of Racist Ideology: The Social and Political Thought of Count on Gobineau* (New York: Weybright and Talley, 1970).
Emily Bilsky (ed.), *Golem! Danger, Deliverance and Art* (New York: Jewish Museum, 1989).
Gisela Bock, *Zwangssterilisation im Nationalsozialismus: Studien zur Rassenpolitik und Frauenpolitik* (Opladen: Westdeutscher Verlag, 1986).
Gisela Bock, 'Racism and Sexism in Nazi Germany: Motherhood, Compulsory Sterilization, and the State', *Signs*, 8:3 (1983), 400–421.
Alexander Bogdanov, *Red Star: The First Bolshevik Utopia* (Indianna University Press, 1984).
Nick Bostrom and Milan Cirkovic (ed.), *Global Catastrophic Risks* (Oxford: Oxford University Press, 2008).
Nick Bostrom and Rebecca Roache, 'Ethical Issues in Human Enhancement' in *New Waves in Applied Ethics*, ed. by Jesper Ryberg, Thomas S. Petersen and Clark Wolf (Basingstoke: Palgrave, 2007), pp. 120–152.

Nick Bostrom, 'A Short History of Transhumanist Thought', *Analysis and Metaphysics*, 5 (2006), 63–69.

Nick Bostrom, 'A History of Transhumanism', *Journal of Evolution and Technology*, 14:1 (2005), 1–25.

Nick Bostrom, 'In Defense of Posthuman Dignity', *Bioethics*, 19:3 (2005), 202–214.

Nick Bostrom, 'Human Genetic Enhancements: A Transhumanist Perspective', *The Journal of Value Inquiry*, 37:4 (2003), 493–506.

Joanna Bourke, *What it Means to be Human, Reflections from 1791 to the Present* (Berkeley, Counterpoint, 2011).

Giuseppe Bottai, 'I miti moderni', *Primato*, (15 Feb., 1942).

Fae Brauer and Anthea Callen (ed.), *Art, Sex and Eugenics* (London: Ashgate, 2008).

Gunnar Broberg and Nils Roll-Hansen (ed.), *Eugenics and the Welfare State: Sterilization Policy in Denmark, Sweden, Norway, and Finland* (East Lansing, MI: Michigan State University, 2005 [1997]).

Franz-Josef Brüggemeier, Mark Cioc and Thomas Zeller (ed.), *How Green Were the Nazis?: Nature, Environment, and Nation in the Third Reich* (Athens, OH: Ohio University Press, 2005).

Allen Buchanan, 'Institutions, Beliefs and Ethics: Eugenics as a Case Study', *The Journal of Political Philosophy*, 15:1 (2007), 22–45.

Allen Buchanan, et al., *From Chance to Choice: Genetics and Justice* (Cambridge: Cambridge University Press, 2000).

Maria Bucur, *Eugenics and Modernization in Interwar Romania* (Pittsburgh: Pittsburgh University Press, 2002).

Carolyn Burdett, 'From *The New Werther* to Number and Arguments: Karl Pearson's Eugenics', in *Transactions and Encounters: Science and Culture in the Nineteenth Century*, ed. by Roger Luckhurst and Josephine McDonagh (Manchester: Manchester University Press, 2002), pp. 204–233

Alberto Burgio (ed.), *Nel nome della razza: Il razzismo nella storia d'Italia, 1870–1945* (Bologna: CLUEB, 1999).

Alberto Burgio and Luciano Casali (ed.), *Studi sul razzismo italiano* (Bologna: CLUEB 1996).

Michael Burleigh, *Death and Deliverance: Euthanasia in Germany, 1900–1945* (Cambridge: Cambridge University Press, 1994).

Michael Burleigh and Wolfgang Wippermann, *The Racial State in Germany: 1933–1945* (Cambridge: Cambridge University Press, 1991).

V. A. S. Careless, *The Ethnological Society of London, 1843–1871* (M. A. Thesis, University of British Columbia, 1974).

A. M. Carr-Saunders, 'Eugenics in the Light of Population Trends', *Eugenics Review*, 60:1 (1968), 46–56.

Francesco Cassata, *Building the New Man. Eugenics, Racial Science and Genetics in Twentieth-Century Italy* (Budapest: Central European University Press, 2011).

Luigi Luca Cavalli-Sforza, *Genes, Peoples, and Languages* (New York: North Point Press, 2000).

Geoffrey Campbell Cocks, *The State of Health: Illness in Nazi Germany* (Oxford: Oxford University Press, 2012).

Ana Cergol, 'Evgenika na Slovenskem v perspektivi spola', *Zgodovinski časopis*, 63:3 – 4 (2009), 408 – 425.
Jeffrey H. Chajes, '*Entzauberung* and Jewish Modernity – on "Magic", Enlightenment and Faith', in *Simon-Dubnow-Institut Jahrbuch* VI (2007), pp. 191 – 200.
Dipesh Chakrabarty, 'The Climate of History: Four Theses', *Critical Inquiry*, 35:2 (Winter, 2009), 197 – 222.
Tielhard de Chardin, *The Phenomenon of Man* (New York: Harper, 1959).
Donald J. Childs, *Modernism and Eugenics: Woolf, Eliot, Yeats, and the Culture of Degeneration* (Cambridge: Cambridge University Press, 2001).
Yuehtsen Juliette Chung, *Struggle for National Survival: Eugenics in Sino-Japanese Contexts, 1896 – 1945* (New York: Routledge, 2002).
Arthur C. Clarke, *2001: Een ruimte-odyssee* (Utrecht: A. W. Bruna, 1969).
Arthur C. Clarke, *Childhood's End* (New York: Ballantine Books, 1964).
Arthur C. Clarke, *The City and the Stars* (New York: Harcourt, Brace and Company, 1956).
Richard Cleminson, *Anarchism, Science and Sex: Eugenics in Eastern Spain, 1900 – 1937* (Oxford: Peter Lang, 2000).
A.J. Coady, 'Playing God', in *Human Enhancement*, ed. by Julian Savulescu and Nick Bostrom (Oxford: Oxford University Press, 2009), pp. 151 – 176.
Matthew Connelly, *Fatal Misconception: The Struggle to Control World Population* (Cambridge, MA.: Harvard University Press, 2008).
Matthew Connelly, 'Seeing Beyond the State: The Population Control Movement and the Problem of Sovereignty', *Past & Present*, 193:1 (2006), 197 – 233.
Peter Conrad, *The Medicalization of Society: On the Transformation of Human Conditions into Treatable Disorders* (Baltimore, Md.: The Johns Hopkins University Press, 2007).
Brian Copenhaver, 'Hermes Trismegistus, Proclus, and the Question of a Philosophy of Magic in the Renaissance', in *Hermeticism and the Renaissance*, ed. by Ingrid Merkel and Allen G. Debus (Washington: Folger Books, 1988), pp. 79 – 110.
Pietro Corsi, 'Le scienze naturali in Italia prima e dopo l'unità', in *Ricerca e Istituzioni Scientifiche in Italia*, ed. by Raffaella Simili (Rome and Bari: Laterza, 1998), pp. 32 – 45.
Allison P. Coudert, 'The Kabbalah, Science, and the Enlightenment: the Doctrines of Gilgul and Tikkun as Factors in the Anthropological Revolution of the Eighteenth Century', in *Aufklärung und Esoterik: Rezeption—Integration—Konfrontation*, ed. by Monika Neugebauer-Wölk (Tübingen: Max Niemeyer, 2008), pp. 299 – 316.
Ruth Schwartz Cowan, 'Nature and Nurture: The Interplay of Biology and Politics in the Work of Francis Galton', *Studies in the History of Biology*, 1 (1977), 133 – 208.
Friedrich Creuzer, *Symbolik und Mythologie der alten Völker, besonders der Griechen*, (Leipzig und Darmstadt: Bei Heyer Und Lesk, 1819).
Roberto Dainotto, '"Tramonto" and "Risorgimento": Gentile's Dialectics and the Prophecy of Nationhood', in *Making and Remaking Italy: The Cultivation of National Identity around the Risorgimento*, ed. by Albert Russell Ascoli and Kristyna von Henneberg (Oxford and New York: Berg, 2001), pp. 241 – 55.
Richard Dawkins, *The Selfish Gene, 2nd Edition* (Oxford: Oxford University Press, 1989).
Fabrizio De Donno, '"La Razza Ario-Mediterranea": Ideas of Race and Citizenship in Colonial and Fascist Italy, 1885 – 1941', *Interventions: International Journal of Postcolonial Studies*, 8:3 (2006), 394 – 412.

G. Dé Rossi, 'La statura degli italiani e l'incremento in essa verificatosi nel periodo 1874 – 1898', *Archivio per l'Antropologia e la Etnologia*, 33 (1903), 17 – 64.

Celia Deane-Drummond and Peter Manley Scott (ed.), *Future Perfect: God, Medicine and Human Identity* (London: Continuum, 2006).

F. Del Greco, 'Elemento etnico e psicopatie negli italiani del mezzogiorno', *Atti della Società Romana di Antropologia (ASRA)*, 3: 1895 – 96 (Rome, 1896), 53 – 87.

Don DeLillo, *Mao II* (London: Vintage, 1992).

Jared Diamond, *Guns, Germs and Steel: A Short History of Everybody for the last 13,000 Years* (London: Jonathan Cape, 1997).

Jose van Dijck, *Imagenation: Popular Images of Genetics* (New York: New York University Press, 1998).

Ewa Domanska, *Biohistory and the Contemporary Human and Social Sciences*, Paper for the VIII International Conversation on History: History and Globalization. Pamplona, University of Navarra, October 6 – 9, 2010.

Svevo D'Onofrio, 'Il fondo Pullé della Biblioteca dell'Archiginnasio', *L'Archiginnasio*, 52 (2007), 473 – 87.

Fyodor Dostoevsky, *The Brothers Karamazov* (New York: The Lowell Press, 1930).

Douwe Draaisma, *Vergeetboek* (Groningen: Historiche Uitgeverij, 2010).

Douwe Draaisma, *Why Life Speeds up as you Get Older: How Memory Shapes our Past*, trans. by Arnold and Erica Pomerans (Cambridge: Cambridge University Press 2004).

Željko Dugac and Marko Pećina, *Andrija Štampar – dnevnik s putovanja, 1931 – 1938* (Zagreb: Srednja Europa, 2008).

Troy Duster, *Backdoor to Eugenics*, 2nd edition (New York and London: Routledge, 2003).

Günter Dux, *Geschlecht und Gesellschaft: Warum wir lieben* (Frankfurt am Main: Suhrkamp, 1994).

Umberto Eco, *The Search for the Perfect Language*, trans. by James Fentress (Oxford; Cambridge, MA.: Blackwell, USA, 1995).

Havelock Ellis, *The Problem of Race-Regeneration* (London: Cassell, 1911).

R. Jacob Emden, *Sefer Birat Migdal 'Oz* (Jhitomir, 1884), fol. 25a.

R, Jacob Emden, *Sefer Mitpaḥat Sefarim*, (Lemberg, 1871).

Merryn Ekberg, 'The Old Eugenics and the New Genetics', *Social History of Medicine*, 20:3 (2007), 581 – 593.

Merryn Ekberg, 'Genetic Expectations', *International Journal of Science and Research*, 2:1 (2006), 41 – 48.

Modris Eksteins, *Rites of Spring* (Boston: Houghton Mifflin, 1989).

Immanuel Etkes, *The Besht: Magician, Mystic, and Leader*, trans. by Saadya Sternberg (Waltham, MA; Hanover, MA: Brandeis University Press; University Press of New England, 2004).

Immanuel Etkes, 'The Place of Magic and the Masters of the Name in the Ashkenazi Society at the end of the 17th and 18th century', *Zion*, 60 (1995), 69 – 104 (in Hebrew).

Stella Fatović-Ferenčić, '"Society as an Organism": Metaphor as Departure Point of Andrija Štampar's Health Ideology', *Croatian Medical Journal*, 49 (2009), 709 – 719.

Francesco G. Fedele, 'I contatti internazionali: Nicolucci e Schleimann', in *Alle origini dell'antropologia italiana: Giustiniano Nicolucci e il suo tempo*, ed. by Francesco G. Fedele and Alberto Baldi (Naples: Guida Editori, 1988), pp. 231 – 43.

Joel Feinberg, 'The Child's Right to an Open Future', in *Whose Child?: Parental rights,*

Parental Authority and State Power, ed. by William Aiken and Hugh LaFollette (Totowa, NJ: Rowman and Littlefield, 1980), pp. 124–153.

Paul Fenton, *Sefer Yesirah ou le Livre de la Création: Exposé de cosmogonie hébraïque ancienne* (Paris: Rivage, 2002).

Adam Ferguson, *An Essay on the History of Civil Society* (Cambridge: Cambridge University Press, 1995 [1767]).

A. J. Festugière, *Contemplation et vie contemplative selon Platon* (Paris: Vrin, 1950).

Eitan P. Fishbane, *As Light Before Dawn, The Inner World of a Medieval Kabbalist* (Stanford: Stanford University Press, 2009).

Henry Ford, *Great Today and Greater Future* (Kila, MT: Kessinger Publishing, 2003 [1926]).

Henry Ford, *My Philosophy of Industry* (New York: Forum Publishing Co., 1928).

J.G. Frazer, *The Golden Bough* (New York, 1890).

Michael Freeden, 'Eugenics and Progressive Thought: A Study in Ideological Affinity', *The Historical Journal*, 22:3 (1979), 645–671.

Wilhelm Frick, 'German Population and Race Politics. An Address by Dr Frick, Reich Minister for the Interior, before the First Meeting of the Expert Council for Population- and Race-Politics in Berlin, June 28, 1933', *Eugenical News*, 19:2 (1934), 36.

Francis Fukuyama, *Our Posthuman Future: Consequences of the Biotechnology Revolution* (London: Profile, 2003).

Francis Fukuyama, *The End of History and the Last Man* (New York: Free Press, 1992).

Hans-Georg Gadamer, *Wahrheit und Methode* (Tübingen: Mohr, 1972).

Francis Galton, 'Eugenics: Its Definition, Scope, and Aims', *The American Journal of Sociology*, 10:1 (July,1904), 1–25.

Francis Galton, 'Eugenics: its definition, scope and aims', *Nature*, 70:1804 (26 May, 1904), 82.

Antonio Garbiglietti, *Sopra alcuni recenti scritti di craniologia etnografica dei dottori Giustiniano Nicolucci e G. Bernardo Davis: Relazione letta alla R. Accademia di Medicina di Torino nella Tornata del giorno 22 giugno 1866* (Turin, 1866).

Clifford Geertz, 'The Integrative Revolution: Primordial Sentiments and Civil Politics in the New State', in *Old Societies and New States: The Quest for Modernity in Asia and Africa*, ed. by Clifford Geertz (New York: Free Press of Glencoe, 1963), pp. 105–57.

Cathy S. Gelbin, *The Golem Returns: From German Romantic Literature to Global Jewish Culture, 1808–2008* (Ann Arbor: University of Michigan Press, 2011).

Ernst Gellner, *Plough, Sword and Book: The Structure of Human History* (London: Collins Harvill, 1988).

Emilio Gentile, 'The Sacralisation of Politics: Definitions, Interpretations and Reflections on the Question of Secular Religion and Totalitarianism', *Totalitarian Movements and Political Religion*, 1:1 (2000), 18–55.

Tudor Georgescu, 'Ethnic Minorities and the Eugenic Promise: The Transylvanian Saxon Experiment with National Renewal in Inter-War Romania,' *European Review of History* 17: 6 (2010), 861–880.

Stefanos Geroulanos, *An Atheism that is not Humanist Emerges in French Thought* (Palo Alto, CA: Stanford University Press, 2010).

Anthony Giddens, 'Living in a Post-traditional Society', in *Reflexive Modernization*, ed. by

Ulrich Beck, Anthony Giddens and Scott Lash (Cambridge: Polity Press, 1994), pp. 56–109.
Oliver Gilkes and Lida Miraj, 'The Myth of Aeneas: The Italian Archaeological Mission in Albania, 1924–1943', *Public Archaeology*, 2 (2000), 109–124.
Aaron Gillette, *Racial Theory in Fascist Italy* (London and New York: Routledge, 2002).
V. Giuffreda-Ruggeri, 'Appunti di etnologia comparata della Sicilia', *Atti della Società Romana di Anthropologia*, 8 (Rome, 1902), 241–263.
John Glad, 'Hermann J. Muller's 1936 Letter to Stalin', *The Mankind Quarterly*, 43:3 (2003), 305–319.
Amos Goldreich, *Automatic Writing in Zoharic Literature and Modernism* (Los Angeles: Cherub Press, 2010) (in Hebrew).
Amos Goldreich (ed.), *Sefer Me'irat 'Einayyim* (Jerusalem, 1984).
Rudolf Goldscheid, *Höherentwicklung und Menschenökonomie. Grundlegung der sozialbiologie* (Leipzig: W. Klinkhardt, 1911).
Nicholas Goodrick-Clarke, *The Occult Roots of Nazism: Secret Aryan Cults and Their Influence on Nazi Ideology* (New York: New York University Press, 1992).
Paola Govoni, *Un pubblico per la scienza: La divulgazione scientifica nell'Italia in formazione* (Rome: Carroce Editore, 2002).
Loren R. Graham, *Science, Philosophy, and Human Behavior in the Soviet Union* (New York: Columbia University Press, 1987).
Arthur Green, 'The Zaddiq as Axis Mundi in Later Judaism', *Journal of the American Academy of Religion*, 45 (1977), 327–347.
Martin Green, *Mountain of Truth: The Counterculture Begins: Ascona, 1900–1920* (University Press of New England, 1986).
Alberto Grilli, *Il problema della vita contemplativa nel modo Greco-romano* (Milano; Roma: Fratelli Bocca, 1953).
Zeev Gries, *Conduct Literature (Regimen Vitae), Its History and Place in the Life of the Beshtian Hasidism* (Jerusalem: Mossad Bialik, 1989) (in Hebrew).
Roger Griffin, *Modernism and Fascism: The Sense of a Beginning under Mussolini and Hitler* (London: Palgrave, 2007).
Alfred Grotjahn, *Die hygienische Forderung* (Leipzig: Tannus, 1917).
Jyotsna Agnihotri Gupta, 'Towards Transnational Feminisms: Some Reflections and Concerns in Relation to the Globalisation of Reproductive Technologies', *European Journal of Women's Studies*, 13:1 (2006), 23–38.
Ithamar Gruenwald, 'Some Critical Notes on the First Part of *Sefer Yezira*', *Revue des études juives*, 132 (1973), 475–512.
Ithamar Gruenwald, 'A Preliminary Critical Edition of Sepher Yetzirah', in *Israel Oriental Studies*, 1 (1971), 132–177.
John Grumley, *History and Totality: Radical Historicism from Hegel to Foucault* (Routledge London, 1989).
Reiner Grundmann and Nico Stehr, *Experts: The Knowledge and Power of Expertise* (Abingdon: Routledge, 2011).
Alessandro Guidi, 'Nationalism without a Nation: The Italian Case', in *Nationalism and Archaeology in Europe*, ed. by Margarita Díaz-Andreu and Timothy Champion (London, UCL Press, 1996), pp. 108–118.

David Gurnham, 'The Mysteries of Human Dignity and the Brave New World of Human Cloning', *Social and Legal Studies*, 14:2 (Jun., 2005), 197–214.
Jürgen Habermas, *The Future of Human Nature* (Abingdon: Taylor & Francis, 2005).
Harvey J. Haimes, T*he Art of Conversion, Christianity & Kabbalah in the Thirteenth Century* (Leiden; Boston: Brill, 2000).
Norman Haire, *Rejuvenation: the Work of Steinach, Voronoff, and others* (London: G. Allen & Unwin, 1924).
Lesley Hall, 'Women, Feminism and Eugenics' in *Essays in the History of Eugenics*, ed. by Robert A. Peel (London: Galton Institute, 1998), pp. 36–51.
Donna Harraway, *Modest_Witness@Second_Millenium.FemaleMan ©_Meets_OncoMouse™: Feminism and Technoscience* (New York and London: Routledge, 1997).
Donna Haraway, 'A Cyborg Manifesto: Science, Technology, and Socialist-Feminism in the Late Twentieth Century', in *Simians, Cyborgs and Women: The Reinvention of Nature*, ed. by Donna Harraway (New York: Routledge, 1991), pp. 149–181.
John Harris, *Enhancing Evolution: The Ethical Case for Making Better People* (Princeton and Oxford: Princeton University Press, 2007).
Carol Harrison and Ann Johnson (ed.), 'National Identity: The Role of Science and Technology', *Osiris, Special Issue* (2009).
Bradley W. Hart, 'Watching the "Eugenic Experiment" Unfold: The Mixed Views of British Eugenicists Towards Nazi Germany in the Early 1930s', *Journal of the History of Biology*, 45:1 (2011), 33–63.
Iuliu Hațieganu, 'Rolul social al medicului în opera de consolidare a statului național', *Transilvania*, 54 (1925), 588.
Gisela Hauss and Béatrice Ziegler, 'City Welfare in the Sway of Eugenics: A Swiss Case Study', *The British Journal of Social Work*, 38:4 (2008), 751–770.
H.A. ten Have, 'Genetics and Culture: The Geneticization Thesis', *Medicine, Health Care and Philosophy*, 4:3 (2001), 295–304.
A. Peter Hayman, *Sefer Yesira, Edition, Translation and Text-Critical Commentary* (Tuebingen: Mohr Siebeck, 2004).
A. Peter Hayman, 'Was God A Magician? *Sefer Yesira* and Jewish Magic', *Journal of Jewish Studies*, 41 (1989), 225–237.
Georg Wilhelm Friedrich Hegel, *The Philosophy of History* (Whitefish, MT: Kessinger Publishing, 2004).
Georg Wilhelm Friedrich Hegel, *Vorlesungen über die Philosophie der Weltgeschichte. Band 1. Die Vernunft in der Geschichte* (Hamburg: Meiner, 1970).
Albert Van Helden and C. Kenneth Waters (ed.), *Julian Huxley: Biologist and Statesman of Science* (Houston: Rice University Press, 1992).
Johann Gottfried von Herder, *Ideen zur Geschichte der Philosophie der Menschheit. Band 4* (Riga und Leipzig: Hartknoch, 1792).
Johann Gottfired von Herder, *Ideen zur Geschichte der Philosophie der Menschheit. Band 1* (Riga und Leipzig: Hartknoch, 1785).
Géza von Hoffmann, 'New Eugenics Society in Hungary,' *The Journal of Heredity*, 11:1 (1920), 41.
Max Horkheimer and Theodor W. Adorno, *Dialectic of Enlightenment* (New York: Continuum, 1972).

David G. Horn, 'Constructing the Sterile City: Pronatalism and Social Sciences in Interwar Italy', *American Ethnologist,* 18:3 (1991), 581–601.

Yvonne Howell, 'Eugenics, Rejuvenation, and Bulgakov's Journey into the Heart of Dogness', *Slavic Review,* 65:3 (2006), 544–562.

D. Hubback, 'Julian Huxley and Eugenics', in *Evolutionary Studies: a Centenary Celebration of the life of Julian Huxley,* ed. by M. Keynes and G.A. Harrison (London: Macmillan, 1989), pp. 194–206.

Aldous Huxley, *Brave New World* (New York: Random House, 2008).

Julian Huxley (ed.), *The Humanist Frame* (London: Allen & Unwin, 1961).

Julian Huxley, 'Transhumanism', in *New Bottles for New Wine,* ed. by Julian Huxley (London: Chatto & Windus, 1957).

Julian Huxley, *Evolution: the Modern Synthesis* (New York and London: Harper & Bros., 1942).

Julian Huxley, 'Social Biology and Population Improvement', *Nature,* 144:3646 (16 Sept., 1939), 521–522.

Julian Huxley, 'Eugenics and Society', *The Eugenics Review,* 28:1 (1936), 11–31.

Julian Huxley, *Religion without Revelation* (London: Benn, 1927).

Moshe Idel, *Kabbalah in Italy, 1280–1510: A Survey* (New Haven: Yale University Press, 2011).

Moshe Idel, *Ben: Sonship and Jewish Mysticism* (London; New York: Continuum, 2007).

Moshe Idel (ed.), *Natan ben Sa'adyah Har'ar, Le Porte della Giustizia,* trans. by Maurizio Motolese (Milano: Adelphi, 2001).

Moshe Idel, *R. Menahem Recanati, the Kabbalist* (Tel Aviv: Schocken, 1998) (in Hebrew).

Moshe Idel, *Hasidism: Between Ecstasy and Magic* (Albany: State University of New York Press, 1995).

Moshe Idel, *Golem; Jewish Magical and Mystical Traditions on the Artificial Anthropoid* (Albany: State University of New York Press, 1990).

Moshe Idel, *Kabbalah: New Perspectives,* (New Haven: Yale University Press, 1988).

Moshe Idel, *Studies in Ecstatic Kabbalah* (Albany: State University of New York Press, 1988).

Moshe Idel, *The Mystical Experience in Abraham Abulafia,* trans. by Jonathon Chipman (Albany: State University of New York Press, 1987).

Moshe Idel, 'On Astral Golems, Dalai Lama and the Maharal', in *Essays for a Jewish Lifetime: The Burton D. Morris Jubilee Volume,* ed. by Menachem Butler and Marian E. Frankston (New York: Hakirah Press, 2012).

Moshe Idel, '*Sefer Yetzirah:* Twelve Commentaries on *Sefer Yetzirah* and the Extant Remnants of R. Isaac of Bedresh's Commentary', *Tarbitz,* 79 (2010), 471–556 (in Hebrew).

Moshe Idel, 'The Image of Man above the Sefirot: R. David ben Yehuda he-Hasid's Theosophy of Ten Supernal *Sahsahot* and its Reverberations', *Kabbalah,* 20 (2009), 181–212.

Moshe Idel, 'Hermeticism and Kabbalah', in *Hermeticism from Late Antiquity to Humanism,* ed. by Paolo Lucentini, Ilaria Parri, Vittoria Perrone Compagni (Turnhout, Belgium: Brespols, 2004), pp. 389–408.

Moshe Idel, 'Golems and God: Mimesis and Confrontation', in *Mythen der Kreativitaet,* ed.

by Oliver Krueger, Refika Sarioender, and Annette Deschner (Frankfurt am Main: Lembeck, 2003), pp. 224–268.

Moshe Idel, 'Magic and Kabbalah in the *Book of the Responding Entity*', in *The Solomon Goldman Lectures*, ed. by Mayer I. Gruber (Chicago: The Spertus College of Judaica Press, 1993), pp. 125–138.

Moshe Idel, 'Hermeticism and Judaism', in *Hermeticism and the Renaissance*, ed. by Ingrid Merkel and Allen Debus (Washington: Folger Books, 1988), pp. 59–76.

Moshe Idel, 'Ramon Lull and Ecstatic Kabbalah', *Journal of the Warburg and Courtauld Institutes*, 51 (1988), 170–174.

Moshe Idel, 'The Magical and Neoplatonic Interpretations of Kabbalah in the Renaissance', in *Jewish Thought in the Sixteenth Century*, ed. by Bernard Dov Cooperman (Cambridge, Ma.: Harvard University Press, 1983), pp. 186–242.

Moshe Idel, 'Inquiries in the Doctrine of *Sefer Ha-Meshiv*', *Sefunot*, 17 (1983), 185–266 (in Hebrew).

Liza Ireni-Saban and Alberto Spekorowski, 'From "Race Hygiene" to "National-Productivist Hygiene', *Journal of Political Ideologies*, 16:2 (2011), 169–193.

Friedrich Heinrich Jacobi, *Briefe über die Lehre Spinozas* (Leipzig: Bey Georg Joachim Goeschen, 1786).

Greta Jones, 'Eugenics and Social Policy between the Wars', *The Historical Journal*, 25:3 (1982), 717–728.

Albert R. Jonsen, *The Birth of Bioethics* (Oxford and New York: Oxford University Press, 1998).

Immanuel Kant, "Idea for a Universal History with a Cosmopolitan Aim," in *Kant's 'Idea for a Universal History with a Cosmopolitan Aim': A Critical Guide*, ed. by Amélie Rorty and James Schmidt (Cambridge: Cambridge University Press, 2009).

Immanuel Kant, *Grundlegung zur Metaphysik der Sitten* (Stuttgart: Philipp Reclam, 1970).

Immanuel Kant, 'Idee zu einer allgemeinen Geschichte in Weltbürgerlichen Absicht', in Immanuel Kant, *Ausgewälte Kleine Schriften* (Hamburg: Felix Meiner, 1965).

Despina Karakatsani and Vassiliki Theodoru, *'Hygiene Imperatives': Medical Supervision and Child Welfare in Greece in the First Decades of the 20th Century* (Athens: Dionikos, 2010) (in Greek).

Lilian Karina and Marion Kant (ed.), *Hitler's Dancers: German Modern Dance and the Third Reich* (Oxford: Berghahn, 2003).

Leon Kass, Life, *Liberty and Defence of Dignity: The Challenge for Bioethics* (San Francisco: Encounter Books, 2002).

Stephen Katz, 'Imagining the Life-span: From Premodern Miracles to Postmodern Fantasies', in *Images of Aging: Cultural Representations of Later Life*, ed. by Mike Featherstone and Andrew Wernick (London: Routledge, 1995), pp. 61–75.

Hans Kellner, *Language and Historical Representation: Getting the Story Crooked* (Madison, Wis.: University of Wisconsin Press, 1989).

Anne Kerr, 'Rights and Responsibilities in the New Genetics Era', *Critical Social Policy*, 23:2 (May, 2003), 208–226.

Daniel J. Kevles, 'Eugenics, the Genome and Human Rights', *Medicine Studies*, I:2 (2009), 85–93.

Ben Kiernan, *The Pol Pot Regime: Race, Power and Genocide in Cambodia under the Khmer Rouge, 1975–1979* (Yale: Yale University Press, 1996).

Hillel Kieval, *Languages of Community: The Jewish Experience in the Czech Lands* (Berkeley; London: University of California Press, 2000), pp. 95–113.
Hillel Kieval, 'Pursuing the Golem of Prague: Jewish Culture and the Invention of a Tradition', *Modern Judaism*, 17 (1997), 1–20.
Andreas Kilcher, *Die Sprachtheorie der Kabbala als Aestetisches Paradigma* (Stuttgart; Weimar: J.M. Metzler, 1998).
Philip Kitcher, *The Lives to Come: The Genetic Revolution and Human Possibilities* (New York: Simon and Schuster, 1996).
Alexandre Kojève, *Introduction à la Lecture de Hegel* (assembled by Raymond Queneau) (Paris: Gallimard, 1947).
Tracy Koon, Believe, *Obey, Fight: Political Socialization of Youth in Fascist Italy, 1922–1943* (Chapel Hill: University of North Carolina Press, 1985).
Mária M. Kovács, *Liberal Professions & Illiberal Politics: Hungary from the Habsburgs to the Holocaust* (Washington, DC: Woodrow Wilson Center Press, 1994).
Nikolai Krementsov, 'From "Beastly Philosophy" to Medical Genetics: Eugenics in Russia and the Soviet Union', *Annals of Science*, 68:1 (2011), 61–92.
Nikolai Krementsov, *Stalinist Science* (Princeton: Princeton University Press, 1997).
Reinbert A. Krol, 'Friedrich Meinecke: Pantheism and the Crisis of Historicism', *Journal of the Philosophy of History*, 4:2 (2010), 195–209.
Giovanni Landucci, 'Mantegazza e Nicolucci', in *Alle origini dell'antropologia italiana: Giustiniano Nicolucci e il suo tempo*, ed. by Francesco G. Fedele and Alberto Baldi (Naples: Guida Editori, 1988), pp. 61–83.
Giovanni Landucci, *Darwinismo a Firenze: Tra scienza e ideologia, 1860–1900* (Florence: L. S. Olschki, 1977).
Christopher Lawrence and Anna-K. Mayer (ed.), *Regenerating England: Science, Medicine and Culture in Inter-War Britain* (Amsterdam: Rodopi, 2000).
Andrew Lees, *Cities Perceived: Urban Society in European and American Thought, 1820–1940* (Manchester: Manchester University Press, 1985).
Fritz Lenz, 'The Position of National Socialism on Race Hygiene', in *The Eugenics Movement: An International Perspective vol. 4*, ed. by Pauline M. H. Mazumdar, (New York: Routledge, 2007), p. 19.
Etienne Lepicard, 'Eugenics and Roman Catholicism: An Encyclical Letter in Context: Casti connubii, December 31, 1930', *Science in Context*, 11:3–4 (1998), 527–544.
Antonis Liakos, Αποκάλυψη, Ουτοπία και Ιστορία [Apocalypse, Utopia and History] (Athens: Πόλις, 2011).
Yehuda Liebes, *Ars Poetica in Sefer Yetzirah* (Tel Aviv: Schocken, 2000) (in Hebrew).
Yehuda Liebes, 'The Messianism of R. Jacob Emden and His attitude toward Sabbataianism', *Tarbiz*, 49 (1980), 122–165 (in Hebrew).
Veronika Lipphardt, *Biologie der Juden: Jüdische Wissenschaftler über 'Rasse' und Vererbung 1900–1935* (Göttingen: Vandenhoeck & Ruprecht, 2008).
Paul A. Lombardo (ed.), *A Century of Eugenics in America: From the Indiana Experiment to the Human Genome Era* (Bloomington, IN: Indiana University Press, 2011).
Monika Löscher. *"...der gesunden Vernunft nicht zuwider...": Katholische Eugenik in Österreich vor 1938* (Innsbruck: Studien Verlag, 2009).
Laura L. Lovett, *Conceiving the Future: Pronatalism, Reproduction, and the Family in the United States, 1890–1938* (Chapel Hill: The University of North Carolina Press, 2007).

David Lowenthal, *The Past is a Foreign Country* (Cambridge: Cambridge University Press, 1985).

Leo Lucassen, 'A Brave New World: The Left, Social Engineering, and Eugenics in Twentieth-Century Europe', *International Review of Social History*, 55:2 (2010), 265 – 296.

Louise Lyle, 'French Perspectives on Eugenics as Seen through Selected Writings of Georges Duhamel', *French Cultural Studies*, 20:3 (2009), 257 – 272.

Mark Lynas, *Six Degrees: Our Future on a Hotter Planet* (Washington, D.C.: National Geographic, 2008).

Adrian Lyttelton, 'Creating a National Past: History, Myth, and Image in the Risorgimento', in *Making and Remaking Italy: The Cultivation of National Identity around the Risorgimento*, ed. by Albert Russell Ascoli and Kristyna von Henneberg (Oxford and New York: Berg, 2001), pp. 27 – 74.

Joe McCarney, *Hegel on History* (London: Routledge, 2000).

Britta I. McEwen, 'Welfare and Eugenics: Julius Tandler's Rassenhygienische Vision for Interwar Vienna', *Austrian History Yearbook*, 51 (2010), 170 – 190.

Angus McLaren, *Our own Master Race: Eugenics in Canada 1885 – 1945* (Toronto: McClelland and Stewart, 1990).

William McNeill, *Keeping Together in Time: Dance and Drill in Human History* (Cambridge, Ma: Harvard University Press, 1995).

William McNeill, *The Rise of the West: A History of the Human Community* (Chicago: Chicago University Press, 1963).

Donald MacKenzie, 'Eugenics in Britain', *Social Studies of Science*, 6:3 – 4 (Dec., 1976), 499 – 532.

John Macnicol, 'Eugenics and the Campaign for Voluntary Sterilization in Britain Between the Wars' *Social History of Medicine*, 2:2 (1989), 147 – 169.

Annemarie de Waal Malefijt, *Images of Man: A History of Anthropological Thought* (New York: Knopf, 1974).

Ilija Malović, 'Eugenika kao ideološki sastojak fašizma u Srbiji 1930-ih godina XX veka', *Sociologija*, 50:1 (2008), 79 – 96.

Peter Mandler, 'Against "Englishness": English Culture and the Limits to Rural Nostalgia, 1850 – 1940', *Transactions of the Royal Historical Society*, 7 (1997), 155 – 175.

J. A. Mangan, *Militarism, Sport, Europe: War Without Weapons* (London: Routledge, 1966).

Joseph Mangan (ed.), *Superman Supreme: Fascist Body as Political Icon – Global Fascism* (Portland, OR: Frank Cass, 1999).

Paolo Mantegazza, *Ricordi politici di un fantaccino del parlamento italiano* (Florence: R. Bemporad, 1896).

Paolo Mantegazza, *Profili e paesaggi della Sardegna* (Milan; Brigola, 1869).

Giovanni Battista Marini-Bettòlo and Rocco Capasso, *Gli scienziati italiani e le loro riunioni, 1839 – 1847: Attraverso i documenti degli archivi dell'Accademia nazionale delle scienze detta dei XL e della Società italiana per il progresso delle scienze* (Roma: Academia Nazionale delle Scienze detta dei XL, 1991).

Zvi Mark, '*Dybbuk* and *Devekut* in the *Shivhe ha-Besht*: Toward a Phenomenology of Madness in Early Hasidism', in *Spirit and Spirit Possession in Judaism*, ed. by Matt Goldish (Detroit: Wayne State University Press, 2003), pp. 257 – 301.

Paul Martin and Robert Frost, 'Regulating the Commercial Development of Genetic

Testing in the UK: Problems, Possibilities and Policy', *Critical Social Policy*, 23:2 (2003), 186–207.
Karl Marx, *The German Ideology* (Moscow: International Publishers Co., 1970).
Pauline Mazumdar, *Eugenics, Human Genetics and Human Failings: The Eugenics Society, Its Sources and Its Critics in Britain* (London: Routledge, 1992).
Friedrich Meinecke, *Die Idee der Staatsräson in der neueren Geschichte* (München: Oldenbourg, 1976).
Immaculada de Melo-Martin, 'On Cloning Human Beings', *Bioethics*, 16:3 (Jun., 2002), 246–265.
Klaus M. Meyer-Abich, 'Herders Naturphilosophie in der Naturkrise der Industriegesellschaft', in *Herder und die Philosophie des Deutschen Idealismus*, ed. by Marion Heinz (Amsterdam: Rodopi, 1997).
Andy Miah, ' A Critical History of Posthumanism', in *Medical Enhancements and Posthumanity*, ed. by B. Gordijn and R. Chadwick (New York: Routledge, 2007), pp. 71–94.
John Stuart Mill, *On Liberty* (London: J. M. Dent, 1910).
Farhat Moazam, 'Feminist Discourse on Sex Selection and Selective Abortion of Female Foetuses', *Bioethics*, 18:3 (June, 2004), 205–220.
Iuliu Moldovan, *Igiena naţiunii (eugenia)* (Cluj: Institutul de igienă, 1925).
Kathleen Montgomery and Amalya L. Oliver, 'Shifts in Guidelines for Ethical Scientific Conduct: How Public and Private Organizations Create and Change Norms of Research Integrity', *Social Studies of Science*, 39:1 (Feb., 2009), 137–155.
Lewis Morgan, *Ancient Society* (Cambridge, Ma: Belknap Press of Harvard University, 1964 [1877]).
George Mosse, *The Crisis of German Ideology: Intellectual Origins of the Third Reich* (New York: Howard Fertig, 1998).
Lion Murard and Patrick Zylberman, "L'ordre et la règle. L'hygiénisme en France dans l'entre-deux-guerres," *Les cahiers de la recherché architecturale*, 15:17 (1985), 42–53.
Thomas H. Murray, 'Enhancement', in *The Oxford Handbook of Bioethics*, ed. by Bonnie Steinbock (Oxford: Oxford University Press, 2007), pp. 491–515.
Antonio Vallejo-Nágera, 'A New Breeding of Spaniards', quoted in *Fascism*, ed. by Roger Griffin (Oxford: Oxford University Press, 1995), p. 190.
John Neubauer, 'How Did the Golem Get to Prague?', in *History of the Literary Cultures of East Central Europe: Junctures and Disjunctures in the 19th and 20th centuries, vol. IV, Types and Stereotypes*, ed. by Marcel Cornis-Pope and John Neubauer (Amsterdam: John Benjamin, 2010), pp. 296–307.
Alfredo Niceforo, *L'Italia barbara contemporanea: Studi e appunti* (Milan and Palermo, 1898).
Giustiniano Nicolucci, *Antropologia dell'Italia nell'evo antico e nel moderno* (Naples: Tip. dell'Accademia delle Scienze, 1887).
Giustiniano Nicolucci, *Lettera del Dottore Cav. Giustiniano Nicolucci al Dottore Cav. Antonio Garbiglietti intorno all'opera del Signor Dottore J. B. Davis intitolata: Thesaurus Craniorum* (Turin, 1868).
Giustiniano Nicolucci, *Delle razze umane: Saggio etnologico del Dottor Giustiniano Nicolucci*, 2 vols. (Naples: Stamperia e Cartiere del Fibreno, 1857–1858).
Friedrich Nietzsche, 'Wille zur Macht,' in *Friedrich Nietzsche. Werke*, vol. 3, ed. by Karl Schlechta (Munich: Carl Hanser Verlag, 1969).

Gedalyah Nigal, *Magic, Mysticism, and Hasidism* (Tel Aviv: Yaron Golan, 1992) (in Hebrew).
Richard Noll, *The Jung Cult* (New York: Simon & Schuster, 1994).
Peter Novick, *That Noble Dream: The 'Objectivity Question' and the American Historical Profession* (Cambridge: Cambridge University Press, 1988).
Onora O'Neill, *Autonomy and Trust in Bioethics* (Cambridge: Cambridge University Press, 2001).
Esra Osyurek, *Nostalgia for the Modern: State Secularism and Every Day Politics in Turkey* (Durham, NC: Duke University Press, 2006).
Laura Otis, *Organic Memory: History and Body in the Late Nineteenth and Early Twentieth Centuries* (Lincoln, NE.: University of Nebraska Press, 1994).
Mona Ozouf, *L'Homme régénéré. Essai sur la Révolution française* (Paris: Gallimard, 1989).
Giuliano Pancaldi, *Darwin in Italy: Science across Cultural Frontiers*, trans. R. Brodine Morelli (Bloomington and Indianapolis: Indiana University Press, 1991).
Giuliano Pancaldi, *Darwin in Italia: the Impresa scientifica e frontieri culturali* (Bologna: Mulino 1983).
Giuliano Pancaldi, 'Nuove fonti per la storia dei congressi: Scritti inediti di Charles Babbage, Carlo Luciano Bonaparte, e Lorenz Oken', in *I congressi degli scienziati italiani nell'età del positivismo*, ed. by Giuliano Pancaldi (Bologna: CLUEB, 1983), pp. 181–201.
Noel and José Parry, *The Rise of Medical Profession: A Study of Collective Social Mobility* (London: Croom Helm, 1976).
Silvana Patriarca and Lucy Riall, 'Introduction: Revisiting the Risorgimento', in *The Risorgimento Revisited: Nationalism and Culture in Nineteenth-Century Italy*, ed. by Silvana Patriarca and Lucy Riall (Basingstoke: Palgrave Macmillan, 2012), pp. 1–17.
Diane B. Paul, 'On Drawing Lessons from the History of Eugenics', in *Reprogenetics: Law, Policy, and Ethical Issues*, ed. by Lori P. Knowles and Gregory E. Kaebnick (Baltimore, MD: Johns Hopkins University Press, 2007), pp. 3–19.
Diane Paul, 'The Value of Diversity in Huxley's Eugenics', in *Julian Huxley: Biologist and Statesman of Science*, ed. by Albert Van Helden and C. Kenneth Waters, (Houston: Rice University Press, 1992), pp. 223–229.
Diane Paul, 'Eugenics and the Left', *Journal of the History of Ideas*, 45:4 (1984), 567–590.
Linus Pauling, *How to Live Longer and Feel Better* (New York: Avon Books, 1986).
Karl Pearson, 'Prof. Karl Pearson's Reply', in *Speeches delivered at a dinner held in University College, London in Honour of Professor Karl Pearson, 23 April 1934* (Cambridge: The University Press, 1934), p. 23.
Karl Pearson (ed.), *The Life, Letters and Labours of Francis Galton, vol. 3* (London: Cambridge University Press, 1930).
Karl Pearson, 'Editorial', *Annals of Eugenics*, 1:1–2 (1925), 3–4.
Karl Pearson, *The Problem of Practical Eugenics* (London: Dulau and Co., 1912).
Karl Pearson, *The Academic Aspect of the Science of National Eugenics* (London: Dulau, 1911).
Ted Peters, 'Perfect Humans or Trans-Humans?', in *Future Perfect: God, Medicine and Human Identity*, ed. by Celia Deane-Drummond and Peter Manley Scott (London: Continuum, 2006), pp. 15–32.

Alan Petersen and Robin Bunton, *The New Genetics and the Public's Health* (London and New York: Routledge, 2002).

Alan Petersen and Deborah Lupton, *The New Public Health: Health and Self in the Age of Risk* (London: Sage, 1996).

Marta Petricioli, *Archeologia e Mare Nostrum: Le missioni archeologiche nella politica mediterranea dell'Italia, 1898–1943* (Rome: V. Levi, 1990).

Yohanan Petrovsky-Shtern, 'The Master of An Evil Name: R. Hillel Ba'al Shem and His *Sefer Ha-Heshek*', *AJS Review*, 28 (2004), 217–248.

Petteri Pietikainen, *Neurosis and Modernity: The Age of Nervousness in Sweden* (Leiden/Boston, MA: Brill, 2007).

Daniel Pike, *Faces of Degeneration: a European Disorder c. 1848–1918* (Cambridge: Cambridge University Press, 1989).

Shlomo Pines, 'Le *Sefer ha-Tamar* et les *Maggidim* des Kabbalists', in *Hommage à Georges Vajda*, ed. by Gerard Nahon and Charles Touati (Louvain: Peeters, 1980), pp. 333–363.

Shlomo Pines, 'On the Term *Ruhaniyyut* and its Sources and On Judah Halevi's Doctrine', *Tarbiz*, 57 (1988), 511–540 (in Hebrew).

L. Poliakov, *The Aryan Myth: A History of Racist and Nationalist Ideas in Europe*, trans. E. Howard (London: Chatto & Windus, 1974).

Russell Powell and Allen Buchanan, 'Breaking Evolution's Chains: The Prospect of Deliberate Genetic Modification in Humans', *Journal of Medicine and Philosophy*, 36:1 (Feb., 2011), 6–27.

Barbara Prainsack and Gil Siegal, 'The Rise of Genetic Couplehood?: A Comparative View of Premarital Genetic Testing', *Biosocieties*, 1: (2006),17–36.

President's Council on Bioethics, *Beyond Therapy: Biotechnology and the Pursuit of Happiness* (Washington: National Bioethics Advisory Commission, 2003).

Todd Presner, *Muscular Judaism: The Jewish Body and the Politics of Regeneration* (London/New York: Routledge Press, 2007).

Todd Presner, '"Clear Heads, Solid Stomachs, and Hard Muscles." Max Nordau and the Aesthetics of Jewish Regeneration', *Modernism/Modernity*, 10:2 (2003), 269–296.

James Cowles Prichard, *Researches into the Physical History of Mankind*, 5 vols. (London: Sherwood, Gilbert and Piper, 1837–1851).

Robert Proctor, *Racial Hygiene: Medicine under the Nazis* (Cambridge, Ma.: Harvard University Press, 1988).

Christian Promitzer, Sevasti Trubeta and Marius Turda (ed.), *Health, Hygiene and Eugenics in Southeastern Europe to 1945* (Budapest: Central European University Press, 2011).

Sandra Puccini, 'Institutionnalisation de l'anthropologie italienne au xixe siècle', *Gradhiva*, 9 (1991), 63–76.

F. L. Pullé, 'Profilo antropologico dell'Italia', *Archivio per l'Antropologia e la Etnologia*, 28:1 (1898), 19–168.

Maria Sophia Quine, *Italy's Social Revolution: Charity and Welfare from Liberalism to Fascism* (Basingstoke: Palgrave, 2002).

Maria Sophia Quine, 'Racial "Sterility" and "Hyperfecundity" in Fascist Italy: Biological Politics of Sex and Reproduction', *Fascism: Journal of Comparative Fascist Studies*, 1:2 (2012), 92–144.

Gregory Radick, 'A Critique of Kitcher on Eugenic Reasoning', *Studies in the History and Philosophy of Biology and Biomedical Sciences*, 32:4 (2001), 741–751.
Ada Rapoport-Albert, 'God and the Zaddik as the Two Focal Points of Hasidic Worship', *History of Religions*, 18 (1979), 296–325.
Dietrich Rasch, *Zur deutschen Literatur seit der Jahrhundertwende. Gesammelte Aufsätze* (Stuttgart: Metzler, 1967).
E. Raseri, 'Materiali per l'ethnologia italiana: Raccolti per cura della Società Italiana di Antropologia ed Etnologia', *Archivio per l'Antropologia e la Etnologia* (AAE), 9 (1879), 259–88.
Hermann Rauschning, *The Voice of Destruction* (New York: G. P. Putnam's Sons, 1940).
Aviad E. Raz, 'Eugenic utopias/dystopias, reprogenetics and community genetics', *Sociology of Health and Illness*, 31:4 (2009), 602–616.
Lucia Re, 'Italians and the Invention of Race: The Poetics and Politics of Difference in the Struggle over Libya, 1890–1913', *California Italian Studies Journal*, 1:1 (2010), 1–58.
Andrés H. Reggiani, *God's Eugenicist: Alexis Carrel and the Sociology of Decline* (New York: Berghahn, 2007).
Elhanan Reiner, 'The Attitude of Ashkenazi Society to the New Sciences in the Sixteenth Century', *Science in Context*, 10 (1997), 589–603.
Chris Renwick, 'From Political Economy to Sociology: Francis Galton and the Social-Scientific Origins of Eugenics', *The British Journal for the History of Science*, 44:3 (2011), 343–369.
Carlo Reynaudi, *Paolo Mantegazza: Note biografiche* (Milan: Fratelli Treves, 1893).
Lucy Riall, *Risorgimento: The History of Italy from Napoleon to Nation State* (Basingstoke: Palgrave Macmillan, 2009).
Lucy Riall, *The Italian Risorgimento: State, Society, and National Unification* (London, and New York: Routledge, 2004).
Angelique Richardson, *Love and Eugenics in the Late Nineteenth Century: Rational Reproduction and the New Woman* (Oxford: Oxford University Press, 2003).
David Roberts, *The Totalitarian Experiment in the Twentieth-Century* (New York: Routledge, 2006).
Pierre Drieu la Rochelle, 'Renaissance de l'homme européen', in *Notes pour comprendre le siècle*, ed. by Pierre Drieu la Rochelle (Gallimard, Paris, 1941), pp. 149–154.
Nikolas Rose, *The Politics of Life Itself: Biomedicine, Power, and Subjectivity in the Twenty-First Century* (Princeton and Oxford: Princeton University Press, 2007).
Nikolas Rose, *Powers of Freedom: Reframing Political Thought* (Cambridge: Cambridge University Press, 1999).
Chad Ross, *Naked Germany: Health, Race and the Nation* (Oxford and New York, Berg, 2005).
Irena Rožman, 'Eugénisme et croyances populaires: le dépistages des infirmités dans le passé', *Ethnologie française*, 42:2 (2012), 301–312.
Vladislav Růžička, 'A Motion for the Organization of Eugenical Research', in *Scientific Papers of the Second International Congress of Eugenics, vol. 2* (Baltimore: Williams & Wilkins, 1923), pp. 452–455.
Sanem Güvenç Salgirli, 'Eugenics for the Doctors: Medicine and Social Control in 1930s Turkey', *Journal of the History of Medicine and Allied Sciences*, 66:3 (2011), 281–312.

Michael J. Sandel, 'The Case Against Perfection: What's Wrong with Designing Children, Bionic Athletes and Genetic Engineering', *Atlantic Monthly*, 292:3 (Apr., 2004), 50–62.

Jacques Sapir, *La Démondialisation* (Paris: Seuil, 2011).

Julian Savulescu, 'Deaf Lesbians, "Designer Disability", and the Future of Medicine', *British Medical Journal*, 325:7367 (Oct. 5, 2002), 771–773.

Julian Savulescu, 'Procreative Beneficence: Why we Should Select the Best Children', *Bioethics*, 15:5/6 (2001), 413–426.

Edgar Schick, *Metaphorical Organicism in Herder's Early Works: A Study of the Relation of Herder's Literary Idiom to his World-view* (The Hague; Paris: Mouton, 1971).

Heinrich Schipperges, 'Natur,' in *Geschichtliche Grundbegriffe. Historisches Lexikon zur politisch-sozialen Sprache in Deutschland*, vol. 4, ed. by Otto Brunner, Werner Conze, Reinhart Koselleck (Stuttgart: Ernst Klett, 1978).

Hans-Walter Schmuhl, *The Kaiser Wilhelm Institute for Anthropology, Human Heredity and Eugenics, 1927–1945: Crossing Boundaries* (Dordrecht: Springer, 2010).

Jane Schneider (ed.), *Italy's "Southern Question": Orientalism in One Country* (Oxford and New York: Berg, 1998).

William M. Schneider, *Quality and Quantity. The Quest for Biological Regenderation in Twentieth-Century France* (Cambridge: Cambridge University Press, 1990).

Gershom Scholem, *Researches in Sabbateanism*, ed. Yehuda Liebes (Tel Aviv: Am Oved, 1991), (in Hebrew).

Gershom Scholem, 'On the Story of R. Joseph della Reina', in *Hokhma Bina veDaat, Studies in Jewish History and Thought Presented to A. Altmann*, ed. by S. Stein and R. Loewe (Alabama: Alabama University Press, 1979), pp. 100–108 (in Hebrew).

Gershom Scholem, 'The Maggid of Rabbi Joseph Taitatchek and the Revelations attributed to Him', *Sefunot*, 11 (1971–1978), 69–112 (in Hebrew).

Gershom Scholem, *On the Kabbalah and Its Symbolism*, trans. by Ralph Manheim (New York: Schocken, 1977).

Gershom Scholem, *The Messianic Idea in Judaism* (New York: Schocken, 1972).

Gershom Scholem, 'R. Isaac of Acre's Commentary on the First Chapter of *Sefer Yetzirah*', *Qiryat Sefer*, 31 (1956), 379–396 (in Hebrew).

Gershom Scholem, 'Hitpatehut Torat ha-'Olamot be-Qabbalat ha-Rishonim', *Tarbiz*, 3 (1932), 33–66 (in Hebrew).

Gershom Scholem, 'Hitpatehut Torat ha-'Olamot be-Qabbalat ha-Rishonim', *Tarbiz*, 2 (1931), 415–442.

Georges Schreiber, 'Actual Aspect of the Problem of Eugenical Sterilization in France', *Eugenical News*, 11:5 (1936), 105.

Dov Schwartz, *Studies on Astral Magic in Medieval Jewish Thought*, trans. by David Louvish and Batya Stein (Leiden: Brill, 2005).

M. Sciuti, *La vita e le opera di Giustiniano Nicolucci: Commemorazione letta all'Accademia Pontaniana nella seduta del 9 aprile 1922* (Naples, 1922).

James C. Scott, *Seeing Like a State: How Certain Schemes to Improve the Human Conditions Have Failed* (New Haven: Yale University Press, 1998).

Nicholas Sed, 'Le *Sefer Yesira*, l'edition critique, le texte primitif, la grammaire et la metaphysique', *Revue des études juives*, 132 (1973), 513–528.

Harold B. Segel, *Body Ascendant: Modernism and Physical Imperative* (Baltimore, MD.: The Johns Hopkins University Press, 1998).

Michael J. Selgelid, 'Ethics and Eugenic Enhancement', *Poiesis & Praxis*, 1:4 (2003), 239–261.
Guiseppe Sergi, *Italia – Le origini: Antropologia, cultura, e civiltà* (Turin: Fratelli Bocca, 1919).
Guiseppe Sergi, *La Sardegna: Note e commenti di un antropologo* (Turin: Fratelli Bocca, 1907).
Guiseppe Sergi, *The Mediterranean Race: A Study of the Origin of European Peoples* (London: Walter Scott, 1901).
Guiseppe Sergi, 'Intorno ai primi abitanti di Europa', *Atti della Società Romana di Antropologia*, 6:1899–1900 (Rome, 1900), 67–89.
Guiseppe Sergi, *Arii e Italici: Attorno all'Italia preistorica, con figure dimostrative* (Turin: Fratelli Bocca, 1898).
Guiseppe Sergi, *Africa: Antropologia della stirpe camitica: Specie eurafricana* (Turin: Fratelli Bocca, 1897).
Guiseppe Sergi, *Origine e diffusione della stirpe mediterranea: Induzioni antropologiche* (Rome: Società Editrice D. Alighieri, 1895).
Guiseppe Sergi, *The Varieties of Human Species: Principles and Methods of Classification* (Washington, D.C.: Smithsonian Institution, 1894).
Guiseppe Sergi, 'Le varietà umane: Principi e metodo di classificazione', *Atti della Società Romana di Antropologia*, 1 (1893), 19–74.
Tom Shakespeare, 'Choices and Rights: Eugenics, Genetics and Disability', *Disability and Society*, 13:5 (1998), 665–681.
Michael H. Shapiro, 'The Impact of Genetic Enhancement on Equality', *Wake Forest Law Review*, 34:3 (Fall, 1999), 561–637.
Byron L. Sherwin, *Golems Among Us: How a Jewish Legend Can Help Us Navigate the Biotech Century* (Chicago: Ivan R Dee, 2004).
Byron L. Sherwin, *The Golem Legend: Origins and Implications,* (Lanham, MD.: University Press of America, 1985).
Lee M. Silver, 'Reprogenetics: How reprogenetic and genetic technologies will be combined to provide new opportunities for people to reach their reproductive goals', in *Engineering the Human Germline*, ed. by Gregory Stock and John Campbell (New York: Oxford University Press, 2000), pp. 57–71.
Lee M. Silver, *Remaking Eden: Cloning and Beyond in a Brave New World* (New York: Avon books, 1997).
A. L. Simonnot, 'Un enjeu éthique du XXe siècle: la question de l'eugénisme', *Annales Médico-psychologiques*, 159 (2001), 23–26.
Alison Sinclair, 'Social Imaginaries: The Literature of Eugenics', *Studies in History and Philosophy of Biological and Biomedical Sciences*, 39 (2008), 240–246.
Mark Singleton, *Yoga Body*, (Oxford: Oxford University Press, 2010).
Glenda Sluga, 'Unesco and the (One) World of Julian Huxley', *Journal of World History*, 21:3 (2010), 393–418.
Daniel Lord Smail, *On Deep History and the Brain* (Berkeley: University of California Press, 2008).
Anthony D. Smith, *Nations and Nationalism in a Global Era* (Cambridge: Polity, 1995).
Vladimir Soloviev, *War, Progress and the End of History: Including a Short Story of Anti-*

Christ. Three Discussions, trans. by Alex Bakshy (London: University of London Press, 1915).
R. Sonn, 'Your Body is Yours: Anarchism, Birth Control, and Eugenics in Interwar France', *Journal of the History of Sexuality*, 14:4 (2005), 415–432.
Claudia Andrea Spring, *Zwischen Krieg und Euthanasie: Zwangssterilisationen in Wien, 1940–1945* (Vienna: Böhlau Verlag, 2009).
Julia Stapleton, *Englishness and the Study of Politics: The Social and Political Thought of Ernest Baker* (Cambridge: Cambridge University Press, 1994).
Nancy Leys Stepan, *"The Hour of Eugenics": Race, Gender, and Nation in Latin America* (Ithaca: Cornell University Press, 1991).
Devon Stillwell, 'Eugenics Visualised: The Exhibit of the Third International Congress of Eugenics, 1932', *Bulletin of the History of Medicine*, 86:2 (2012), 206–236.
Richard Stites, *Revolutionary Dreams: Utopian Vision and Experimental Life in the Russian Revolution* (Oxford: Oxford University Press, 1989).
Dan Stone, *Breeding Superman: Nietzsche, Race and Eugenics in Edwardian and Interwar Britain* (Liverpool: Liverpool University Press, 2002).
Pierre-André Taguieff, 'Eugénisme ou décadence? L'exception française', *Ethnologie Française*, 24:1 (1941), 81–103.
Jakob Tanner, 'Eugenics before 1945', *Journal of Modern European History*, 10: 4 (2012); 458–479.
Frederick Taylor, *The Principles of Scientific Management* (New York: Harper Bros, 1911).
Keith Thomas, *Religion and the Decline of Magic* (New York: Scribner, 1971).
Ben Thorne, 'Assimilation, Invisibility, and the Eugenic Turn in the "Gypsy Question" in Romanian Society, 1938–1942', *Romani Studies*, 21: 2 (2011), 177–205.
Isaiah Tishby, *Netivei Emunah u-Minut* (Ramat Gan: Massada, 1964).
Lynn Thorndike, *The Place of Magic in the Intellectual History of Europe* (New York: AMS Press, 1967).
Lynn Thorndike, *History of Magic and Experimental Science* (New York: McMillan, 1925–1928).
Karl Toepfer, *Empire of Ecstasy: Nudity and Movement in German Body Culture, 1910–1935* (Berkeley: University of California Press, 1997).
Arnold Toynbee, *A Study of History* (Oxford: Oxford University Press, 1935–1954).
Balázs Trencsényi, *The Politics of "National Character": A Study in Interwar East European Thought* (Abingdon: Routledge, 2012).
Leon Trotsky, *Literature and Revolution* (Chicago, IL: Haymarket Books, 2005).
Marius Turda, *Modernism and Eugenics* (Basingstoke: Palgrave, 2010).
Marius Turda and Paul Weindling (ed.), *Blood and Homeland: Eugenics and Racial Nationalism in Central and Southeast Europe 1900–1940* (Budapest: CEU Press, 2007).
Edward Burnett Tylor, *Primitive Culture: Researches into the Development of Mythology, Philosophy, Religion, Art and Custom* (London: J. Murray, 1871).
Sandra Valabregue-Perry, *Concealed and Revealed, 'Ein Sof and Theosophic Kabbalah* (Los Angeles: Cherub Press, 2010).
V. Vitale, 'Gli Abruzzi', *Atti della Società Romana di Anthropologia*, 8 (Rome, 1902), 214–40.
Wolfgang Voigt, 'The Garden City as Eugenic Utopia', *Planning Perspectives* 4 (1989), 295–312;

Mark Walker, 'The "National" in International and Transnational Science', *The British Journal for the History of Science*, 45:2 (2012), 1–18.
Richard D. Walter, 'What became of the Degenerate? A Brief History of the Concept', *Journal of the History of Medicine and Allied Sciences*, 11:4 (1956), 422–429.
LeRoy Walters and Julie Gage Palmer, *The Ethics of Gene Therapy* (Oxford: Oxford University Press, 1997).
James D. Watson and Francis Crick, 'Molecular Structure of Nucleic Acids', *Nature*, 171:4356 (Apr. 25, 1953), 737–738.
Margarethe Wegenast, *Hölderlins Spinoza-rezeption und ihre Bedeutung für die Konzeption des "Hyperion"* (Tübingen: Niemeyer, 1990).
Paul Weindling, 'Julian Huxley and the Continuity of Eugenics in Twentieth-century Britain', *Journal of Modern European History*, 10: 4 (2012), 480–497.
Paul Weindling, 'The Origins of Informed Consent: The International Scientific Commission on Medical War Crimes and the Nuremberg Code', *Bulletin of the History of Medicine*, 75:1 (2001), 37–71.
Paul Weindling, 'International Eugenics: Swedish Sterilization in Context', *Scandinavian Journal of History*, 24:2 (1999), 179–197.
Paul Weindling, *Health, Race and German Politics between National Unification and Nazism, 1870–1945* (Cambridge: Cambridge University Press, 1989).
Sheila F. Weiss, *The Nazi Symbiosis: Human Genetics and Politics During the Third Reich* (Chicago: University of Chicago Press, 2010).
Sheila F. Weiss, *Race Hygiene and National Efficiency: The Eugenics of Wilhelm Schallmayer* (Berkeley: University of California Press, 1987).
Tzahi Weiss, 'Soft and Hard: More Comments on the Syrian Context of *Sefer Yesira*', *Kabbalah*, 26 (2012), 229–241 (in Hebrew).
Uwe Wesel, *Der Mythos vom Matriarchat* (Frankfurt am Main: Suhrkamp, 1980).
Hayden White, *Figural Realism: Studies in the Mimesis Effect* (Baltimore: Johns Hopkins University Press, 1999).
Elvi Whittaker, 'Adjudicating Entitlements: The Emerging Discourses of Research Ethics Boards', *Health*, 9:4 (2005), 513–535.
Raymond Williams, *Keywords. A Vocabulary of Culture and Society*, Revised edition (New York: Oxford University Press, 1985).
Evan Willis, 'Public Health and the "New" Genetics: Balancing Individuals and Collective Outcomes', *Critical Public Health*, 12:2 (Jun., 2002), 139–151.
Ian Wilmut, et al., 'Viable Offspring Derived from Fetal and Adult Mammalian Cells', *Nature*, 385:6619 (Feb. 27, 1997), 810–813.
Edward O. Wilson, *The Future of Life* (New York: Knopf, 2002).
Langdon Winner, *Autonomous Technology: Technics-out-of-Control* (Cambridge, Ma.: MIT Press, 1978).
Maria A. Wolf, *Eugenische Vernunft: Eingriffe in die reproductive Kultur durch die Medizin, 1900–2000* (Vienna: Böhlau Verlag, 2008).
Tamsen Wolff, *Mendel's Theatre: Heredity, Eugenics and Early Twentieth-Century American Drama* (Basingstoke: Palgrave Macmillan, 2009).
Aliza S. Wong, *Race and Nation in Liberal Italy, 1861–1911: Meridionalism, Empire, and Diaspora* (New York; Basingstoke: Palgrave Macmillan, 2006).

Kiene Brillenburg Wurth, *The Musically Sublime: Indeterminacy, Infinity, Irresolvability* (New York: Fordham University Press, 2009).

Limore Yagil, *L'Homme Nouveau' et la Revolution Nationale de Vichy, 1940–1944* (Villeneuve d'Ascq: Presses Universitaires du Septentrion, 1977).

Gad Yair and Michaela Soyer, *The Golem in German Social Theory* (Ladham, MD.: Lexington Books, 2007).

Frances A. Yates, *Giordano Bruno and the Hermetic Tradition,* (Chicago: University of Chicago Press, 1979).

Rory Yeomans, *Visions of Annihilation: The Ustasha Regime and the Cultural Politics of Fascism, 1941–1945* (Pittsburgh: University of Pittsburgh Press, 2013).

Robert Young, 'The Development of Herbert Spencer's Concept of Evolution', in *Actes du XIe Congrès International d'Histoire des Sciences* (Warsaw: Ossolineum, 1967), 273–278.

John Zammito, *Kant, Herder, and the Birth of Anthropology* (Chicago and London: Chicago University Press, 2002).

John Zammito, 'Herder, Kant, Spinoza und die Ursprünge des deutschen Idealismus', in *Herder und die Philosophie des deutschen Idealismus*, ed. by Marion Heinz (Amsterdam: Rodopi, 1997), pp. 107–144.

John Zammito, *The Genesis of Kant's Critique of Judgment* (Chicago: Chicago University Press, 1992).

Yevgeni Zamyatin, *We: New Edition* (London: Penguin Books, 1993).

Andrew Zimmerman, 'Anti-Semitism as Skill: Rudolf Virchow's "Schulstatistik" and the Racial Composition of Germany', *Central European History*, 32:4 (1999), 409–429.

Online Materials

http://www.theberendelfoundation.com/node/100 [accessed 7/09/2011]. Crafting Humans.

http://www.nickbostrom.com/papers/dangerous.html [accessed 7/09/2011]. Nick Bostrom, 'Transhumanism: the World's Most Dangerous Idea'.

http://humanityplus.org/learn/transhumanist-declaration/ [accessed 11/11/2011].

http://www.fhi.ox.ac.uk/ [accessed 7/09/2011]. The Future of Humanity Institute.

http://www.nickbostrom.com [accessed 11/11/2011].

http://humanityplus.org/about/ [accessed 1/11/2011].

http://humanityplus.org/learn/transhumanist-faq/#answer_20 [accessed 1/11/2011]. 'What is a Posthuman?'

unitednations.ispnw.org/archives/breivik-manifesto-2011.pdf [accessed 12/01/2012]. Andres Breivik, *2083. A Declaration of European independence* (London, 2011) 1180.

http://www.greatwar.nl/books/meinkampf/meinkampf.pdf [accessed 12/01/2012]. Adolf Hitler, *Mein Kampf* trans. by James Murphy, p. 32.

http://teachers.sduhsd.k12.ca.us/tpsocialsciences/world_history/dem_ideals/robespierre.htm [accessed 12/01/2012].

Index of Names

Abraham 44–49, 57
Abulafia, Abraham ben Samuel 45–48
Agamben, Giorgio 63, 66, 68
Agar, Nicholas 67, 90, 95, 153–156, 166
Alemanno, R. Yohanan 47, 56 seq.
Antal, Lajos 124
Aschheim, Steven 75

Baden-Powell, Robert 76, 79
Bársony, János 120
Bauman, Zygmunt 81 seq., 84
Benn, Gottfried 78, 155
Bertillon, Alphonse 142
Beveridge, William 117
Bismarck, Otto von 129
Bogdanov, Alexander 64
Bostrom, Nick 101 seq., 104, 154–156, 161–164, 166 seq.
Bottai, Guiseppe 87
Breivik, Anders 86 seq.
Broca, Paul 137
Burckhardt, Jacob 20
Burke, Edmund 31

Cavalli-Sforza, Luigi Luca 14
Chakrabarty, Dipesh 16, 35 seq., 69
Child, Charles Manning 73, 93, 95 seq., 99–103, 111, 115, 121, 157
Cirkovic, Milan 163 seq.
Clarke, Arthur C. 26–33, 35, 76
Crutzen, Paul 36

Darwin, Charles 17, 106, 121, 128, 132, 156

Davis, Joseph Barnard 129, 131, 139
Dawkins, Richard 14
Del Greco, Francesco 145
DeLillo, Don 71
Diamond, Jared 14
Domanska, Ewa 10, 15
Dostoevsky, Fyodor 71
Draaisma, Douwe 29 seq.
Drieu la Rochelle, Pierre 83 seq.
Duster, Troy 97
Dux, Gunther 15

Eksteins, Modris 76
Ellis, Henry Havelock 116 seq.
Emden, R. Jacob 52, 57–61

Feinberg, Joel 102
Ferguson, Adam 14
Ficino, Marsilio 55 seq.
Fischer, Eugen 120
Frick, Wilhelm 121 seq.
Fukuyama, Francis 26, 65 seq., 107

Galton, Francis 80 seq., 90, 110–112, 125 seq., 142
Gastev, Alexei 65
Gentile, Emilio 58 seq., 62, 81, 150
Giddens, Anthony 103
Gobineau, Joseph Arthur de 128, 133–135
Goldscheid, Rudlof 117
Grotjahn, Alfred 118 seq.
Gurnham, David 99

Habermas, Jurgen 68

Haeckel, Ernst 73
Haldane, J. B. S. 155 seq., 159
Hamy, Ernest 137
Haraway, Donna 69, 107
Harris, John 100, 103, 155 seq., 162, 166 seq.
Haţieganu, Iuliu 119
Hegel, Georg Wilhelm Friedrich 13, 18 seq., 21, 23 – 29, 31 – 33, 35 seq., 64 – 66, 73
Henry, Thomas 65, 129, 156, 158
Herder, Johann Gottfried 9, 16 – 18, 20 – 25, 33, 35 seq.
Hitler, Adolf 72, 76, 79, 84 – 86, 120, 122, 170
Hoffmann, Geza von 31, 119
Höppener, Hugo 74
Horowitz, R. Pinehas 61
Huxley, Aldous 65, 156, 155 – 167
Huxley, Julian 125, 153, 155 – 163, 165 – 167

Jacobi, Friedrich Heinrich 18 seq.
Jahn, Friedrich 82
Jeremiah 48 – 52

Kant, Immanuel 9, 17 – 25, 31, 33 – 37, 64, 73, 76
Kellogg, John Harvey 77
Kerzhentsev, Platon Mikhailovich 65
Klutschak, Franz 61
Kneipp, Sebastian 77
Kojève, Alexandre 63, 65 seq.

Laplace, Pierre-Simon 17
Lawrence, D. H. 75, 78, 114
Le Bon, Gustave 28
Lenz, Fritz 120
Lombroso, Cesare 140, 142, 145
Lorgna, Antonio 132
Loria, Lamberto 150
Lundborg, Herman 119
Luzzatto, R. Moshe Hayyim 59
Lynas, Mark 35

Mann, Thomas 40, 44, 46 – 48, 50, 52 – 54, 61, 78, 94
Mantegazza, Paolo 128, 132, 140 – 146, 151 seq.
Martini, Ferdinando 150 seq.
McNeill, William 11, 13, 32
Meinecke, Augustus 20
Mendelssohn, Moses 59
Meyer-Abich, Klaus 22
Meyrink, Gustav 61
Mill, John Stuart 101
Moazam, Farhot 96
Mochi, Aldobrandino 150
Moldovan, Iuliu 123 seq.
Muller, Herman J. 121
Murat, Gioacchino 130
Mussolini, Benitto 72, 83, 120, 170

Niceforo, Alfredo 144 seq.
Nicolucci, Giustiniano 128 – 140, 142, 150 – 152
Nietzsche, Friedrich 10 seq., 13, 71, 73, 75, 90, 112, 153, 155
Nordau, Max 82

Paul, Diane 44, 64, 75, 80, 90 seq., 94, 97, 110, 113, 155, 157, 163
Pauling, Linus 158
Pearson, Karl 111 seq., 117, 120 seq.
Pico della Mirandola, Giovanni 45, 56
Pierce, William 86
Pol Pot 85 seq.
Presner, Todd 82
Prichard, James Cowles 129
Prokofiev, Sergei 75
Pullé, Francesco L. 146 seq.

R. Isaac ben Samuel of Acre 46
Raseri, Enrico 143
Rava 47 seq., 52, 58
Robespierre, Maximilien 29, 85
Rossi, Gino Dé 143 seq.
Růžička, Vladislav 113 seq.

Saint John the Evangelist 63
Sandel, Michael 103 seq.

Index of Names

Savulescu, Julian 96, 100, 156
Schelling, Friedrich Wilhelm Joseph 18 seq., 23
Schiff, Maurizio 142
Schliemann, Heinrich 131
Schopenhauer, Arthur 20, 29
Schreiber, Georges 122 seq.
Sergi, Guiseppe 128, 132 seq., 136, 145, 147–149, 151 seq.
Shakespeare, Tom 15, 90, 96
Shaw, George Bernard 121
Shelley, Mary 39, 61
Silver, Lee M. 102, 153
Soloviev, Vladimir 64
Spencer, Herbert 147
Spengler, Oswald 13, 77
Spinoza, Baruch 9, 18–21, 23–25, 30 seq., 33, 36
Stalin, Joseph 72, 85, 121
Steinach, Eugen 158
Steiner, Rudolf 9, 75, 78, 115

Tarde, Gabriel 28
Trotsky, Leon 65

Ungewitter, Richard 77

Vallejo-Nágera, Antonio 113
Vernadsky, Vladimir 161
Vico, Giambattista 16, 18, 20, 24 seq., 27, 33 seq.
Virchow, Rudolf 131, 142 seq.

Wells, H. G. 80, 121, 156 seq.
Wiener, Norbert 41, 59
Wilson, Edmund 15, 35, 120

Yates, Frances Amelia 46, 54–57

Zammito, John H. 9, 18, 20 seq., 23–25
Zannetti, Arturo 142
Zinoviev, Alexander 87

Reflections on (In)Humanity

Volume 1: Longxi Zhang (Hg.)
The Concept of Humanity in an Age of Globalization
ISBN 978-3-89971-918-5

This book calls for the reclaiming of humanism as an effective response to the conflict, turmoil, and violence we witness in the world today.

Volume 2: Stefan Reichmuth, Jörn Rüsen, Aladdin Sarhan (Hg.)
Humanism and Muslim Culture
Historical Heritage and Contemporary Challenges
ISBN 978-3-89971-937-6

The papers of this volume move from the abstract scheme of an intercultural humanism of the future to concrete cultural expressions of humanism within the Muslim culture of different times up to the present.

Volume 3: Mihai Spariosu, Jörn Rüsen (Hg.)
Exploring Humanity – Intercultural Perspectives on Humanism
ISBN 978-3-8471-0016-4

The principles and practices of intercultural humanism as an inclusive vision for humanity.

Volume 4: Christoph Antweiler
Inclusive Humanism
Anthropological Basics for a Realistic Cosmopolitanism
ISBN 978-3-8471-0022-5

This book offers an anthropologically informed foundation for addressing pertinent questions of intercultural exchange.

V&Runipress
For further information and sample sections see www.vr-unipress.de
Email: info@vr-unipress.de | Tel.: +49 (0)551 / 50 84-301 | Fax: +49 (0)551 / 50 84-333